The shell that held the seed –
the seed that seeks a shell
Kathryn Berthelsen

Magic Afoot

Textualities

Textualities
8 Lauriston Street
Edinburgh EH3 9DJ

Editor: Jennie Renton

Tel: (+44) 0131 228 4837
the.editor@textualities.net
www.textualities.net

ISSN 1751-2034
ISBN 0-9552896-0-2
978-0-9552896-0-6

Textualities 1~Magic Afoot
All content © the contributors, 2006

Printed and bound in the UK
by the Cromwell Press Ltd,
Trowbridge, Wiltshire.

Textualities is supported by

Editorial

Textualities~Magic Afoot began to take shape when Kathryn Berthelsen showed me her beautiful sequence of poems about Rosslyn Chapel. The Rosslyn strand grew; a mystical novella by Suhayl Saadi materialised; and Gordon Bruce, curator of the Scottish Magic Archive, came up with the intriguing story of a quest in which the grail was the lost identity of a historian of conjuring. A further magical dimension was provided by Harriet Lyall and Claire Thomson with their observations on Hans Christian Andersen. Interwoven poems, stories, images, essays and an interview carry through the themes of magic and illusion. Searching the web for representations of the Snow Queen, I discovered the painting by Stefan Blöndal which became our cover image and suggested the title *Magic Afoot*.

On the very day I put the final element in place, part of 'The Rosslyn Canon of Proportions' was broadcast for the first time – music derived directly from the medieval carvings in Rosslyn Chapel, according to its composer Stuart Mitchell. Aware that sound waves also manifest as patterns, he used cymatics – the study of this phenomenon – to interpret symbols carved on the 213 cubes on the arches of the chapel. Working back from image to sound vibration, he established that each pattern does indeed represent a note and went on to interpret the encoded music in his composition.

As I listened, it struck me that the genesis of his musical piece was analogous to the way *Magic Afoot* had come together. What these pages contain was submitted to the printer in the form of electronic code. Before that, ideas and impressions were brought forth by language, a mysterious attribute of sentience and the movement of the breath. Everything is a source of wonder. There is nothing fully explicable in our experience. In these terms, Rosslyn Chapel is a singular manifestation of the universal enigma.

Jennie Renton

The cover image, *The Snow Queen*, is by Danish artist Stefan Blöndal. He interprets Hans Christian Andersen's Snow Queen 'untraditionally', representing her crystalline coldness with ice, which 'plays both a decorative and psychological role' and 'forms her castle and realm, which she sets foot on with high stilettos of ice.' Examples of Stefan Blöndal's work can be found at www.stefanblondal.com and at www.galeriehelth.dk. Thanks are due to Arne Helth, proprietor of Galerie Helth, for putting us in touch.

*

Textualities' online counterpart, textualities.net, is a literary review offering hundreds of articles about books and writers, contemporary and collected, with new material normally posted weekly. Since its launch in 2005, it has attracted healthy traffic with visits from over sixty countries. To subscribe to the textualities.net newsletter, please email the.editor@textualities.net.

Textualities~Magic Afoot
Contents

Waylaid by Rosslyn
Poetry, fiction and essays inspired by Rosslyn Chapel and Roslin Glen

1	Ten Poems on Rosslyn Chapel	Kathryn Berthelsen
9	Rosslyn Aloes in Veritas?	Brian Moffat
16	The Wandering Road to Rosslyn	Mark Oxbrow
21	Roslin Glen	Tess Darwin
26	Captain Wedderburn's Courtship	Anon
29	Snow White and the Prince	Regi Claire

Literally Fabulous
The genius of Hans Christian Andersen

44	Andersen for Adults	Harriet Lyall
57	A Land of Machines	Claire Thomson

Conjuring with Identities
Two magician book detectives and the materialising of Mr Watson

83	Watson Sherlocked	Gordon Bruce
86	Searching for Arthur Watson	Bob Read
106	Conjurers	Arthur Watson

Casinos, Clubs & Co.
Linocuts by Paul Ballingall

133	Linocuts	Paul Ballingall

Space Booked
Four Edinburgh bookshops

197	Photographs	Ariadne Xenou

Britain in Print Project
Early travel writing at the Mitchell Library

146 Be There Dragons?   Zsuzsanna Varga

Rorschach Ruminations
Lawrence Krauser, puppets and lemons

175 Puppet Theory (excerpts)   Lawrence Krauser
184 Lawrence Krauser Interview   Jennie Renton

Novella
Carved in stone, etched in metal, written in flesh
217 The Saelig Tales   Suhayl Saadi

Miscellany – Poetry

67   Little Traveller   David Campbell
     The Despot Dwarf
     Ghost Lover
70   maybe   Anita Govan
144 Epithalamium   Tom Leonard
154 'Oma'   Julia Rampen
     Beach Secrets
     Hunter's Point
     One liquid summer's day
163 You think it's crazy here...   Gwen Suominen
169 Obituary   Dilys Rose
     Maeve's Hair
     Hilda's Aura
     Peter's Shadow
174 Dalguise   Michael Brown
188 Sushi   Shampa Ray
     Russian Doll
     This is just to let you know
     After reading John Clare
     Poetry
     Walking Out

192 Whisper   Valerie Lawson
    Resolution
206 Hogmanay   Janis Mackay
207 Young Snow   Gerry Cambridge
208 Perfiekt Sjætlin   Robert Alan Jamieson
    Perfect Shetlandic
    Da Veksæsjin a Nemin
    A Problem of Definition
212 Scribe   Elizabeth Burns
    'Rummers and Ladels'
    Strawberries
273 Mummy   Nuala Ramage
    Ray Catoot

Miscellany – Fiction

 37 Patchouli, Loulou and Opium   Regi Claire
 71 Careless   Ruth Thomas
    Balloon Shaped World
158 William's New Friend   Tim West
194 Fragments   Susie Maguire

Waylaid by Rosslyn

Kathryn Berthelsen

The Chapel Addresses the Pilgrim

Are you the brave one?
Are you the small one?

Do you know your carvings?
Do you know how to read mine?

We shall see.
Come inside.

View to Rosslyn Chapel from Arthur's Seat

You are nowhere to be seen,
only sensed by passing
my fingers over the braille

of landscape. To identify you
would be to find a mere dot,
to miss the spread of a line

upon the green, a sentence raised
by us, our mounds and houses
scrolling over the hills in a pattern

more runic than even you.
It is this texture upon which
your mystery is written,

the horizon our limitless desk,
the sun a lamp to light our studies.

Baptism

She lets out a cry,
loud, tinged with fuchsia –

a holy utterance
flung high above us,

a newborn firetongue
calling out hosannas

to the forge. Water soothes
her homesickness to a taper,

a new spire cools
against the sky.

Lungs

You remember your century and a half
without windowpanes.

Even with your modern glazing,
wind does not move around you,

it moves through you,
inhaled in rafter drafts

exhaled through open doors.
My lungs breathe within yours.

Salamander

'Note the botanical carvings on the
southeast buttress, possibly Spanish in design.'

The guidebook points her out to me,
mistakes her for a flower.

True, she lives among the vines,
whose tendrils encircle her body.

She hides as salamanders do.
But I cannot deny her form:

head oval like a matchstick tip,
torso slender as a glassblowing rod,

tail curled into a fire-eater's tongue.
Seeing her for what she is,

I keep a wary eye.
At any moment, she may ignite.

Acoustics

She sings from the crypt:
her notes rise and hang

in the summer air, then pour
down like new honey at sunset,

slow to fall, luminous in my mind –
and then the flicker of wings

across my skin, stillness
becomes a gathering of those that fly,

unseen bees returning to the hive.

Kirkyard, February

Spread of snow gauze:
winter ashes scattered
into a veil between centuries,
eyelid thin.

I walk my curious pattern
around the kirkyard,
my footsteps melt the moment,
form foot-shaped windows

through which I see ancient Rosslyn,
her barons living on as minerals,
nourishing the infant iris, a green
thing unconcerned with time.

River Esk at Dawn

And I come to a bridge
    that exists only for me

to linger above the seeming
    that sheens this water:

below my feet the river,
    rustling like jet and chocolate

coloured feathers in wait
    for fire, restless for light

to rise to the angle of alchemy.
    Two minutes pass,

and then for a minute only
    the river reveals itself

as a peacock tail, a shimmering
    surface for blue and green

and a hundred gold-rimmed eyes
    glistening back towards the sun.

Colour

We are so fond of speaking
    as if we know you, as if answers

to our questions hover around you
    in a milquetoast halo.

We have even painted your carvings
    white to keep your truths

preserved, placid. But there are
    openings in your stone,

places where your skin shows bare,
    and, if only for a few inches, I can see

the rose, the amber, the dusky tamarind
    yellow hues that tell me of your origins.

You were not sired by an alabaster god,
    but as a child of currents, sand grains

laying down with the tide, offering themselves
    to be pressed through water into stone.

Their merging was the quickening
    of your veins that now flow

under the white like rivers,
    serpents, question marks.

Ceiling of Flowers: A Nocturne

Night opens,
ink slips
from the sky-well.

The moon
walks its path
among stars

that gleam foolishly
white: proud
immortal daisies.

Men sleep enclosed
in the grey cloak
of desert dunes.

They dream
of lilies arching
into bloom.

They dream
of roots turning filigree
below the sand.

A word
is on their tongues,
a word that dawn

will pluck
from their mouths,
a red petal

she will leave
on the horizon's
doorstep as a gift

to twilight, a gift
she gives to say –

    I remember you.
        Forget me not.

Brian Moffat

Rosslyn Aloes in Veritas?

PHOTOGRAPH © MARK OXBROW

IN THE INTRODUCTION to her *opus majus, Observation and Image-making in Gothic Art* (2005), Jean A. Givens poses three questions. Did medieval artists work from first-hand observation? How would we know? And why does this question continue to attract the attention of scholars? She rejects overall naturalism and prefers to dwell on descriptive specifics.

It is my intention to apply these questions to some rather ill-sorted accounts of the plants carved in the interior of Rosslyn Chapel, Midlothian. The chapel fascinates and impresses all with its sheer profusion of carvings: natural, supernatural, and preternatural; directly represented and emblematic; plain and mysterious. It is a *jeu d'esprit,* but what of the plants selected for carving within? How do they compare with those studied, assessed and analysed elsewhere?

From the beginning, Rosslyn Chapel stirred curiosity and wonder: chronicler, Walter Bower, in his *Scotochronicon,* wrote in circa AD 1447, 'in Fabricando sumptuosam structuram apud Roslyn'. Hundreds of visitors have provided effusive accounts of its richly diverse and densely packed carvings – and often report the painful crick in the neck to have been worth it.

Yet the architectural historian Colin McWilliam was not impressed by the chapel's quality of carvings: he writes in Pevsner's series, The Buildings of Scotland, that they 'are nowhere of specially high quality and their placing takes no account of their subject matter'. Dissimilar images jostle each other, almost rioting! Whereas McWilliam confines himself to carving on strictly religious themes – angelic choirs and musical ensembles, the Seven Deadly Sins, the Seven Acts of Mercy and numerous scenes from the life of Christ – others study the converse only.

McWilliams' restrained, scholarly account seems not to have been read by the numerous commentators thriving in 'the esoteric tradition'. Guidebooks – official, semi-official, and extraorbital – abound. The latter dwell on the non-Christian images (notably a count of 120 images of the Green Man), the Templar and Masonic symbolism (Sinclairs of Rosslyn were, we are told, prominent in both movements) and the Gnostic (often a catch-all category for what remains ambiguous and puzzling).

Representations of plants at Rosslyn present particular difficulties. Niven Sinclair's *Beyond a Shadow of a Doubt* (1997) has been enormously influential in that his polemic has been repeatedly examined in over sixty substantial newspaper features. Roughly one-third take it at face value; another third point out shortcomings; the remainder (among whom I count myself) consider the polemic to be a string of highly improbable or even preposterous circumstances, as follows. Henry Sinclair, Earl of Orkney and owner of Rosslyn, took absence from home and crossed the north Atlantic to north-east Canada. An arch-riddler, Sinclair left an Orcadian-style brooch, a rock carved with a broadsword, and Micmac folk-tales in the New World, and brought back images of two New World plants to have them, fifty years later, carved in no prominence, in Rosslyn Chapel.

Niven Sinclair is an enthusiastic celebrant and populariser of Rosslyn but has certainly overstepped the mark by calling it 'a medieval pharmacy in stone'. For this to have any meaning, the carving of particular, named plants must be accurate and naturalistic, and identification must always be secure and unambiguous. Potent plants kill and cure – and it matters which. These are exalted standards, and are called for. A much studied though very brief Naturalistic Period has been noted in the late thirteenth century, in north-west Europe. It involved carving in stone as well as other artistic media – including illustrated herbals. The buildings that incorporate 'vividly observed leaves, fruits and flowers' are the cathedrals of Exeter, Naumburg (on River Saale, south-west of Leipzig – in what was East Germany), Reims; Minsters of Southwell (Notts.), York; the Sainte-Chapelle of Paris. Much the most thoroughly studied is Southwell, the key-stone of Givens' work, and the focus of Pevsner's *The Leaves of Southwell* (1945).

And what plants would merit the phrase 'pharmacy in stone'? Pevsner provides a quantification of the Southwell images, as follows: Field Maple, 34; Oak, 33; Common Hawthorn, 24 (possibly one is the localised Midland Hawthorn); the Buttercups, 22; the Grapevine, 15; Ivy, 14; the Hop, 12... and much less prominent, the Roses and hybrids of species, 3 each; White Bryony, 2; and one each for Beech, Blackthorn, (wild) Cherry, Fig, a Geranium, Hollyhock, a trilobate Liverwort, Mugwort, cultivated Pea, a Thistle, and Wormwood. All these species are native or had been long introduced in the Middle Ages. At Rosslyn, I have noted all plants listed to Ivy, but to no high standard, in low-status, coarse-grained sandstone, and normally with bare leaves. A pharmacy, then? Givens uses the phrase 'unrepentedly useless plants', but there *is* little scope for debate on which plant is being examined. Leaves are complete with flowers or fruit, and stand proud in a number of perspectives. At Rosslyn, leaves are pressed flat in a uniform regularity.

Why select this Southwell Flora – which Givens notes is not dissimilar from the other naturalistic Floras? What are they intended to say and mean? Givens first chides Pevsner, as he 'conspicuously lacks an attempt to weave the sculptures into a tidy iconographic scheme', and goes on to hold the idea of the medieval herbal pharmacopoeia up to the light. The lists, she says, do not match – but we may go further: there are far too many woody species and the herbs are the wrong ones. As a medieval rule, the medically useful, woody species are the Spices... experienced, if at all, in powdered form. Givens cites the much-depicted Buttercups, a plant family almost unused. Only one Buttercup is widely used; it is absent, with its cordate leaf, from Southwell. To Cumbrians, it is the specific, Pilewort.

If Southwell falls short of a pharmacopoeia, and Rosslyn lags far behind, what then qualifies as a pharmacopoeia? All plants have had some use and usefulness – if this is assiduously delved for. An instance from everyday medieval medicine ought to assist: much the most widely distributed medieval herbal in Macer's *De Viribus Herbarum* (Concerning the

Powers, or Strengths of Plants). It is ever-present, in multiple copies in all the monastic and noble library catalogues left to us. It simply has no clear rival. Written before AD 1100 somewhere in northern France, it uses as its raw materials the Flora of northern Europe. Why prescribe what is not to hand, in the locality? Seventy-seven chapters centre on the seventy-seven crucial herb species, with spices and other exotics forming addenda. This compares with twenty-two clear-cut species at Southwell, and a rough and ready dozen at Rosslyn. Niven Sinclair's phrase 'the myriad of physic plants' is a gross and specious exaggeration.

Givens then goes on to what I will call Christian didacticism and considers the Eucharistic reference inherent in the Grapevine, the Maria symbolism of the Roses, noting that much of the Southwell Flora has little lore. Head of the list, the Field Maple, is a nondescript hedge-plant. As with Pevsner, 'no tidy iconographic scheme' is to be had from Givens.

She then turns to the agrarian environment or that part of it apart from the Cereals, Legumes (the Pea excepted), and much fruit. Cereals and pasture-grasses can scarcely be 'trained' to garland the usual site for carvings, at the capital of pillars. Garlanded and convolved on man-made tree-trunks, it is hard not to see this as an architectural metaphor, a stone microcosm raised in praise of the macrocosm of Creation. Medieval farmers integrated their livelihood more with the use of woodland and woodland-pasture than their modern equivalents. They lopped particular trees and shrubs for winter fodder; as Givens notes, this has only been re-discovered in recent years – Ivy, Holly (not at Southwell but elsewhere), and company. I will add that no plant toxic to livestock though is depicted… Buttercups are left severely alone.

Finally, we turn to two allegedly American plant species that have been 'discerned' at Rosslyn. At the outset, we have to query the circumstances of any early traveller incorporating exotic plants in the design and building of a late-medieval chapel. To most onlookers, exotics would be strange, unknown and without meaning. To paraphrase McWilliam, the Rosslyn stonemasons worked from a pattern-book endorsed through tradition and, one assumes, a degree of official sanction. Rather than reach for a contrived extraordinary explanation, might a more orthodox explanation fit better? The first New World plant in question is Maize, Indian Corn, or Corn on the Cob; the second, Aloes. There is no citation of either in the *Oxford English Dictionary* before the mid-sixteenth century.

Does any plant figure in orthodox medieval ecclesiastical stone-carving

that closely resembles Maize? A French scholar who devoted a lifetime to the systematic study of naturalistic stone-carving in French churches, Denise Jalabert (Fɪ. 1930–45), provides the answer. She simply recompiles the pattern-book from the carvings *in situ* – centred on the Arum Lily or Lords and Ladies (*Arum maculatum*). It fruits, with ranks of orange-red berries erect on the spadix, and surrounded by a spathe of leaves. The natural Arum Lily has been stylised to fantastic heights of abstraction. The plant itself is common and widespread, was valued for medicinal properties and its starch content, and was rich in lore. A glimpse of Arum Lily prompts recollection of the tale; its spotted or splodged leaves remind us that the plant grew beneath Christ on the Cross – and so became marked for all time. The Arum Lily, carved, stands for the Crucifixion – indirectly, yet plainly. Other spotted plants attract the same lore, and persistent '*maculatum*' suffix: Dead-nettle (*Lamium*); Hemlock (*Conium*); Orchid (*Orchis*).

On the day I write of the inherent improbability of Maize, a staple yet mundane American field-crop, being transmitted devoid of meaning like a blank postcard, larger events intrude. There are reports of a newly discovered early Mayan, paint-on-plaster mural. This splendid, unprecedentedly large mural – (3 ft. high, 30 ft. long) – unearthed in a tunnel near San Bartolo, in modern Guatemala, depicts the 2200-year-old Mayan account of creation, with the Maize God, his birth, death and resurrection, and the God's son's sacrifices towards the creation of earth, water, air, and paradise. It is impossible to imagine what Maize then stood for – to Mesoamerican Mayan adepts – but what scintilla of this splendour reached far-off Canada one millennium and more later is beyond conjecture. The searchers for the esoteric will, of course, embrace this mural as their own. If the splendour inherent to Maize deities for the Maya did diffuse into North America and beyond, the band of Maize-plants on show at Rosslyn is as flattened, as devoid of meaning, and broken down as any corn-circle.

Turning to Aloes, matters are complex. The name stands as such in Latin, English, French... and this, in medieval Spicery, indicates it was a commodity in international trade. Aloes (*sic*, the plural is the norm) stands for three distinct groups of plants (i) tree-like succulents of the order *Liliaceae* (lilies) that yield an inspissated sap (ii) two tree species of the order *Leguminosae* (pulses) bear a heartwood called Aloes Wood or High-Aloes (iii) the Agaves of American Aloes belong to the order *Ameri-yllidaceae* (bulbous-rooted like *Liliaceae*, but distinct). Before modern times, the plant-groups were confined to (i) south and east Europe (*A. vulgaris*), around the mouth of the Red Sea (*A. Socotrina*, after the island of Socotra) with other originating in the Middle East and Far East (ii) indigenous to Indonesia and Indo-China (iii) arid and semi-arid Mexico and Central America. Aloes, group one, has been traded throughout the Classical and medieval periods; group two also figures in trade – prized as incense, in embalming – and it figures thus in the Talmud, the Bible and the Koran; group three is recorded in etymological dictionaries from the mid-sixteenth century, and was first imported to Spain in 1561.

If Aloes from Central America was carved within Rosslyn, it would be genuinely astonishing; New Brunswick lies 2700 miles from the Rio Grande (compared with 2800 miles from Guatemala and its mural). There is a clear indication that Niven Sinclair, and those who follow him, believe Aloes to be peculiarly or particularly American in origin. This is fallacious, as the Aloes in common knowledge, used in medicinal, quasi-medicinal and cosmetic preparations, is Aloe vera (the true Aloes); this has been transferred to *A. barbadensis* or the more costly *A. socotrina*. In the Herbal of Rufinus, compiled in AD 1240, he classifies and grades the quality of Aloes as a drug: *Aloes caballinus* is good (lit. Horse Aloes); *Aloes (h)epaticus* (liver/liverwort shaped); *Aloes socotrinus* (or *cico-*; from Socotra) is the best.

As an ingredient, Aloes is manifestly at the costliest end of the market. It stands out in accounts of royal households, but only the wealthiest and least austere of monastic households. It was prominent in medications given to Edward I during his final illness in 1307, and also in preparations for his embalming. 'The Pills of Pope Alexander' are first mentioned in much copied recipes from as early as AD 1200 and comprise: *Calamus aromaticus* (Sweet Flag), *Cynamonis* (Cinnamon), *Cubebes* (*sic*), *Nucis muscate* (Nutmeg), *Macis* (Mace), *Spice nardi* (Spikenard), *Masticis* (Mastic Gum), *Gariofili* (Cloves), *Agarici* (Agaric toadstools), *Reu barbari* (Rhubarb), *Sene* (Senna), and *Aloes epatici vel socotrini* (Liver[-wort] shaped Aloes), to the weight of the other ingredients, and to be taken with Oximel, purified honey plus acetic acid plus water (5:1:1). This will 'above all, regulate the human body'. But hold fast, Aloes – quite unlike Maize – signifies the lucrative international trade in medicinal drugs. Aloes is traded in the form of sap or resin, or heartwood; the consumer will never see the plant that yielded the commodity. It is a truism that the origin of spices – the plant and place of origin – are not a matter of general knowledge until well into the nineteenth century. Niven Sinclair's American Aloes is too highly stylised to permit even speculative identification. Again, at the most stylised end of Denise Jalabert's reconstructed pattern-book, are Acanthus leaves, part of the medieval and Biblical environment.

I have examined leaves of all the commoner and most used Aloes and Agave species – all succulents taking a tight rosette form of bladed leaves. Many are savagely spined along their length. The studded effect on Rosslyn Aloes may be said to flatten leaves with a spined saucer-like section into a single plane, though I can trace no trilobate-leaved Aloe or Agave species. These leaves may as readily be seen as a studded trident bludgeon. In common with the majority of Rosslyn's foliage, little life is on display and precious little nature.

If I have taken the heaviest of scholarly hammers to crack this nut, so be it. I believe I have defined the nut for what it is: some highly speculative 'esoteric' argument that has co-existed with the likes of *The Leaves of Southwell* but has resisted illumination by it.

Mark Oxbrow

The Wandering Road to Rosslyn

'SO, WHY DID you write a book about Rosslyn? Was it because of *The Da Vinci Code*?' This is the first question people ask when they find out that I'm the co-author of *Rosslyn and the Grail*. The answer is a simple 'no'. I first visited Rosslyn about twenty years ago, and have been researching and lecturing on its legends and history for over a decade. *Rosslyn and the Grail* is the product of six years' collaboration with my co-author, Ian

Robertson. But the roots of the project reach back into my childhood.

I grew up in a house full of books – I even learned to walk by pulling myself upright on bookcases. My family are book hoarders, especially my grandfather, whose garage was full of odds and ends that 'might come in useful'. I vividly remember the day we built a bookcase together. He had it sketched out on the back of a brown envelope and he hummed and hawed as he sized up his motley materials – broken fruit crates, odd bits of pine and chunks of knotty two-by-four. My job was to work the vice on the bench and help saw the wood. I fetched jars of nails, poured them out and picked through for the straightest ones. He held the wood still, and I tried to hammer them in straight. Slowly the bookcase took shape – not a terribly accurate shape. By the end of the afternoon it was as finished as it was ever going to be. It may have been wobbly, but it held every book I possessed.

On a high shelf in the living room, well out of my reach sat *The Lord of the Rings,* three imposing hardbacks, their dust jackets marked with the red eye of Sauron. But our paperback copy of *The Hobbit* was a cosy thing that lived at my level. It sat about on the floor and curled up in the comfy armchair by the fire. I read it until it fell to pieces. Mirkwood, the Running River and the Lonely Mountain became part of my world. We lived beside an ancient drove road that wound from the fields and farms beyond the Pentland Hills to Edinburgh, plummeting downhill to meet the Braidburn River and follow it through the Hermitage. I could stand at the top of the hill in winter when the trees were bare and trace the old path all the way to the castle.

All around my neighbourhood were curious buildings with heavy iron doors and no windows. These were well-houses, which capped natural springs, but we children used to scare each other by saying they were full of man-eating goblins and trolls. My primary school badge had the four birds and animals of the springs: the swan, the fox, the peewit and the hare, while local streets were named after Swan Spring and Fox Spring. I later discovered that the seventeenth-century system that brought spring water from Comiston to the Royal Mile was devised by George Sinclair, the author of *Satan's Invisible World Discovered,* in which his interest in supernatural tales is plain: he asks his readers for information about 'Spirits, Witches, and Apparitions... Second Sight, Charms, Spells, Magic, and the like'. In years gone by, natural springs and wells were thought to be protected by goddesses and haunted by fairies. On the first morning of May, people would gather at these sacred places to wash in the healing waters and sometimes tie rags to nearby bushes in the belief that their maladies would fade as the cloth rotted away.

My parents were both ecologists. Despite having a scientific tilt to my understanding of the natural world, I always felt drawn to its folklore. Science seeks to understand the universe by studying the evidence but you can't weigh or measure the magic of things. From an early age I immersed myself in tales from the Highlands and Islands, Border ballads and Arthurian legends. Stevenson, Burns, Conan Doyle, Scott, Buchan, MacDonald and Lang introduced me to the underground stream of the supernatural that runs through Scottish literature. With my interest in Scottish History and folklore whetted by such masters, Rosslyn was an obsession waiting to happen.

I went there for the first time when I was sixteen, lured by a mention in an old gazetteer. As I walked down the lane towards the chapel, the glen below was an autumnal tangle of gold, orange and brown. A murder of crows rose and swirled into the air above the chapel's topmost pinnacles, which pointed like stone arrows to the lowering sky.

A heavy wooden door in a high stone wall swung open and an old lady in a nice cardigan led me into the grounds. I seemed to be the only visitor. Talking quickly and quietly, she told me that the chapel had been founded over five hundred years ago as the Collegiate Church of St Matthew the Evangelist. Its founder was Sir William St Clair, third and final St Clair Earl of Orkney and lord of Rosslyn. It had taken a small army of masons, carvers and carpenters almost forty years to build.

It had been raining, and now the gargoyles and hobgoblins on the north wall above us were spewing out water from the downpour. The guide beckoned and I followed her through a door, with no idea that I was about to enter a new chapter in my life.

The interior of the chapel teemed with life. Dragons, elephants, unicorns, green men, lions, griffons and monkeys – everywhere I turned, there were fabulous creatures and grotesques from medieval bestiaries. Angels and devils, saints and sinners, kings and queens. A heavenly host of medieval musicians. The pillars and arches were adorned with fruit and flowers and in the stone ceiling was a field of stars, the sun, and a crescent moon. The effect was overwhelming. Rosslyn Chapel was a Book of Hours set in stone.

The guide told me the story of the young man who had dreamed of carving a wonderful pillar. I stared at the dragons at the base of the Apprentice Pillar, tracing the foliate vines that spiralled like ribbons around a maypole. She told me about the master mason who struck his apprentice dead in a jealous rage. The carved heads of the murdered apprentice (with gashed forehead), his grieving mother and the master mason stared down at us. I learned that beneath the chapel was a vault where generations of St Clair knights and lords lay buried, uncoffined, in suits of armour. She told me much more – of Robert the Bruce, of the carved piper, of how Dorothy and William Wordsworth had championed the restoration of the chapel when they found it falling into dereliction in the early nineteenth century. The guide held me completely rapt. I had fallen under Rosslyn's spell.

Over the years that followed, researching the history and traditional tales of Rosslyn became a compelling pursuit. At the National Library of Scotland I immersed myself in printed and manuscript accounts of the chapel. It was there that I found *The Traditionary Tales of Roslin Castle and the History of Margaret Hawthorn, more generally known in the Lothians by the name of Camp Meg with poems and songs of the Glens,* by John Rigby of Rumbletyne Cottage, Hawthornden, 1860. The library's copy I consulted was defective, with duplicate and missing pages, but Rigby gives perhaps the most extraordinary version of the story of the White Lady, a maiden of the St Clair line. When she spurned the advances of Lord Soulis, he made a pact with the devil and imprisoned her in a secret chamber beneath Rosslyn Castle, where she is said to sleep to this day, guarding the fabled treasure of the St Clairs and awaiting the brave knight who will free her from her spell. I read legends, ghost stories and traditional tales, collected accounts of black dogs, evil wizards and chivalrous knights. There was much to learn about the St Clair family, who fought in the Wars of Independence, signed the Declaration of Arbroath, allied themselves by marriage with the Douglas Clan and remained devoted servants of Mary Queen of Scots and the Catholic Faith. I devoured every new book about Rosslyn. Increasingly they reflected the murky world of conspiracy theory and speculative alternative history about Templar knights, the embalmed head of Jesus and the Holy Grail. They often defied common sense and documented history. Some said that Rosslyn Chapel was not a Christian building. The St Clairs were supposed to have hidden the treasure of the Templars, they guarded the secrets of the marriage of Jesus and Mary Magdalene – perhaps they were descendants of Christ? Some said the crypt held a terrible secret that would bring the Catholic Church crashing down.

Not to put too fine a point on it, this was all rubbish. In my researches I had found a Latin transcription of the trial of the Templars in Scotland

and had it translated into English for the first time. This shows that in 1309 the St Clairs of Rosslyn publicly denounced the Templar Order. In reality the St Clairs had clung to their Catholic faith and Rosslyn Chapel was built as a Catholic place of worship – and indeed, it was full of Christian imagery and Biblical scenes.

About ten years ago I met Ian Robertson, who shared my passionate interest in Rosslyn and we embarked on a collaboration to tell its real story. Writing *Rosslyn and the Grail* was an organic process; our book evolved into 300 pages of legends, history and secrets.

When I first found my way to Rosslyn Chapel, it seemed impossible that I would ever make sense of its thousands of carvings. They appeared almost random. But as I immersed myself in study of the chapel, I came to realise they were nothing of the kind, and that the story they tell is clear.

The carvings in Rosslyn Chapel can be 'read'. Beginning with the carving of an angel holding an open book and ending with the one of the angel cradling a closed book – clockwise from east to south, south to west and west to north – the wall carvings tell the story of the birth, life, passion and resurrection of Christ and the stories of the Bible from the Garden of Eden to the Day of Judgement. In the east, birth, spring and the dawn; in the south, life, summer and the light; in the west, twilight and autumn; and in the north, death, winter and darkness – here is the cycle of the seasons set in stone. Why did it become such a mystery? Probably because the meaning, which would have been plain to medieval worshippers, was lost the way so much knowledge is lost – incrementally, through the passage of time. Released from distortions, its conception has a purity that is stunningly beautiful in itself.

Since the *The Da Vinci Code,* hundreds of thousands of people have visited Rosslyn Chapel and it has become a very busy place. Moments of solitude are few but in those moments the potent Rosslyn magic still resides. One frosty winter's night not long ago, after a shoot in the chapel for a television programme, I was the last one out. As I turned off the electric lights, I looked back into the interior. The image will never leave me. Moonlight pouring in, turning the sandstone a deep midnight blue – and a thousand tiny faces staring out of the shadows.

Tess Darwin

Roslin Glen

'A place formed by Nature for heavenly contemplation'

T WAS A surprise on the first visit, discovering this deep glen nestling in the folds of landscape. It cast a spell over me that has never lessened; on every visit I am re-enchanted. The chapel is astonishing, the castle dramatic, but it is the glen that has drawn me to Roslin so many times over the last twenty years.

I always approach by the same route: down the brae to the right of the old inn beside the chapel, then left along the track that winds towards the castle between two halves of the graveyard, the old and the new. From the castle causeway you can take a raven's view down into the woodland, but you must descend the steep steps that wind beneath the castle walls to experience the primeval wildwood of Roslin Glen.

Here, the thread of life connects us through many generations of trees to ancient times, before human history; here, we can experience the nearest we have to a remnant of the wildwood that once covered the Lothians. Inconspicuous in the undergrowth sprouts evidence of continuous forest cover: wood-rush, wood sorrel, dog's mercury, ramsons and opposite-leaved golden saxifrage.

This is my cathedral, sacred space, where the voices of birds and trees sing their accompaniment to the chanting of the River Esk. Where water shows its power, stronger than stone, and the river creates and dictates the path I will follow, while the spirit of Robin Hood – the original Green Man, celebrated in Roslin until recent times – flits through the trees.

I rarely meet a human soul on my walks, but I am aware of the many local folk who work to keep the glen a special place: the tree planters and removers of invasive species; the path makers, who over the years have repaired and restored the network of paths around Roslin – occasionally coming into conflict with the conservationists, for this is a Site of Special Scientific Interest for its geology.

The glen has a long, troubled and dramatic human history. At times soldiers were a common sight camped in the open spaces; after the Battle of Roslin in 1303 the river ran red with blood and the fields downstream of Roslin were marled white with the bones of the slaughtered. This is remembered in local place names: Killburn, Stinking Rigg, Shinbanes, Hewan Bank. Over the centuries many fugitives, maybe including William Wallace, sought hiding places in the caves of this secluded glen.

Two hundred years ago the glen was frequented by the first tourists, artists, writers, poets and elegant day-trippers from Edinburgh who came with picnics. After Dorothy Wordsworth visited in 1803, she wrote that she had 'never passed through a more delicious dell than the glen of Roslin'.

On hot summer days when my children were small, we often retreated to the cool shadows of Roslin Glen; they spent many hours playing in the shallow golden river while I watched the changing light on the rose pink sandstone and tried to sketch the trees. Sometimes we met with friends for impromptu suppers on the riverbank at twilight, which comes early in the glen. On one memorable occasion close friends got married there, a long summer's day of celebrations in the woods and meadows, along the river, in the chapel and the castle – a colourful and fitting mix of Pagan and Christian ritual, of sacred and sensual, leaving the shady woods with the scent of crushed grass and wildflowers in our noses to enter the dim and musty chapel, exchanging birdsong and the hum of insects for hymns and the rustling leaves of prayer books, with the trunks of stone sprouting around us and the Green Men watching, approving.

All this, the trees witness and remember. They may not all be the same species that grew here before humans came and tried to 'improve' on nature, but the ancestral memory of the trees is in the soil made of their flesh and it is tangible even today. There are many curiously shaped trees in Roslin Glen, as in most old woods. One characterful sweet chestnut by the remains of Rosebank House, once the dower house a few minutes' walk from the castle, is thought to be up to 450 years old. Walking the high path towards Hawthornden Castle, you pass a trunk shaped like an angel with folded wings. In winter, others with twisted shapes are revealed. Big old trees fall and the paths and river have to find a way around them.

Three miles downstream is Dalkeith Old Oak Wood; for nearly ten years I worked in an office five minutes walk from these ancient trees, which became dear friends that I visited many times for a hug and half an hour of repose in their peaceful riverside home. Each one is a venerable character with great presence; the aura of such antiquity in a living being is palpable. As T.G. Johnston puts it in 'Dalkeith Old Oak Wood' (*Scottish Forestry* 56, 2002): 'Dalkeith Old Oak Wood possesses an aesthetic mystique which provides a living link with the Dark Ages. It is unique in Scotland and is of great importance ecologically, just as Roslin Chapel some three miles upstream on the River North Esk is of great importance architecturally.'

King David I declared Dalkeith a royal hunting forest in 1163; it is not impossible that some of the trees still growing in the wood today may have seen David himself hunting the deer; it is certain that many of them are several hundred years old. We know people were hunting in this forest more than a thousand years before King David's time: archaeological remains from the Bronze Age have been found there. The forest was already about five thousand years old by then: it must have been a primordial place of massive gnarled boles, standing, toppled, rotting.

Trees were the life-support system for prehistoric people. They supplied all the basics of survival: timber for boats, tools and shelter; fuel for light, warmth and cooking; fibres and bark for ropes and containers; branches for brushes and scourers; resin for glue and medicine; food from leaves, fruits and nuts. With so many practical, essential uses, trees were to be respected and used wisely. But did the first peoples of Scotland take the relationship further than that – did they revere trees?

Surely they felt awe when contemplating these magnificent beings which lived far longer than the human lifespan – might even, for all they could tell, be immortal. Beings which, sustained only by sun, water, air and soil, grew so tall and strong with roots hidden deep in the earth and limbs stretching to the skies. They shed their leaves and seemed lifeless in winter, then magically came back to life each spring. Which of us alive today has not been moved by the annual spectacle of buds bursting, tender bright leaves and blossoms unfurling? Who can feel indifferent to the glories of autumn?

Scotland's first people must have known fear when venturing into the wildwood, that darkened, different world with its own unique atmosphere and sounds and smells. In Dalkeith oak wood today one can feel that sense of unease, uncertainty, not knowing who or what could be hidden or watching. Imagine then how much greater the fear when the woods were completely unexplored, unmapped, and contained real dangers from wolves, wild boar and stags that could kill a person. It must have been awe-inspiring and mystifying when wildwood that had been cleared for farming kept claiming back its territory; when individual trees cut to a stump miraculously sprouted new stems; when huge old fallen trees with hollow trunks just kept on growing at new angles.

The woods we see today in Roslin and Dalkeith have been managed since at least the fourteenth century, probably much longer, for timber and pasture as well as hunting; the wildwood is long gone but the trees remain as a living link with the past. As well as two species of oak (sessile and pedunculate), the woods contain ash, elm, holly, hawthorn and birch. The dead wood supports many kinds of fungi, lichens and invertebrates, including some rare species. There are green and great spotted woodpeckers, tawny owls, sparrowhawks, jays, spotted flycatcher and many other birds.

Life below ground is equally important and fascinating. Half a tree's biomass may be within the earth. Trees grow simultaneously up towards the light and downwards into the dark. Embracing one of Dalkeith's ancient oaks, you can sense the immense life force within, energies flowing in networks nearly as complex as those in our own bodies. Bound to one place for its entire life, the tree moves in its own dance of time, responding to the daily rhythms of light and dark, wind and weather; the seasonal cycles of each passing year. In the growing rings around its girth the tree records every detail of the changing climate; its bark tells the story of the animals that have nibbled and rubbed and rested against it.

In *Women Who Run With the Wolves*, Clarissa Pinkola Estes asks 'What is the basic nutrition for the soul?... For some women, air, night, sunlight and trees are necessary. For others, words, paper and books are the only things that satiate. For others, colour, form, shadow and clay are the absolutes. Some women must leap, bow and run, for their souls crave dance. Yet others crave only a tree-leaning peace.'

I like to sit in silence for a while – a long while – resting my back against an old oak, or on a rock above or beside or in the river Esk, and listen to the stories the trees are whispering. I murmur my appreciation as the attentive water does. The stones also speak. They have borne witness to all that has passed, from the beginning of time: the forces of earth movements, weather and water, the follies of humans. I read their stories as I run my hands across their scarred and sculpted bodies.

I can spend whole days watching the changing light and colours of the stone and water, filtered through leaves or branches. I have visited in every season and all weathers, by day and by night. I am in thrall to the trees of Dalkeith and Roslin. It seems obvious to me why the chapel was built there. Its verdant pillars are the forest rendered in stone, watched over by all the Green Men, the spirits of the land. But the real thing lies below, 'a place formed by Nature for heavenly contemplation'.

The description of Roslin Glen as 'a place formed by Nature for heavenly contemplation' was first made in the Edinburgh Magazine *in 1761.*

Captain Wedderburn's Courtship

The Lord of Rosslyn's daughter gaed through the wud her lane,
    And there she met Captain Wedderburn, a servant to the king.
    He said unto his livery-man, Were't na agen the law,
    I wad tak her to my ain bed, and lay her at the wa.

'I'm walking here my lane,' she says, 'amang my father's trees;
    And ye may lat me walk my lane, kind sir, now gin ye please.
    The supper-bell it will be rung, and I'll be missd awa;
    Sae I'll na lie in your bed, at neither stock nor wa.'

He said, My pretty lady, I pray lend me your hand,
    And ye'll hae drums and trumpets always at your command;
    And fifty men to guard ye wi, that weel their swords can draw;
    Sae we'll baith lie in ae bed, and ye'll lie at the wa.

'Haud awa frae me, kind sir, I pray let go my hand;
    The supper-bell it will be rung, nae langer maun I stand.
    My father he'll na supper tak, gif I be missd awa;
    Sae I'll na lie in your bed, at neither stock nor wa.'

'O my name is Captain Wedderburn, my name I'll neer deny,
    And I command ten thousand men, upo yon mountains high.
    Tho your father and his men were here, of them I'd stand na awe,
    But should tak ye to my ain bed, and lay ye neist the wa.'

Then he lap aff his milk-white steed, and set the lady on,
    And a' the way he walkd on foot, he held her by the hand;
    He held her by the middle jimp, for fear that she should fa;
    Saying, I'll tak ye to my ain bed, and lay thee at the wa.

He took her to his quartering-house, his landlady looked ben,
    Saying, Monie a pretty ladie in Edinbruch I've seen;
    But sic 'na pretty ladie is not into it a':
    Gae, mak for her a fine down-bed, and lay her at the wa.

'O haud awa frae me, kind sir, I pray ye lat me be,
    For I'll na lie in your bed till I get dishes three;
    Dishes three maun be dressd for me, gif I should eat them a',
    Before I lie in your bed, at either stock or wa.

''Tis I maun hae to my supper a chicken without a bane;
    And I maun hae to my supper a cherry without a stane;
    And I maun hae to my supper a bird without a gaw,
    Before I lie in your bed, at either stock or wa.'

'Whan the chicken's in the shell, I am sure it has na bane;
    And whan the cherry's in the bloom, I wat it has na stane;
    The dove she is a genty bird, she flees without a gaw;
    Sae we'll baith lie in ae bed, and ye'll be at the wa.'

'O haud awa frae me, kind sir, I pray ye give me owre,
    For I'll na lie in your bed, till I get presents four;
    Presents four ye maun gie me, and that is twa and twa,
    Before I lie in your bed, at either stock or wa.

''Tis I maun hae some winter fruit that in December grew;
    And I maun hae a silk mantil that waft gaed never through;
    A sparrow's horn, a priest unborn, this nicht to join us twa,
    Before I lie in your bed, at either stock or wa.'

My father has some winter fruit that in December grew;
    My mither has a silk mantil the waft gaed never through;
    A sparrow's horn ye soon may find, there's ane on evry claw,
    And twa upo the gab o it, and ye shall get them a.

'The priest he stands without the yett, just ready to come in;
    Nae man can say he eer was born, nae man without he sin;
    He was haill cut frae his mither's side, and frae the same let fa; fa?
    Before I lie in your bed, at either stock or wa.'

'Death is greener than the gress, heaven higher than thae trees;
    The devil's waur than women's wish, hell's deeper than the seas;
    The cock craws first, the cedar buds first, dew first on them does fa;
    Sae we'll baith lie in ae bed, and ye'se lie at the wa.'

Little did this lady think, that morning whan she raise,
    That this was for to be the last o a' her maiden days.
    But there's na into the king's realm to be found a blither twa,
    And now she's Mrs Wedderburn, and she lies at the wa.

In *The English and Scottish Popular Ballads* (five volumes, 1882–98), Francis James Child presented three different versions of 'Captain Wedderburn's Courtship'; the one above is number 46b in the collection.

Regi Claire

Snow White and the Prince

LIKE A LITTLE girl I've waited and waited for this day. The date is engraved on my heart; no doubt it'll be found there, seared into my flesh, the scar still fresh, when they open me up after death.

Twenty-seven minutes past four. Dusk has fallen outside, silvering the uncurtained bay window with a sheen of dampness. I switch on the table lamp. My gold watch ticks the seconds away ever more loudly, and the Roman numerals on its face seem to blur into each other as though the glass lid had lost its lustre, demanding an extra polish on the sleeve of my blouse. It's my best blouse, reserved for Sundays – for special days.

Twenty-nine minutes past four. I'll give it another half-hour. Five o'clock on a Sunday is a more decent time to telephone almost-strangers; they'll have had their afternoon nap and won't yet be sitting down to supper.

There goes the cat flap, a muffled double-bang that breaks up the sluggishness of waiting.

'Trixie?'

She is a killer, this one, a tiger right down to the stripes, with slitted demon eyes it's hard to outstare. I just hope she hasn't caught a bird again. She's brought home two already this past week. A small sparrow, torn and mute, barely alive, its eyes black with terror until I helped it out of its misery. Then a dead blackbird, an old female with gnarled, twig-like feet and a trace of mould round the base of its beak. It looked so pathetic I wouldn't let her eat it. I found a Cadbury box, lined it with twigs, moss and leaves like a nest, and tucked the sorry creature inside.

Twenty-eight minutes to five. I've always cherished this watch, ever since that day fifty-one years ago when Sean said in his Irish lilt-and-drawl, 'Florence! Surprise, surprise, close your eyes!' and fastened it round my wrist. Sleekly cool the gold had felt on my skin – but then Sean kissed me, and the metal began to glow with our love; the warmth spread through my body, from my arm into my shoulder and all the way down and everywhere – and even now at times I can feel a small ripple of it, as if a trace of that heat had been forever trapped in my body's memory.

It had taken us two-and-a-half years to reach the first stage of the courting ritual. The first and last stage, as things turned out. The rings never happened. Instead, a decade later, I 'inherited' a wedding ring (no question of an engagement ring from the man who'd asked for my hand, not my heart). 'Have this as my mother's blessing,' my late husband said, slipping it on my finger. The metal was dulled by drudgery, etched with the tiny filigree lines that come from too much scouring, washing and cleaning. I was quick on the uptake. Learnt to patch and mend the already patched and mended curtains of what used to be *her* house. Learnt to beat the rugs and sweep out the cold ash from the hearths just as *she* used to do. Learnt to air the sewn-up old overcoat which protected the mattress from the springs of the double bed that used to be *hers*. The three children, at least, were mine. I bought them new beds, new curtains and new rugs for their rooms. Sometimes I pictured my dead mother-in-law supervising me from the spirit world, and I stuck out my tongue at her.

'Trixie, puss, puss.' No bird today, thank God. 'Here, jump on up. That's better, isn't it? Cosier for both of us.'

We seemed an item, Sean and I. The architect-to-be and the hairdresser. Both sculptors of sorts, we would joke. To this day, I can reel off facts and figures about Georgian, Victorian or Edwardian buildings. And I can still feel the thick, silky texture of Sean's hair between my fingers as I scissor-snipped it into shape. Near-white it'll be by now.

I hoped he would never graduate. Never leave. I'd grown to hate the long summer holidays he spent away from me, in Ireland. Hated the parting kisses at Caley Station that made me burst into tears and take refuge in St Cuthbert's Cemetery, flinging myself down on De Quincey's grave.

Then came Sean's finals. Then the graduation ceremony. The evening before he returned to Belfast for good I desperately clung to him in the doorway of my lodgings. When at last we'd said our goodbyes and I watched him cross the street towards Marchmont, it felt like a stab in the heart. I knew this was the beginning of the end, knew it in a flash, beyond doubt – and I also knew he would always, always be my love.

'Poor you, Trixie. Not many eligible toms in the neighbourhood, are there?'

For the next year or so Sean and I carried on visiting each other across the Irish Sea. He'd doss down on some architect friend's floor here in town – we were so damnably proper! – and I'd stay with his family. Then his sister got engaged. His mother took me aside soon afterwards and said with a big smile: 'Isn't Shonagh's engagement ring lovely, Florence? And only six months since the gold watch!' (I'd had my own gold watch for seventeen months.) Perhaps this was just the proud mother speaking. Perhaps. But for me it was the last straw.

I'd been annoyed for ages that Sean was continually surrounded by his friends when I was in Belfast. They stuck to him like limpets. Came to the house, showed up in pubs, joined us for walks, dances, the pictures. It was always him and his friends – and me. Quite unlike our closeness in Edinburgh.

'What do you mean, 'never alone'?' Sean said, his voice suddenly hard and liltless. 'They're my friends! I've known them all my life.'

'I am your friend too. Your best friend, I hope.'

'That's different. You're my *girl*. They're my *friends*.'

'But surely you can get them to back off a bit while I'm here? For a day or two?'

'Don't you want my friends?'

'Don't you want me?'

We were talking in circles, vicious ones. Back in Edinburgh I became sick, my heart felt bruised, and I had to take time off work. In the end I sent him a letter. I tried to explain myself. Tried to explain without sounding like a prima donna, all whiny and jealous. I was twenty-six years old and I knew I'd passed on the love of my life. He wrote back by return. Pleaded. Asked why? What had he done? Didn't I want to share my life with him? But I'd made up my mind.

Five months after we'd finished I received a small package. Inside was the narrow leather box with my grandfather's amber-and-wrought-silver cigarette holder I'd given Sean. Again he begged me to reconsider.

Twenty more minutes. Time has slowed to a snail's pace. I wish I could curl up like you, Trixie, and purr away the minutes in happy oblivion. My feet, gnarled and brittle as the dead blackbird's, are too unsteady now for a good long hike to tire out body and soul.

It must have been the summer after Sean and I split up, one of those luscious, sultry Sundays when people went to church for coolness, not worship. I could think of a better place to escape the heat, skipped the service and – none of my friends being around for company – took the train out to Roslin all by myself. My mother was from Rosewell and her best friend lived in one of the houses in the glen, long before it became the Country Park. I used to run wild with the glen children. We'd play hide-and-seek in the woods, splash about in the North Esk with its gungy, coloured foam from the carpet factory; we'd race up and down the steps of Jacob's Ladder, sneak along the fence of the gunpowder mill to watch the horses pull their dangerous loads, naively holding our ears closed in case there was an explosion; or we'd explore the gorge and Wallace's cave, and dare each other to go near the castle at dusk. But hope as I might, I never once met the black knight on horseback, never once saw the white lady, and never once heard the baying of the phantom hound.

The glen echoed with voices on that hot, bright Sunday afternoon. Picnic rugs and folding chairs dotted the river banks; some people were enjoying a late lunch, others sat chatting and smoking; children chased by dogs were paddling in the water or throwing balls.

The shade of the trees felt refreshing as I strolled along past families, past couples with happy, shining faces. I chose the paths at random, up and down, left and right, zigzagging – keeping my favourite spot, the castle, for last.

When I finally stood on the giant stone bridge in the glittering sunlight, the sheer drop down into the glen took my breath away, yet again. I raised my arms in greeting – and froze. The glass lid of my treasured gold watch, where was it? I almost cried out. Compulsively checked and re-checked the rolled-up sleeves of my blouse, inside my handbag, under the waistband of my skirt. Sweating now, I retraced my steps along the cobbles of the bridge. The trees started to close in on me, forming malevolent, endlessly winding tunnels of darkness, penetrated only here and there by dusty, uncertain shivers of light. I strained my eyes, scanned the ground, scanned roots which had turned into sinuous arms and hands, grasping, scanned mouldering leaves, the soil beneath giant horsetails and ferns. Nothing. Not a glint. Above me in the trees I could hear the swish of wings, heavy, portentous. A woodpecker drilled mechanically. There were rustles in the undergrowth. Shouts rang out from the river, and laughter. Barks.

It was hopeless, of course. Like trying to find a needle in a haystack. The lid could have fallen off anywhere. It might have dropped into the water from the footbridge. Or perhaps someone had picked it up and kept it for luck – there were enough people about, after all. Not that I had the courage to accost any of them.

Just then, I noticed a middle-aged couple coming towards me, tall, well-dressed, arm in arm. The woman, in a lovely, ivory-coloured frock, had a pale, genteel face and silvery curls. On an impulse I decided to speak to her.

She pre-empted me. 'Can we help you?' she asked kindly.

I stuttered, explained. After hearing me out, the woman just smiled and pointed down to my feet. 'There,' she said, 'look, it's right there, next to your shoe.' And so it was. The small glass disk was quite whole, without a single scratch. I stared up at the woman. She was still smiling, but her eyes seemed to flicker, very briefly.

How I got home that day I can't remember; I might have flown for all I know. It was as though, for a fleeting moment, I'd been allowed a glimpse of the invisible pattern that governs our lives.

One evening three years later I came out of the hairdressing salon in George Street where I worked and set off towards South Charlotte Street as usual when, up ahead, standing deep in conversation, I saw Sean.

Surely it couldn't be? Surely not? His tell-tale round shoulders were stooping now, no doubt from bending over the drawing board too much (if he'd stayed with me, I'd have made him stop and relax). I recognised the other man too; it was George Kerr, one of his friends. I felt paralysed by a sense of déjà vu. As if there was a film stored inside me, ready to roll. Presently Sean would spot me and come rushing up, laughing, shouting: 'Florence! Hey, Florence!' Suddenly giddy, I grabbed hold of the window ledge behind me.

Something was wrong with the film. Or perhaps it was the wrong film. Because Sean didn't turn round, didn't spot me. He walked off. And I followed blindly, like a dog. Just as I summoned up the courage to go up to him, he was joined by a woman who had emerged from a shop. They kissed, crossed the street and together disappeared inside the Roxburghe Hotel.

Instead of trundling home by tram, I ran. Ran all the way up Lothian Road and through the Meadows to my lodgings. Ran as fast as I could so my heart would break, at last.

But some hearts take a lot of breaking.

Once inside, I poured myself a large G&T, then rang up my friend Kitty, who used to know Sean well. Would she mind telephoning the Roxburghe and speak to him, for old times' sake?

She called me back three-and-a-half G&Ts later. The receptionist had said Mr O'Connor wasn't in and Kitty had hazarded: 'What about Mrs O'Connor?' Mrs O'Connor was out too. Kitty had left her number for Mr O'Connor.

Sean was married. MARRIED! To someone else.

I let myself drop into the fusty old armchair beside the telephone and started crying.

'Hey, Florence, there are plenty more fish in the sea. Thousands and thousands.'

I merely snuffled.

Kitty told me the rest. Sean had rung her back and, after they'd talked about this and that – life in Belfast and Edinburgh, their respective careers (Kitty was a nurse at the Sick Children's Hospital), how he'd met his wife (she'd replaced him as architect at Stormont when he set up his own business) – he had finally brought the conversation round to me, asking was I married.

'Oh, no,' she'd replied, 'not Florence. She has never looked at another man.'

There'd been a long silence. Then, like a little boy stamping his foot, Sean had blurted out, 'But my parents saw her at the Braemar Highland Games – with her husband, they said. They were positive it was her.'

I gasped and interrupted her: 'I haven't been to those games in my life, I swear to God!'

'Don't worry, Florence, that's exactly what I told Sean. He went dead quiet after that.'

At noon next day I was in the middle of doing a blue rinse for one of the Turtle-Necks (as we used to nickname them, though the woman must have been a good bit younger than I am now), when the salon bell dinged. The other hairdresser and the apprentice were out at lunch so I tugged open the cubicle curtain –

And there he was. Leaning against the counter by the door.

The salon bell kept dinging in my ears as I stared at him, unable to move. Sean. *My* Sean. Seconds later he'd dashed up to me and we embraced.

We kissed…

Until the old lady began to complain about the blue rinse trickling down her face. As I got busy cleaning her up, Sean hovered by my side, touching my arm every so often. 'Can't you spare ten minutes, Florence? Please?' I shook my head, jerked my chin towards Turtle-Neck, whose hair dye needed rinsed off (I couldn't risk the scant remainder of her locks falling out, could I? But for one mad moment I caught myself thinking, 'Dammit, she can wear a wig!').

Sean only had another quarter hour before the conference on architecture resumed after lunch. 'At least give me a ring at the hotel tomorrow,' he said as we kissed goodbye. 'I'll be in Edinburgh again in a few months' time. I'll look you up then, I promise.'

That was forty-six years ago.

But now the waiting is over. It's five o'clock. Yes, Trixie, no use pretending surprise. I can feel my body quivering, on the brink of one last adventure. Easy to picture that poor blackbird of yours, jerkily poised on the grass, its mouldy beak probing the earth – while you lurk unseen...

I've already checked with international directory enquiries (did that this morning, like an impatient young thing). Spelt his name, spelt Belfast (for good measure), and, lo and behold, his number was revealed to me, digit by digit. Not that this guarantees he's still alive. But I'm too old now not to take risks.

'Hello?' A woman's voice, rather frail. Which makes me ask more firmly, 'Could I speak to Sean O'Connor, please?'

When she inquires who should she say, I nearly weep with relief. 'Just say someone from Edinburgh,' I reply, almost airily.

He gives his name in the familiar lilt-and-drawl, and hearing it after all these years cuts my heart, yet again. I want to shout, 'It's Florence! *Your* Florence!' Instead I say, 'This is someone from Edinburgh.'

'From Edinburgh?' He sounds puzzled and I can imagine his frown. Even as a student he had a vertical line between his eyes; by now it will be a furrow.

How could he have forgotten *me*? How could Edinburgh not mean the *one and only* thing to him? How could he have forgotten my *voice*? How?

In the end I have to tell him. 'It's Florence,' I say, hurt and crestfallen. Then I add, 'Chalmers.' Because I couldn't bear him not recalling me at all; I'd start blubbering and never stop.

'Ah, Florence!' A spark of recognition now, thank God. 'How *are* you?' But there's something in his tone that warns me to tread softly. He, at least, has had a good marriage, it seems. I wish him many happy returns on his seventy-fifth birthday.

'You remembered after all this time?'

'Of course.' *And I've been waiting*, I want to shout, *waiting and hoping silly little-girl hopes*.

For a while we talk about nothing very much. I mention that I've been widowed for almost twenty years, mention the shop, the children, grandchildren, the cat. Soon, we hang up.

'What else is there to say, eh, Trixie? I'm so glad you are a fighter and a killer. You'll survive.'

The winter dark creeps up on us; the windowpanes are tarred black now, with the table lamp a feeble glow in the far left corner. Trixie stretches, yawns and leaps down to the floor where she slides and squirms in and out of my legs, doing figure-eights accompanied by miaows. Then she jumps up again, begins to paw at my hands, her claws out for more effect. A cunning little beast. If only I'd been born a cat.

'I'm coming,' I say wearily and for a moment she gazes up at me with her big, slitted demon eyes. She springs off my lap as I force myself to my feet. I feel wobbly all of a sudden. 'Yes, yes, Trixie, I'm coming.'

I have decided.

I leave her seven dishes heaped high with the contents of seven tins, leave her seven bowls filled to the rim with fresh water. As if she was all the seven dwarfs rolled into one. And I Snow White. I chuckle. I've been saving up my sleeping pills.

Then I look at my gold watch. It has stopped. The pattern, I know, is complete.

I might just allow myself a last few slices of apple. Not that there's much hope of me choking on them. And even if I did, my prince will never arrive. Will never ride across the seven hills. Never brave the stormy seas.

Patchouli, Loulou and Opium

COUNTRY FOLK, I thought, would be kinder. But now they've barricaded my doors and windows from the outside, shutting me in like a wild beast. The police will be here soon.

Everybody goes crazy once in a while, don't they?

I can hear Jeanie yapping from Weekend John's doorstep up the lane, where she's guarding my things. There are muffled voices now, and shouts. The barking has stopped. Surely those men wouldn't harm my dog?

Forty, I told myself after my wife had divorced me and taken the kids, forty would be the cut-off point: either by then or never. So when I had the accident at thirty-nine, falling off a telescopic ladder and permanently injuring my back, I knew it was time. I sold my bungalow in Sheffield, put my belongings into storage, traded in my car for a camper van, and set off in search of new beginnings. The Scottish Borders seemed perfect: the air smelled sweeter, the people smiled when they greeted me, the houses were affordable, and Jeanie delighted in exploring the wonders of rabbit holes, true to her mixed Jack Russell and dachshund ancestry.

Jeanie's yapping again, frenziedly. Poor dog. What will happen to her if the police take me away? Robert McBain might have been right when he said they'd lock me up and throw away the key. But I'm not a menace to the public, he is wrong about that.

The first time I came here, sixteen months ago, was one of the happiest days of my life.

'Excuse me!' I called out across a dry-stone wall into the rampant summer wilderness of a cottage garden from where I could hear laughter and the clink of glasses. 'Excuse me!'

Jeanie was scuffling up on her hind legs to peer through a gap when two yellow labs came pelting through the high grass on the other side and, spittle flying, lunged and barked at us.

'Stop it, boys, stop it!' A tall, floppy man had appeared from the back of the house, dressed in sun-bleached shorts and a sleeveless black T-shirt, and holding a half-full glass of red. At his approach, the two dogs sat back on their haunches, tongues lolling. 'Sorry about that,' he said with a smile. 'Their bark's worse than their bite.' The evening sun gave his face a handsome bronziness and made his white hair stand out halo-bright. Not that he was that old, late forties at most.

I apologised for intruding, then explained I was interested in buying Briar Cottage in the side lane. Could he tell me when the McBains, who had a key, would be home?

The man swirled the wine round his glass. 'I've no idea. But hang on, I'll ask.' He returned to say his wife had seen them drive off a couple of hours earlier. 'That could mean anything,' he commented. 'They're retired.'

I thanked him and stepped away from the wall. 'I'll take Jeanie for a walk and try again later. Or tomorrow if needs be. My camper van won't mind.' I laughed, rather girlishly, and had to put a quick hand over my mouth.

The man wished me luck, adding that Briar Cottage could be really nice 'with a bit of work.' Flanked by the two labs, he started back towards the chatter of voices, then suddenly swung round again. 'Hey, why don't you join us? We're having a barbecue.' He grinned as he held out his hand: 'They call me Weekend John.'

I signed the contract for Briar Cottage at the beginning of October, ten days before my fortieth birthday.

What would Jeanie say, I wonder, if her barks could be translated into words? That she lost her sunny back garden in the city, her pals in the park? In exchange for what? A cottage which reeked of damp, bred armies of woodlice, spiders and beetles that invaded her bed, crept into her fur and drowned in her water bowl, a cottage which required so many licks of paint it gave her lip a permanent curl of disgust and her coat a Disney dapple of cherry-blossom pink and silver-moon blue? Or would she talk about me? How, after settling down at last, I changed hairstyles, clothes, ornaments and took up the guitar again, singing softly, much more softly than before, moaning almost? How the worn flagstone floors were suddenly hidden under fuchsia-red rugs, the sofa and armchairs smothered in fuchsia-red cushions, the windows covered by fuchsia-red blinds? But dogs don't see colours, do they?

And Briar Cottage itself, what does it whisper at night to the wind, to the owl as its shadow touches the roof? Sometimes, lying in bed, I can hear a groaning in the old ceiling beams, a strained sighing in the walls as if the laths were short of breath, and sometimes there's the ping of a tile as it splinters in half.

Two days after my birthday I went to see my new GP, complaining of a (phantom) pain in my heart – not too far off the truth, after all. The doctor was fat and pleasant. So, during another appointment – for a nonexistent cough – I screwed up my courage and told him about the vows I'd made to myself in childhood whenever I glimpsed a falling star or caught the bigger part of a wishbone. Soon afterwards I was sent to a female psychiatrist, for weekly sessions.

'Why is it,' I asked her just before Christmas, 'that sadness produces such a clear liquid? Shouldn't sadness be murky, dark and troubled?'

She glanced at me without saying a word.

'You know,' I continued, 'I've started to collect my tears. I keep them in a small glass phial in my bathroom cabinet, next to the three flasks of perfume I've allowed myself: Patchouli, Loulou and Opium.'

This time, I'd grabbed her attention. She stared at me.

With my most sincere smile I said, 'Please give me a chance. A three-month trial of those pills would be enough for me to find out whether this is truly what I want.'

Her lips were pursed as she slid her gaze down my face – from undulating hairline, modest nose and mouth to generous expanse of chin – keeping well away from my eyes. Finally she shrugged and said she'd arrange for a referral to the local hospital where they had a specialist to assess cases like mine. When I thanked her, she shook her head quietly. 'Let's just wait and see, shall we?' she said. 'Meanwhile, take these.' And she handed me a pack of anti-depressants.

The New Year cards I sent out were designed, printed and laminated in my very own living-room office – with a photo of Jeanie in a reindeer hat, holding a beribboned bone in her mouth, and a verse I'd written a few months earlier and tried unsuccessfully to turn into a pop lyric. Thanking everyone in the hamlet for their friendly reception of me, a virtual stranger, in their midst, I said how grateful I was for being allowed at last to explore my own destiny. I used my new name to sign it: 'Michelle.'

A few days after Hogmanay, Weekend John and his wife arrived in their beat-up diesel VW. Escaping from the city to spend their time battling with the temperamental old stove in their freezing cottage. Sure enough, I could soon hear John's axe ring out through the cold, still air, punctuating the chatter of blackbirds, sparrows and yellow-hammers as they fought over the crumbs and seeds on my kitchen sill. Half an hour later I was ready for my walk with Jeanie.

'Happy New Year, John!' I leant my elbows on the dry-stone wall and Laurel and Hardy, the two yellow labs, bounded up for a biscuit each.

'Oh hello,' John looked round, 'Michelle.' He straightened and came over, leaving his axe stuck in a half-split log. 'And a happy New Year to you, too. Thanks for your card. Very nice and professional.' He patted his dogs, but he was grinning, thank God, his face red and shiny with sweat.

'Well,' I tucked back a blonde strand of the wig I'd bought and my new gold bracelet tinkled, 'if you're ever in need of desktop publishing services, you'll know where to come.' I glanced down at the flecks of ice on the stones in the wall which, even as I watched, seemed to form themselves into recognisable shapes, one of them an oddly familiar face in profile, with a large, square chin and a snub nose.

'Blonde suits you, I must say.' John's voice sounded admiring. He'd bent down to pick up a tennis ball and Laurel and Hardy shot off.

'Thank you.' I smiled, just a little coquettishly. Then, with another tinkle of the bracelet, I pulled the present from my jacket pocket. 'Something I would like you to have, John.' And I held out my black balaclava.

Jeanie leapt up trying to snatch it away. 'Jeanie, no,' I said, nearly shouting at her.

John turned the hat over and over in his hands. Finally he replied, 'That's very kind of you, Michelle. It'll certainly keep me warm – both outside and inside the cottage!'

'I'm so glad,' I blurted out. 'You see, I won't need it now.' I could feel myself blush. But there was nothing wrong with blushing like a girl, of course. Not any more.

I've never felt at ease in ladies' wear departments, though I have the same right as anyone to be there, have the same right to fondle the materials, then disappear into the changing rooms. I can teeter on my heels with the best of them (I practised in front of my bedroom mirror for hours on end). When I present the garments to the cashier, I always do so with an elegant flick of the wrist and a charming smile. Why is it they never smile back?

Overnight, it seemed, the rowan tree in my back garden had flung on its bridal gear, the cream-white splashes vying with the sappy new green, bursting to let nature transform them from frothy nothings to heavy clusters of berry red. To me it felt like a signal. After all those carefully planned shopping trips, I was kitted out to perfection.

From that day on, Old Farmer Johnston and the McBains did their damnedest not to ogle me and my fake-fur coat when we met in the lane.

You're lovely, I keep telling myself, don't worry. Soft, blonde curls reaching all the way down to your shoulders, gold hoop earrings, a honey-coloured complexion, courtesy of Revlon, glossy pink cupid-bow lips, blue eyes shimmer-shadowed a deeper blue, eyebrows plucked into sculpted arches, deft, strong fingers (the nails, admittedly, could be less raggedy, and cleaner), slim hips, legs perhaps a bit on the short and sturdy side, though the high heels easily make up for that. A pleasing sight, don't you think? Especially when you smile like you're doing now, and the two dimples show in your cheeks. Cute, even at forty-one.

Yes, you have come far, achieving all this in only a year. Discovering the freedom of being yourself, exploring it so whole-heartedly, so totally, it's like living in a brand-new element. Even your flesh feels different, softer somehow, more pliable, wanting so much to be touched, and to touch. Your blood, too, looks different, thicker, more viscous, a deeper crimson – as you noticed when cutting yourself this morning by accident. Your taste buds have evolved and now discriminate between too much and too little salt, and you suddenly smell things you didn't before: stones hot from the sun, fresh rain on leaves, the brisk coldness of snow. Maybe, of course, it's simply a matter of allowing yourself at long last the time and pleasure to care. And care you do. God, you wouldn't mind caring for others like you. Helping them reach this stage in life. Everybody goes crazy once in a while, don't worry.

After the DIY jobs necessary to spruce up my cottage, I started on the sun-trap back garden. Pruned the apple and plum trees, trained a young pear tree against the kitchen wall, dug over and planted the vegetable patch. Building a pond – an old dream of mine – was next, complete with a solar-powered fountain, ornamental stones, shells and marbles I'd collected over the years, exotic marsh plants and water lilies I hoped would serve as sun lounges for the neighbourhood frogs. Soon, frogs did find their way there. I often watched them lazing about, flicking their thin long tongues with lightning speed whenever an insect or spider ventured too close. That was before the herons arrived.

I advertised my designer skills in the shop windows of the nearby town, but doing the occasional layout job for church leaflets, take-out menus and self-published authors, laminating business cards, or writing song lyrics for myself didn't keep me busy enough. Weekend John's straggly garden seemed the ideal project. His wife was so grateful she called round one day and sat in my fuchsia-smothered armchair, making small talk for a full hour while studiously avoiding looking at my legs, which I'd forgotten to shave that morning.

The rowan berries have long since been pecked at by birds, blighted by rain, scattered by the winds, trampled and mashed underfoot by creatures of the night. Autumn in these parts is dank and miserable when the mists won't lift. So I was glad to hear the clank of the letter box this morning. Picking up the airmail envelope from my daughter, who is to be married soon, I was even gladder. Then I read the message, which had travelled all the way across the chill Atlantic:

Hey there, Dad/Michelle

Listen, I don't want to hurt your feelings but all things considered, I'd rather you didn't turn up at the wedding. Just imagine how awkward it would be for everyone... I'm truly sorry. Take care, Kirsty.

PS. Thanks for the money. It'll buy us a top-of-the-range Dyson.

I was halfway through a bottle of cognac when I saw a heron flap past the kitchen window and swoop down to the pond. Its long beak began to stab into the water, *my* water with *my* frogs, lovely, vulnerable frogs, stab-stab-stab, like a drilling machine.

I ran shouting into the back garden, pursued by Jeanie. At the same moment the heron lifted itself into the air, just missing Jeanie's teeth and banking sharply over my head in triumph and derision, with a soft, mottled body in its beak – the last of my frogs. My pond was dead now, black and dead. If I'd had a gun, I would have gladly shot that bastard of a bird.

Instead I chased it. Out through the gate and into the drizzly morning emptiness of the village lane. I was still in my satin nightgown, and my feathery white slippers made hollow sucking noises on the wet cobbles. I kicked them off. Jeanie tried to retrieve them, but her mouth was too small for both and she ended up scurrying to and fro, yapping like a banshee.

The heron suddenly veered to the left and vanished behind some trees. I went on racing up the lane, unthinking and unstoppable now like a wind-up toy that's been kept in a box for too long.

The nightgown with its flounces billowed out behind me, a gleaming seashell pink in the watery dreichness. I whipped it off. Flung it down on Weekend John's doorstep together with my wig, and the real blonde hair stirred slightly in the damp breeze.

Fifty yards ahead, the school bus was idling at the corner.

I jogged up to it. The door had just slid shut behind the last straggle of children. The driver stared at me through the slowly swishing windscreen wipers, open-mouthed. The children gaped. Some of them sniggered. Others cheered. Still others shrank away, hiding their faces.

I know now I should have simply carried on and down the track between Old Farmer Johnston's fields, pretending to be out and about, communing with nature. Why didn't I? Why did I have to break my stride and hammer on the bus windows with my fists? Why did I have to shout, over and over again, 'Look at me! Just look at me, for pity's sake!'?

By the time the driver had recovered his wits and was revving the engine and sounding his horn to alert the villagers, my knuckles were bleeding and my voice had grown hoarse. The bus pulled away so abruptly I landed on my hands and knees, just as Robert McBain came panting up the lane, swinging his gnarled walking stick.

To give him his due, he didn't hit me, merely poked me in the ribs as I got to my feet. 'Damn disgrace!' he exclaimed. 'What do you think you're doing? In front of the kids, too! Be lucky if they don't put you on that sex offenders' list. And take off those stupid plastic breasts. Just look at yourself. Ridiculous. Go home now and get dressed. Then stay put.' His stick started to push and prod me like a farm animal back along the lane.

Jeanie was lying on top of my wig and nightgown, the slippers next to her. She grinned proudly and wagged her tail. 'Come here, Jeanie,' I called, but my voice was weak, sapless, and the dog remained where she was.

I'm feeling better now; I'm ready for them. Underneath the kimono, my skin is slick with perfume, like a wrestler's body covered in oil: Patchouli for the legs, Loulou for buttocks and belly, Opium for arms, chest and throat. The bottle of cognac seems to have emptied itself and I've had to start on the vodka.

Jeanie is howling, but there's nothing I can do for her now; she will have to fend for herself. I can hear sirens in the distance and, like a fire sucking in a sudden rush of oxygen, the voices in the lane outside flare up into a roar. My neighbours have begun to tear off the boards they nailed across my door – eager to feed the flames.

43

Harriet Lyall

Literally Fabulous
Andersen for Adults

HANS CHRISTIAN ANDERSEN is regarded primarily as a children's author, his fairytales occupying a niche on every nursery bookshelf with those of the Brothers Grimm. The paradox of ostensibly naive children's literature is that it is often produced by the most sophisticated and mature intellects. Lewis Carroll is a case in point, as are Louisa May Alcott, Robert Louis Stevenson, C.S. Lewis and J.R.R. Tolkien. Andersen was just such a sophisticated writer and he well repays detailed analysis. The diminutive category of 'fairytales', assigned by the English language to his best-known stories, is merely an approximate translation of the more serious term 'Eventyr', derived from the Latin 'aventura', or adventure, by which his works are known in his native Danish.

Like many another, I first encountered Andersen when, as a child, I received a copy of his tales as a Christmas present. Certain passages and expressions in the Victorian translation were beyond my understanding at that time. What I did respond to was his ability to evoke atmospheric scenes in the imagination.

Returning in my mid-thirties to Andersen, I read 'The Little Match Girl'. To my surprise and embarrassment, I found tears gushing onto the page. I hoped I might fare better with 'The Nightingale' and did keep my lachrymal glands under control until the final section, in which the Nightingale beguiles Death with her song. What extraordinary power had this writer, I wondered, to shake me body and soul despite my efforts at resistance?

I heard Andersen's name again in 1997, in an unexpected context: the Adelphi Hotel in Liverpool, at a conference on EU Public Procurement conducted by a Danish consultant. Over dinner, the conversation turned to Danish literature. Jørn, the consultant, asserted: 'My native language has only ever produced one truly great writer.' 'Who might that be?' I asked, expecting him to name anyone but the obvious. 'Hans Christian Andersen, of course!' was the reply.

So omnipresent in the collective psyche are Andersen's creations that their influence is often overlooked. Never a day goes by but the phrases 'ugly duckling' or 'Emperor's new clothes' occur in conversation or journalism, often without the speakers, writers or readers being aware of their origin. Reading 'The Snow Queen' alongside *The Lion the Witch and the Wardrobe*, one can hardly fail to observe the latter's debt to the former. C.S. Lewis's White Witch, with her wintry power and her propensity to beguile arrogant young lads into her sleigh, is but a re-creation, or extrapolation of Andersen's glacial *femme fatale*.

To return to the question that perplexed me: how does Andersen achieve his effects? To answer this, it is necessary to look at his way with the words themselves, bearing in mind that, while Andersen is read by more English speaking readers than readers in his native tongue – and thus counts as a classic author in English – those said Anglophone readers can only ever approach him via translation.

The Power of Words

Andersen's literary technique is unsurpassed. Both in structure and in detail, 'The Snow Queen' is a masterpiece of lyricism, metaphysics and morality, expressed within a perfectly controlled *Novelle*. Around the plot involving Kay and Gerda is a framework – *Rahmentechnik* – describing the distorting Magic Mirror invented by the trolls at wickedness school.

The Mirror's fragments spike the heart and eyes with cold indifference and a distorted moral vision. This 'framework' has in one sense nothing to do with the main plot and in another everything to do with it: the splinter in Kay's heart will soon make him cold to Gerda and in thrall to the Snow Queen, thus convincingly setting in motion the machinery of the entire subsequent plot.

Andersen proceeds briskly from the moral allegory of the Mirror, with its folkloric cast and props, to the sunlit daytime world, the little Eden of Kay and Gerda:

> In a large town where there are so many houses and people that there is not room enough for everyone to have even a little garden, and where many have to be content with a few plants in pots, there dwelt two poor children, whose garden was somewhat larger than a flower-pot. They were not brother and sister, but they loved each other as much as if they had been, and their parents lived in two attics which were exactly opposite each other. The roof of one house nearly joined the other, the gutter ran along between, and there was in each roof a little window, so that you could stride across the gutter from one window to the other. The parents of these children had each a large wooden box in which grew herbs for kitchen use,

and they had placed these boxes upon the gutter, so near that they almost touched each other. A beautiful little rose-tree grew in each box; scarlet-runners clustered over the boxes, and the rose-bushes threw out long shoots that were trained round the windows; the whole looked almost like a triumphal arch of leaves and flowers. The boxes were very high, and the children knew that they might not climb over them; but they often got leave to sit on their little stools, under the rose-trees, and thus they passed many a delightful hour. In winter there was an end to these pleasures. The windows were often quite frozen over, and then they heated pennies on the stove, held the warm copper against the frozen pane, and thus made a little round peep-hole through which they could see each other. …

'Those are the white bees swarming there!' said Kay's old grand-mother one day when it was snowing…

Andersen, like his own 'Old Street Lamp', has the gift of creating pictures in the mind's eye. His subtly coloured descriptions of the Snow Queen and his portrayal of her character are effected in depth, yet with marvellous economy:

She was wonderfully fair and beautiful, but made entirely of ice, glittering, dazzling ice. She was alone and her eyes sparkled like two bright stars, but there was no rest or repose in them. She nod-ded at the window, and beckoned with her hand. The little boy was frightened and jumped down from the chair; and at that moment he seemed to see a large bird fly past the window.

Andersen's thoughts fly at such breathless speed we can barely keep pace and his images remain with us, like dreams we can never forget.

The Andersen Aesthetic

You will remember that the Queen of Fairyland, in another tale of male abduction by a beautiful lady, shows Thomas the Rhymer a 'third way' which is neither Evil nor purely Good in the saintly sense, but is 'the way to Fairyland', to poetic inspiration, fantasy and artistic creation. Un-doubtedly, Andersen is a master of pathos ('The Little Match Girl') and satire ('The Emperor's New Clothes'), but between the two, in the purely aesthetic genre, is where his genius lies:

> Just then a few snowflakes fell, and one, the largest of them, remained lying on the edge of one of the flower-boxes. This snowflake grew larger and larger, till at last it took the form of a lady dressed in the finest white crape, which looked like millions of star-like snowflakes joined together. She was wonderfully fair and beautiful, but made entirely of ice, glittering, dazzling ice...

or, from 'The Nightingale':

> The palace of the Emperor of China was the most beautiful palace in the world. It was made entirely of fine porcelain, which was so brittle that whoever touched it had to be very careful.

> The choicest flowers were to be seen in the garden; and to the prettiest of these, little silver bells were fastened, in order that their tinkling might prevent anyone from passing by without noticing them. Yes! Everything in the Emperor's garden was wonderfully well arranged; and the garden itself stretched so far that even the gardener did not know the end of it. Whoever walked farther than the end of the garden, however, came to a beautiful wood with very high trees, and beyond that to the sea...

and in the following passage, the aesthetic element is suffused with an exquisite morbidity:

> And Death gave up all these treasures for a song. And the nightingale sang on. She sang of the quiet churchyard where white roses blossom, where the lilac sends forth its fragrance, and the fresh grass is bedewed with the tears of the sorrowing friends of the departed. Then Death was seized with a longing to see this garden, and, like a cold white shadow, flew out at the window...

The 'Snow Queen' is a Romantic celebration of nature in all her contrasting facets and moods, but especially the snow-covered landscape of the northern winter, magical in its other-worldly beauty and without which we would be less able to appreciate the miracles of spring and summer when they come.

Christian Values in 'The Snow Queen'

The emotional dynamic of the story is the tug-of-love between the Snow Queen, who is cold and domineering, and Gerda, who is warm, loving and giving – Christian 'Caritas' in person. They are struggling for possession of the heart and soul of Kay.

The Snow Queen, unlike C.S. Lewis's White Witch, cannot be considered a truly evil figure, any more than an iceberg or other force of nature can be evil. Her eyes may have 'no peace in them' but there is no moral inflection to Andersen's characterisation of her. True, she kidnaps Kay, but he initiates his own abduction by hitching his sledge to her wagon.

However, the Snow Queen is the catalyst for the moral development of Kay and Gerda and their redemption through suffering. In this role, she may be seen as the agent of a moral Providence. Once Kay and Gerda are united in her icy realm, she does not attempt to oppose them but simply melts away to attend to other business (as does Death, on hearing the Nightingale's music). Andersen depicts real evil elsewhere. In 'The Red Shoes' and 'The Rose Elf', the horrors are the fault, not of any supernatural or ultra-natural figure, but of human beings indulging their familiar sins of vanity and hatred.

'The Snow Queen' is a geographical journey over vast distances in the world's most inhospitable and deadly terrains: Lapland, Finland and the North Pole; this parallels the moral journey from loss to reunion, childhood to maturity, estrangement to love, heartlessness to self-knowledge, arrogance to humility, bewilderment to enlightenment.

Each stage on the journey has its own distinct character and register: The Enchanted Garden, where Gerda has an illusory sense of security but is being held back from her goal; The Prince and Princess episode, in which she is well-treated and assisted, but where her hopes that she has found Kay are dashed; with the Robbers, where she is in jeopardy but where she makes the first real breakthroughs in her quest; in Lapland and Finland, where she gets 'warmer' although the temperature drops; and, finally, in the Snow Queen's Palace – the veritable Heart, not of Darkness but of its equally terrifying opposite, utter Whiteness – where, paradoxically, she finds her heart's desire. Nothing can be concealed in such dazzling brilliance. The scales fall from Kay's eyes and his moral vision is restored; and so it is shown that the rewards of maturity and fulfilment are achieved only by pushing through pain, ignorance and resistance.

Having attained the Heart of Whiteness, Gerda and the rescued Kay retrace their steps, back from terrifying maturity, with all its choices and uncertainties, to the scenes of their contented childhood. Andersen intends his story to illuminate his Biblical quote, 'except ye become as little children'. His ultimate value is the transcendent power of love, supported by the pillars of courage, conscience and steadfastness. Gerda is ever more true to her goal. The 'happy ever after' she and Kay attain, while being a fairytale convention, is also consistent with Andersen's moral and religious message.

Devices, Conceits and Metaphors

Andersen's prose is bestrewn with devices which are not so much figures of speech as philosophical concepts in deceptively naïve literary clothing. They often have a scientific or metaphysical content: the placing of the heated penny against the window to melt the ice is one such, as is the observation of the perfect six-sided snowflakes which coagulate to form the Snow Queen. When Gerda is smuggled into the Princess's palace by the talking raven, she creeps along the corridors trying not to make any noise. Andersen tells us that a few dreams rustle past. What a strange and lovely conceit, that dreams could actually detach themselves physically from the dreamer and become discernible.

In the Snow Queen's palace, the windows are made of the cutting winds. How can a window, which is a solid barrier to keep the wind out, itself be made of wind? This may seem pure poetic licence, but it is a physical fact that very strong winds, although made of nothing but air, can constitute both an impassible, albeit transparent, barrier and an irresistible force to solid objects. The beautiful and mysterious Aurora Borealis is explained nowadays as the interaction of solar wind particles with the magnetism at the North Pole, and force fields created by electro-magnetism and other invisible phenomena are by now a familiar dramatic device in science fiction. The most intellectually tantalising, yet aesthetically exquisite device of all is at the climax of 'The Snow Queen', where Kay tries to form the word 'Eternity' from pieces of ice. Does Andersen mean the symbol of Eternity, the circle or the mathematical symbol, which looks like a figure eight on its side, or does he mean the actual word? Or, are words and symbols meant to be indicative of Eternity itself? How are we to understand what Kay is trying to do? Is it an impossible mathematical task, like squaring the circle, or is it grasping at an elusive philosophical concept?

Thinking along these lines leads me to wonder whether the character of Kay is based on Søren Kierkegaard, outstanding philosophical genius of the Danish Golden Age whose particular brand of anguished asceticism may be fancifully depicted in Kay's task. Kay's name is also Kierkegaard's initial, 'K'. Furthermore, Kay is something of a mathematical whizz and can do fractions in his head, although, in the presence of the Snow Queen, he wonders if he knows so very much after all.

Kierkegaard's life was never the same again after his broken engagement with Regine Olsen. He left her, not for anything so ordinary as another girl, but in pursuit of his own austere commitment to philosophy. Veiled allusions to Regine inform many passages in his philosophical writings. The concepts of eroticism and the demonic, and the persona of Don Juan provide the inspiration for some of Kierkegaard's greatest metaphysical fugues, in which the significance of Regine's name (Regine is the Frenchified version of the Latin word for 'Queen') has been remarked upon. Is Regine represented in the character of the Snow Queen, or in Gerda, the faithful girl next door? From my reading of Kierkegaard's biography, I see philosophy as his personal Snow Queen, for whom he abandoned the satisfactions of bourgeois domesticity, and I believe that Kierkegaard's philosophy is the intellectual hard core of Andersen's tale. The dazzling purity of the Snow Queen is an untainted absolute value, a Platonic ideal, and a metaphor for the mathematical underpinning of nature, which unfailingly produces phenomena such as perfect six-sided snowflakes.

The Enchanted Garden where summer time stands uneasily still, masking the reality of autumn outside is a reworking of a recurrent folk motif. In the story of Thomas the Rhymer, Thomas is kidnapped to fairyland for what seems like a few days, returning to find that seven years have elapsed. Conversely, in other stories, the central character lives a whole life elsewhere in the twinkling of an eye in ordinary time. The false Indian summer is reminiscent of the fairy gold which fades to withered leaves at dawn, as well as being indicative of life's brevity. August Strindberg wrote: 'Once I sat on a verandah under green leaves, now my life is nothing but ashes. I was like someone who fell asleep in a beautiful palace and awoke in a hovel.' Or in William Blake's words, 'But my time of youth is fled/And grey hairs are on my head.'

According to Stephen Hawking, 'there are two sorts of Time: real, objective time and psychological time.' And, in Einstein's relativistic universe, with its black holes, time itself becomes bendy. before them both, Andersen had the intellectual mettle to convey in popular literary form the most challenging scientific and metaphysical concepts.

Feminism and Gender Bending

Practically every character in 'The Snow Queen' is female, most notably its eponymous central figure. The main man of the story, immature and arrogant, is the passive object of both the Queen's seduction and Gerda's redeeming love. Other characters are all shamanesses, with a bluestocking (the Princess) and a tomboy (the Robber Maiden) for good measure. The Reindeer, who is a male, spends his time *chez* the robbers in a state of funk. Going by this evidence, Andersen finds women more morally courageous and admirable than his own sex.

The femininity of Gerda is no wise compromised by the fact that she takes the active role in rescuing Kay, and we identify with her all the more, precisely because she is just an ordinary girl subjected to superhuman trials of strength and endurance.

Is it feasible that dutiful Gerda would drop everything in pursuit of too-clever-by-half Kay, who has thrown her over? Andersen anticipates this question, albeit subliminally, putting it into the mouth of the Robber Maiden, who calls Kay a 'graceless truant'. The Robber Maiden may be seen as Gerda's feminist alter ego. Andersen depicts her no-nonsense swagger and independence with distinct approval.

For all her alarming outbursts and mannish manners, the Robber Maiden is an attractive character. Andersen admired her type in real life and indulged one of his unrequited passions for the boisterous French actress Rachel. Contrary to what is often supposed, not only do men forgive girls for smoking cigars, drinking with the boys and even having a moustache *à la* Frida Kahlo – they find such characteristics positively endearing. 'Good blokes', such girls are called. The Robber Maiden may carry a knife and throw her weight around, but she is of greater assistance to Gerda's quest than any previous character. Gerda's encounter with her is the *Wendepunkt* of the *Novelle*.

The Snow Queen herself is the *deus ex machina* of the tale. She is not purely supernatural: she has an external, objective existence of her own. She can be interpreted variously as a metaphor for the seductive, deadly beauty of winter, or for a certain type of woman, the cold-hearted siren, the Swedish Queen Christina or Russian Catherine the Great, chatelaine of innumerable 'Winter Palaces' in various parts of her snowbound empire.

The story's psychological structure of a series of trials to which its characters must submit to become better people and win their heart's desires is common in folklore, as is: the girl who goes through hell and

high water to win her prince. Examples are Cinderella, Rapunzel and, in Greek mythology, Psyche. It is often the girl, supposedly the weaker vessel, who endures trials of body and mind in these tales. The fact that women are traditionally expected to adopt a more passive role adds piquancy and drama to this gender reversal.

Eroticisim in 'The Snow Queen'

Literature, like life, is full of ironies. The myth of Hans Christian Andersen is of someone unworldly, childishly naïve, a stranger to adult erotic relationships. His fairytales are read as children's fantasies. Like Jane Austen, he is wrongly perceived as a person of spinsterish gentility.

'The Snow Queen' is suffused with discreet eroticism: the whole story hinges on the romantic relationship of Gerda and Kay. There is a conventional fairytale-within-a-tale, namely the episode of the Princess who has chosen a husband by public competition, which is a common theme in Grimm's *Kinder- und Hausmärchen*; in Celtic legends, Norse mythology (Skadi chooses Njord by mistake for Balder); in *Turandot* and also in the *Arabian Nights*. Andersen progresses beyond the bounds of convention by taking us into the bedroom and showing us the Prince and Princess asleep together in their sumptuous bed.

'The Snow Queen' has echoes of many 'quest' and 'trial and tribula-
tion' fairytales, in which the erotic or romantic impulse to find a mate is
the key emotion and impetus of the action.

Andersen's poetic aestheticism, his perception of the beauties of nature
and of people, are the distillate of Romanticism. Each female character
has her own personal perfume, be it icy and ozonic in the case of the
Snow Queen, wholesome as new-baked bread in that of Gerda, expensive
and classic for the Princess, and exotic, spicy, with a hint of tobacco and
leather – the Robber Maiden. Even the Lapland and the Finland Women
sweltering in their saunas, must reek of birch twigs, smoked fish, Stock-
holm tar and whale-oil, no doubt a turn-on for those who like that sort
of thing!

Andersen's literary eroticism was at odds with the difficulties he experienced in fulfilling his real-life romantic aspirations, although he was an
eternal optimist and never forgot his first love, Riborg Voigt, whose letters
were found on his person when he died. Throughout his life he formed
deep attachments, including one to the 'Swedish Nightingale' Jenny Lind.
His bachelor status left him free to romanticise romanticism. Had he married, banal reality might have alienated his artist's nature and frozen his
feelings. He might have become like Kay, numbed in a barren relationship
to his polar Queen, his heart transpierced by a splinter of ice.

Andersen and Small Things

Humble things have great significance for Hans Andersen. Be these small
things in the form of inanimate objects, plants or creatures, his sharp eyes
spot them among the dust and debris under our feet or half-concealed
among the roof tops over our heads, and invest them with personality,
drama and ethical portent in inverse proportion to their physical size,
social status or monetary value. He constructs story after story around
the Christian theme of humility ('The Red Shoes', 'The Little Match Girl',
'The Angel', 'The Daisy' etc.) The spiritual importance of those who are
lowly in worldly terms is a value to which Andersen returns habitually
and which he treats in every genre at his Protean command.

At the beginning of 'The Snow Queen', Kay and Gerda inhabit an
Eden constructed from the humblest of materials. I can attest that his
observation of the improvisational self-sufficiency of childhood games is
acute. When I was a child, our gang would search the woods behind our
home for any interesting items which people might have dropped. On one

occasion, we found a spelling book, on another, a brightly-coloured wrapper from a packet of stockings and on another, an oval piece of pink plastic. All of these were scrutinised and their significance debated before they were stowed carefully in a hollow under a hedge. I remember creating a banquet of soap foam dyed pink, with 'burgers' of dried mud. Andersen's goblin feast in 'The Elfin Hall' is similar:

> In the kitchen, frogs were roasting on the spit; while other choice dishes, such as mushroom seed, hemlock soup, etc. were ready or were being prepared. These were to supply the first courses. Rusty nails, bits of coloured glass, and such like dainties, were to come in for the dessert.

In 'The Goloshes of Fortune', even the bacteria in ditch water come in for the Andersen treatment:

> The water splashed up among the green branches above, and the clerk thought of the millions of tiny creatures that must have been hurled upwards in those drops of water. To them it must have been as fearful as it would be for us to be suddenly whirled high into the regions of the clouds.

Andersen and Horror

Passages of horror in Andersen's stories are anchored with other, quite different emotions, resulting in a complex structure of complementary or contradictory ideas. In 'The Red Shoes', it is the fact that Karen is such a pretty little girl, guilty of little more than mere frivolity, which makes it so especially horrific that she is eventually reduced to begging the executioner to cut off her feet. Prior to that, she has been unable to control her dancing feet, so that she gives her benefactress many a kick on the shins when they are riding together in the carriage. The underlying nightmare is losing control, through a kind of Tourette's syndrome, so that one's body behaves objectionably despite desperate efforts to bring it to heel. It is the fear of losing parts of one's body integral to one's whole self-image, which gives 'The Red Shoes' such potency: in other words, fear of losing control sends a shudder through the subconscious, which abhors its own annihilation above all else. It is not even as if Karen is able to rid herself of her feet by having them cut off: in a variant of the macabre 'Hand of Glory' idea – where a severed hand holding candles is an accessory at witches' sabbaths – Karen's bleeding feet dance before her, disbarring her attempts to return to church.

However, in 'The Snow Queen' and 'The Nightingale', the reader does not experience either the Snow Queen or Death as evil. They are cast as forces of nature. And in the final analysis, they are no match for Art and Love respectively.

This world's phenomena fleet away: ice caps melt, people age and die, possessions decay and even relationships falter. Material reality is ultimately insubstantial. What abides, however, is the power of our ideas and our dreams, indestructible because incorporeal, through which we realise the hidden significance of all things and apprehend the Eternal Verities of Goodness, Truth and Beauty. Surely this is what Andersen, like a seer or a pilgrim bringing riches from the spiritual realm, a wise man in the guise of a fool, means us to understand.

Claire Thomson

A Land of Machines
Time, Technology and Otherness
in some tales by Hans Christian Andersen

WALTER BENJAMIN ONCE mused that 'each epoch dreams the one to follow'; he was quoting Michelet, but the mutually-illuminating relationship between past and future eras that this axiom sets up is key to Benjamin's writings. Kaja Silverman has paraphrased this with the eloquent formulation: 'We awaken from the dream of the century that preceded our own by relating our 'now' to its 'then'. That is, the seeds of our own epoch are sown in the previous one, we 'actualise' our forebears' dreams; but this has little to do with a linear conception of progressive history, which Benjamin was keen to discourage. Rather, the most fruitful way to 'use' history was, for Benjamin, to bring the past into a constellation with the present:

> Historicism contents itself with establishing a causal connection between various moments in history. But no fact that is a cause is for that very reason historical. It became historical posthumously, as it

were, through events that may be separated from it by thousands of years. A historian who takes this as his point of departure stops telling the sequence of events like the beads of a rosary. Instead, he grasps the constellation which his own era has formed with a definite earlier one. Thus he establishes a conception of the present as the 'time of the now' which is shot through with chips of Messianic time.

Elsewhere in his 'Theses on the Philosophy of History', Benjamin was also critical of the modern tendency to imagine time as 'homogeneous' and 'empty', or as a kind of tunnel through which the progress of humankind would flow. For him, the twin ideas of linearity and progress (scientific, moral, æsthetic, etc.) cannot be rent asunder; to critique progress requires a critique of this kind of conception of time, and vice versa.

Hans Christian Andersen might be said to prefigure Benjamin's view of history in his thoughts about what the future would bring in the way of æsthetic developments and technological advances. There is a distinctive turn in the narrative voice of the storyteller when he wonders about 'The New Century's Muse' or the young American tourists who will visit 'Old Europe' in their airships a few millennia from now. That Andersen was fascinated by, and well-informed about, contemporary science is well-established. Ljudmilla Braude has traced the thematic cross-currents between his travelogues and his tales and Brigid Gaffikin convincingly shows that the fairytale world of Andersen was in fact deeply rooted in everyday material culture and practices.

What concerns me here is the meeting of technology and history in three of Andersen's tales, written in the 1850s and 1860s. But I am not so concerned with technology as a border-crossing between the fictional fairytale world and the material world in which Andersen lived and wrote, anchoring the tales in a particular epoch and stage of technological advancement. Technology functions in some of Andersen's tales as a means to think through what it might mean to live in history, to open up an imaginative space in which contemporary events and phenomena can be contextualised not simply as part of a sequence of events in the history of his time – Benjamin's beads on a rosary – but as part of a constellation which future eras might map out and interpret. I would like to suggest that Andersen's tales celebrate technological advances without projecting a teleology of progress onto the forward march of history. Instead, technology is seen to interact with humankind and with nature to produce transformations in the world, but without accelerating into what we would today call a post-Enlightenment historical narrative.

There is a very simple example of this in 'Vænø og Glænø' (Vænø Island and Glænø Island). In this tale, the two islands are ravaged by a storm one night, and one disappears. The temporality is typical fairytale: 'Der laae engang... En Nat blev det et forfærdeligt Veir' (Once upon a time there was... One night, there was a terrible storm) – and Vænø sinks beneath the waves only to bide its time, and wait for Glænø to join it. The reader is then addressed directly by the narrator, recounting that s/he was on the beach gazing out towards Glænø, but then goes out into the world for an indeterminate length of time and, on returning, is astonished to find that Glænø has disappeared – when was the second great storm? But in fact it is 'Menneskekløgt' (human ingenuity) that has taken Glænø away: built a dam, drained the watery inlet and made the island part of Zealand. In a dizzying reversal of the expected perspective, the explanation sounds like this:

Det var ikke Vænø, som hentede Glænø, det var Sjælland, som med lange Dige-Arme greb til og med Pompernes Mundveir blæste og læste Trylleordene, Formælingens Ord, og Sjælland fik mange Tønder Land i Brudegave.
(It was not Vænø Island that took Glænø Island, it was Zealand that reached out with the long arms of its sea-walls and with the mouth music of the pumps pronounced the words of enchantment, the nuptial vows, and Zealand gained many acres of land as a dowry.)

The twist in this tale is that the expected disappearance of Glænø is not an act of nature but an act of humankind. The mix of imagery here is interesting: the dams and pumps become part of the body of the eager bridegroom, the marriage vows are described as conjuring words as well as nuptial vows, and the dowry is a stretch of land. Thus a truce is established around this event, as the narrator refuses to criticise the engineers' interference in nature, the reclaiming of land from the sea, preferring to romanticise it as a physical union between Zealand and Glænø which has the blessing of both magic and religion. And it has taken place behind the back of the unsuspecting addressee of the text, who has left the area for a period which is left vague and described only in the fateful language of fairytale time. 'Og dog ere Glænø's Dage talte; vi kunne ikke sige, hvor mange de ere, men der ere talte, en skjøn Morgen er Øen forsvunden'(And yet Glænø Island's days are numbered; we cannot count them, but they are numbered, and one fine morning the island is gone). The technology responsible for this transformation is simply incorporated into the time – and the ontological logic – of the fairytale.

More of a panoramic view of the interaction of human ingenuity with the landscape is given in 'Om Aartusinder' (In Thousands of Years). Here, some young Americans, a few millennia in the future – 'Om Aartusinder komme de!' (In Thousands of years they will come!) – fly over the European continent in an airship, and what they see, as well as what they associate with the now-vanished civilisations, is described to us by a narrator who is not omniscient enough to know what has happened between our time and theirs, or even how much time has passed. The storyteller does not position himself in some imagined future epoch and look back. Rather, the narrator fudges the issue of the passage of time between the crumbling of Old Europe and the arrival of the tourists. They fly over the ruins of towns on the Danube which 'vor Tid ikke kjendte' (our time did not know); in Paris, they get excited about 'Helte, Skjalde og Videnskabsmænd, som vor Tid ikke kjender, men som skulle fødes paa Europas Krater: Paris' (Heroes, poets and scientists, which our time does not know, but who would be born in the crater of Europe: Paris). The sights and names which 'our time' does not know, however, are interspersed with the great cities, natural wonders, and famous names which the mid-nineteenth century has inherited from a jumble of different eras. The British Isles, known both as the land of Shakespeare and as 'a land of machines', have been joined to France by a channel tunnel. The geysers of Iceland have ceased to steam, Germany's network of canals and railways has gone, and the splendours of Rome have crumbled into dust and desert, leaving only a fragment of St Peter's, whose very authenticity is questionable.

This last comment on authenticity by the narrator is interesting, because it raises the possibility that the material ruins of Europe are reduced to something even less material than dust – they are just stories, fragments invested by the guidebooks with the aura of an ancient civilisation. And in fact the last line of this tale mentions a guidebook used by the travellers, *Europa Seet i otte Dage* (Europe in Eight Days), the author of which is not named, but referred to only as 'a name belonging to their time'. Their time, presumably, is 'millennia hence', which is one translation of the Danish title of 'Om Aartusinder', but I prefer to think of 'om' here in the sense of 'about', so that the tale becomes 'about millennia' – 'about' how the piles upon piles of years and centuries lie spread out before the future traveller, whose own era, its point of view distilled into the guidebook, brings the past into a constellation according to its own needs: 'every image of the past that is not recognised by the present as one of its own concerns threatens to disappear irretrievably', as Benjamin puts it. Fundamentally, though, the 'needs' of this undefined future time are dictated by the possibilities for travel which the tourists' epoch accords them. They travel in a 'Luftskib' (airship), 'paa Dampens Vinger' (on the wings of steam), and the size of their party has already been communicated via an under-sea electromagnetic cable. Their experience of the remains of the past in the landscape of Europe is, then, inseparable from the touristic practice which their technology affords them.

A relaxed acceptance of historical contingency is at work in these tales. The permanence of the landscape, geo-political centres and borders, the organisation of industry, literary canonicity and transportation practices are not the natural order of things, though the contemporary epoch may be comfortable in its conception of them as such; they are transient and contingent. It is the shift in perspective in both these tales that reveals the storyteller's fascination for how future epochs will see the mid-nineteenth century and its own pasts.

Things look different – the coast of Zealand after the incorporation of Glænø, and the landscape of Europe after the ravages of untold centuries. The corollary for the storyteller in 'Om Aartusinder' is that the

cultural map of Europe also looks different; it has different landmarks, they mean different things, and the chronological chasms that separate previous epochs, at least for the mid-nineteenth century reader, are etiolated by the passage of time and the needs of the imagined future present. The temporal depth of the European cultural heritage is flattened and its history spatialised.

It is instructive to contextualise this kind of angle on history by thinking of what the prevailing literary representation of history in the mid-nineteenth century is supposed to have been. This is the era in which, according to Benedict Anderson's thesis of the burgeoning of the imagined national community in Europe, the mass-circulation, realist novel disseminated a particular conception of national community as territorially bounded, and constantly progressing to some limitless future through 'homogeneous, empty time' – his point being that the very conception of historical time which Benjamin critiqued as irrevocably tied to political and economic progress is also tied to the novel.

Andersen's tales arguably constitute a mass-circulation counterpoint to the realist, historical novels that Danes such as Ingemann produced in the wake of Walter Scott. Mid-nineteenth century Danes were reading – and performing – tales which discuss and structure time as something other than linear, homogeneous and empty, and (national) space as permeable and relative. They were also reading tales which were deeply engaged with the material culture of the time and 'learning' how to think about the relationship between technology, society and history.

I'm now going to turn to 'Det nye Aarhundredes Musa' (The New Century's Muse), which is not really a tale, although it appears in the 1861 collection *Nye Eventyr og Historier* (New Tales and Stories). It is more of a rumination on the development of culture in a new age which somehow grows out of the present. But, again, there is the impression of two epochs – literally, in this text, spacetimes – standing in relation to each other, growing out of each other, the one defining the other: 'Hvert Aarhundrede, hvert Aartusinde kan der ogsaa siges, har sit Storheds Udtryk i Poesien; født i det afsluttende Tidsrum, træder den frem og raader i det nye kommende Tidsrum' (Each century, each millennium can also be said to find the expression of its greatness in poetry; born in the epoch that is coming to an end [literally, 'time-space'], it steps forward and reigns in the new era). And the Muse understands her debt to many epochs: 'Forstandens Lynglimt fik hun, i alle Prismets gjennem Aartusinder skiftende Farver, der vurderedes efter modefarven' (she catches the lightning bolt of intellect in all the colours of the prism as they shift from one millennium to the next, judged by the colours of fashion). Like Benjamin, she sees the contingency – the shifting fashions – of understandings of the past.

The central figure is, indeed, a muse, who remains a small child for most of the text, and the narrator describes her cultural and genetic heritage. The Muse is, naturally, cosmopolitan (she has Holberg bound in one volume with Molière, Plato and Aristophanes, but mostly reads Molière). Her nursery is lined with the great epics of Iceland, Germany and the Orient, and she has heard Mozart and Beethoven. She has her 'blood and soul' from her mother and father, each representing an aspect of the people: on her father's side she is 'Folkets Barn' (a child of the folk), hale and hearty, while her mother is rather more bourgeoise: 'den høibaarne academi-opdragne, Emigrantens Datter med de gyldne Rococo Erindringer' (the high-born, academy-educated, emigré's daughter, with the golden Rococo memories).

With this migrant blood in her, where she might eventually arrive from is a subject of some speculation for the narrator. Will it be America, the Arab world, the Far East, from Britain (this time described as 'Steenkuls-Øen, hvor Shakspeare er Herskeren fra Elisabeths Tid' – the Isle of Coal, where Shakespeare prevails from Elizabeth's time). And she is even-handed as far as national traditions are concerned: 'Nationaliteternes Hjertslag, hver er kun eet Bogstav i det store Udviklings-Alphabet, men hvert Bogstav griber hun med lige Kjærlighed, stiller dem i Ord og slynger Ordene i Rythmer til sin Nutids Hymne' (The heartbeat of nations, each is only one letter in the great alphabet of development, but she grasps every letter with the same love, makes them into words and casts the words into the rhythms of the hymns of her present). Again, the imagery is couched in terms of an arrangement of riches from the past, from many sources, this time in the form of letters emanating from different national heritages, brought into meaningful synthesis. Benjamin also related his constellations to writing, arrangements of words on paper.

The narrator's assumption is that this New Century's Muse has already been born, though when she will spring into action he does not know. He does, however, know where she was born: in the great factory of the present. The sound of her arrival was stifled by 'klapprende Maskiner, Locomotivets Piben, Sprængningen af materielle Klipper og Aandens gamle Baand' (clattering machines, the locomotive's whistle, the blasting of great cliffs and of the old fetters of the spirit). And her technological environment is further enriched by the gifts she is given in her cradle:

af Dykkerklokken er rystet vidunderligt >>Nips<< fra Havets Dyb. Himmelkortet, dette ophængte stille Ocean med de Myriader Øer, hver en Verden, blev lagt aftrykt som Vuggeklæde. Solen maler hende Billeder; Photografien maa give hende Legetøi.

(From the diving bell tumbles wonderful bric-à-brac from the depths of the sea. The map of the skies, that still, suspended ocean with the myriad islands, each its own world, was printed as a blanket for her cradle. The sun paints pictures for her; photography must give her playthings.)

The allegory is obvious enough – that the new century's Muse will have at her disposal knowledge of the map of the universe and of the Earth's oceans, and she will be able to exploit the new medium of photography. The inextricable linkage between technology and nature which we saw in the two other tales is also fundamental here. Technology makes possible exploration and explanation; and thereby it makes possible a new cultural epoch, which grows out of the present.

It strikes me that that the New Century's Muse is not so far from a cyborg – a particular kind of cyborg, of course. This may seem an outrageous suggestion, but think of Donna Haraway's seminal essay from the mid-1980s, 'A Manifesto for Cyborgs', in which she develops the cyborg as a metaphor for feminist action in late-twentieth century society:

...my cyborg myth is about transgressed boundaries, potent fusions, and dangerous possibilities which progressive people might explore.

The dichotomies between mind and body, animal and human, organism and machine, public and private, nature and culture, men and women, primitive and civilised are all in question ideologically.

Cyborg writing is about the power to survive, not on the basis of original innocence, but on the basis of seizing the tools to mark the world that marked them as other [...] The tools are often stories, retold stories, versions that reverse and displace the hierarchical dualisms of naturalized identities. In retelling origin stories, cyborg authors subvert the central myths of origin of Western culture.

I will not labour the question of the extent to which Andersen's writing seizes 'the tools to mark the world that marked [him] as other', or to what extent his stories 'reverse and displace the hierarchical dualisms of naturalized identities'. But this Muse from some future epoch is not afraid to take up her technological tools and exploit them to carve out the cultural expressions of her time. After all, to borrow a Danish expression, she drank in technology with her mother's milk. But neither is she a stranger to nature. She rides on dolphins as well as on locomotives, through tunnels and over viaducts. And her rearranging of the fruits of previous epochs is certainly all about 'transgressed boundaries, potent fusions, and dangerous possibilities'.

Towards the end, the narrator finds one possible answer as to when the Muse will arrive. For all the Orientalism – albeit cosmopolitan Orientalism – that roams the pages of Andersen's collected tales and travel writings, the new technologies of transport and communication carry his travellers toward a meeting with another epoch, as much as toward geopolitical boundaries and ethnic Others. He anticipates the expansion of the European railways as far as China, and, he says, then the Great Wall of China will fall – whether it will literally crumble, as in the Europe of 'Om Aartusinder', or if this is metaphorical, is unclear. But when 'Asiens aflukkede Cultur-Archiv' (the locked-away cultural archive of Asia) is opened and 'de to Cultur-Strømme mødes' (the two streams of culture meet), what sounds will ring out! It will be a kind of Ragnarok, and both eras and races will disappear, leaving only some images of each to float like lotus flowers on the stream of eternity. Then says the narrator, we will recognise that we are all of the same flesh, but in different attire. In this case, not only does technology change the landscape and draw borders and boundaries closer together, even dissolving them (an early stab at the concept of spacetime compression!), it is the catalyst for the new era with the cyborg muse, an era in which contemporary nationalities, contemporary Others, are re-arranged and synthesised.

These tales, then, do not deny or ignore chronological progression, but they display a resistance to history as 'beads on a string' – what is interesting to the narrator in each case is the relationship between one century or millennium and another. Thus the other epoch becomes the Other; it must, as Benjamin insists, 'dream the next', but the gaze of succeeding epochs transforms it. The New Century's Muse, says the storyteller, has read a terrifying amount, and must learn what to forget: 'grumme Meget maa glemmes igen og Musaen vil forstaae at glemme' (an awful lot must be forgotten again and the Muse will know how to forget), so that history can be interpreted according to the needs of her present.

References

Andersen, Hans Christian (1989; 1905): *Samlede Eventyr og Historier. Jubilæum-sudgave*. Odense: Hans Reitzels forlag, Flensteds forlag.

Anderson, Benedict (1991): *Imagined Communities: Reflections on the Origin and Spread of Nationalism*. London: Verso.

Benjamin, Walter (1999): 'Theses on the Philosophy of History' in *Illuminations*. Introduced by Hannah Arendt. Translated from the German by Harry Zohn. London: Pimlico.

Braude, Ljudmila (1999): 'Hans Christian Andersen's Writer's Manifesto In Sweden – Andersen and Science', in Johan de Mylius, Aage Jørgensen and Viggo Hjørnager Pedersen (eds): *Hans Christian Andersen. A Poet in Time. Papers from the Second International Hans Christian Andersen Conference 29 July to 2 August 1996*. The Hans Christian Andersen Center, Odense University, Odense University Press.

Gaffikin, Brigid (2004): 'Material Witnesses. Hans Christian Andersen's 'Tingseventyr' and the Memories of Things', in *Edda: Scandinavian Journal of Literary Research* 2004:3, pp. 186–200.

Haraway, Donna J. (1991): 'A Cyborg Manifesto: Science, Technology and Socialist-Feminism in the Late Twentieth Century', in *Simians, Cyborgs and Women: The Reinvention of Nature*. London: Free Association Books.

Silverman, Kaja (2002): 'The Dream of the Nineteenth Century', in *Camera Obscura* 51, 17:3, pp. 1–29.

Note

The translations from the Danish in 'Land of Machines' are by Claire Thomson.

The illustrations accompanying the articles by Harriet Lyall and Claire Thomson are by Vilhelm Pedersen (1820–59), Andersen's own favourite illustrator of his work.

David Campbell

Little Traveller

Hailed by love to the
               sanctum sanctorum
Little one
               I have felt you grow
Found the woman's wonder
               of a womb
Where in our secret dark
               enigma you
Decoded into human form
And when
               I ran to scan
               and see the news
Those who could decipher
               the encrypted signs
Let me know that now
               you lay within me dead
               my womb your tomb
And how to say farewell when
               yet we never met
A double grief, to bring you here
               and to your grave
Yet I know
               amidst this drowning salt
That you have been
               however briefly
               and will somewhere be.

The Despot Dwarf

Comfortable, alone
We sit in our bath
The tyrant and I.
He sleeps and allows
me to plan
to sneak off and escape him
awhile:
such a pampered little
wrapped up in a shawl
cosy vole-like
blind pink little
wrinkled manikin;
settled asleep there
on his arsenals
of more than
new clear power
in the red woods.
Does he stir?
As little as a thought's
shadow : action.
He waits and schemes
requisitions my body and mind,
billets his patience,
intents, in my thoughts,
his spies in MI5 fingers
'Come on dears', my words;
dictates the night
yet there he sleeps
baby tyrant
pink-snug
in his bath
the pygmy ruler
of our world.

Ghost Lover

You came to me
                        in sun-bright day
Hot your lips
                             with poetry
You sought my song
                                I gave my soul
Your laughter rang
                             as if in tune
You mined my eyes
                       jewels of surprise
Then how you glowed
                             as if on fire
And from you flowed
                    such strange desire
That sucked my youth
                     in slakeless drouth
I'd never met
                       the living dead
Nor known the dread
                     that can't be fed
And haunts to seek
                   life from the quick
You were not there
                  you were not there
And so in lies
                   you lay with me
Ghost lover
          nor eyes nor thighs nor song
Can salve your pain
                        begone

Anita Govan

maybe

maybe it's not to be known
or given a name

maybe it's not to try, tie it down
place it, make it fit

maybe it's not to understand
but to take for what it is

maybe it's not to ask why or how
but let flourish without constraint

maybe it's not to be questioned
but allowed to be heard

maybe it's not to figure out
but for us to hold in faith

maybe it's not to be feared
but held and then embraced

maybe it's not about the future
but the present we live

Ruth Thomas

Careless

THERE WERE A lot of people in Accident and Emergency, and they all seemed to be bleeding. Everyone looked up as Joseph walked in, then away again, uninterested. They had all entered a new world, where bleeding was normal.

'What did you do?' the receptionist asked, glancing at the bright red Kleenex around Joseph's hand.

'I cut it with a chisel.'

'Chisels can be lethal,' the receptionist said, proferring a slip of yellow paper. 'You should be careful.'

She sighed and looked around the foyer, at all the careless people.

In the waiting-room Joseph found the last empty seat and sat down. There was a television fixed very high to the wall, showing a day-time chat show. *Help! I'm losing my mind* said the writing across the screen. But nobody was watching. Everyone was just sitting there in chastened silence, parts of themselves in makeshift bandages.

After a while a nurse called Joseph's name, and he got up and plodded into a little sectioned-off part of the room, behind a thin, pink and blue-striped curtain.

'What's been going on here, then?' the nurse asked.

'I cut it with a chisel.'

'Joseph the carpenter.' the nurse said.

'Mm.'

'What were you doing? Carving something?'

'Trying to.'

'Bet it hurts.'

'Just a bit.'

'Oh well', said the nurse. She uncurled the dried-up Kleenex from Joseph's hand and looked at the cut. A gash, three inches across his palm. The chisel had slipped just as he was turning a corner; he had been holding it wrong, not thinking, and this was what had happened.

'You'll need some stitches in that, dear,' the nurse said. She wiped the cut with a disinfectant and gave Joseph a professional-looking swab to put on it. Then she told him to go back to the waiting room.

The thing he had been carving was a present for his girlfriend. A small, wooden box, made out of pearwood. A box to keep things in. Necklaces, earrings. He had always been good at carpentry, and had been carving her name onto the top of it. CARA. The letters were difficult to get right, and he wished he'd chosen a squarer type-face instead of something with so many curlicues. Each letter had taken him a whole evening, sitting at the kitchen table until it had grown dark outside and he'd had to get up and switch the light on. CAR – he had just got to the end of the R when Cara told him she didn't want to be his girlfriend any more.

'What?' he said.

'We're drifting apart, aren't we?' said Cara.

'What?'

Cara sighed and picked up her coat and keys from his bed.

'I mean,' she said, 'you never even want to go out in the evenings any more. You just spend all the time hunched up over that bit of wood.'

'It's that prat in your Metaphysical lectures, isn't it?' Joseph said.

'No,' she said.

She had tears in her eyes, but that didn't seem to make any difference to her decision. 'Bye,' she said, walking to the bedroom door and quietly closing it behind her.

So now he just had this box that said CAR.

Since that weekend, he had done a lot of stupid things. He had fallen over playing five-a-side football with his flat-mates, gashing his knee on the astroturf; he had knocked three little espresso cups from the washing-up rack, watching them smash, one after the other; he had managed, somehow, to poke himself painfully in the eye. And now this, with the chisel.

There were a lot of people far worse off than him; he realised that. It was very humbling. But still. His hand hurt. He was bleeding.

With his good hand he picked up a magazine.

Beat the Christmas Rush: Our best recipe yet for a fabulously boozy cake. Detox the Celebrity Way! True Story: I walked my way out of heartbreak.

'They're all about four years old, son,' said a woman sitting down beside him. She was holding onto her elbow.

'Probably doesn't matter,' Joseph replied, letting the magazine flop back on the table. On the TV, the chat show ended and a soap opera began.

But Doug, I told him there was a storm forecast. I told him it was dangerous to go surfing.

An old man was wheeled past very slowly, a plastic tube dangling from beneath a pale blue tartan blanket. Joseph sighed. At least he wasn't an old man under a tartan blanket.

Cara had been his first serious girlfriend. Except their relationship hadn't been serious. It had been lighthearted. Maybe, he thought, if he hadn't done anything so serious as carving her name into a wooden box, they would still be together. Maybe if he had not answered the phone when she rang; not been there when they arranged to meet. To be loved, he had begun to realise, you had to be careless.

They had both belonged to the same tutorial group: Seventeenth Century Italian Literature at 3pm. They had met on the very first day of their very first year at university. Joseph had sat opposite Cara on a noisy, slightly broken chair, and thought how beautiful she looked. And how bright her questions were. And how good her voice sounded when she read Petrarch. They were eighteen. In the middle of the autumn term he had asked her out for lunch. 'Sure,' Cara had said, staring at him with her round brown eyes and twisting a kirby grip back into her falling-down hair. The following Monday they had sat together in the student union refectory, on either side of a compass-scratched table, contemplating two enormous, inadequately-topped pizzas.

'So,' Joseph said, 'are you a fan of pizza?'

Sometimes he wondered what she had seen in him. How on earth had he managed to interest a girl like her? But he had often heard girls describe him as sweet. Sweet and innocent. Ah, bless, they said, look at his wee dreamy face.

The soap opera ended and children's programmes began. A blonde woman jumped around the screen, singing about trains. Then there was a cartoon involving bears and a zookeeper.

At last someone called, 'Joseph Turner' and he creaked up out of his seat and walked across the room towards the nurse, holding his hand upright.

'How are you, Joseph Turner?' the nurse asked, leading him down a corridor towards another curtained-off section.

'I've been better,' Joseph replied.

'We'll soon have you sorted out,' said the nurse, drawing the curtain back on squeaking rails and walking away.

Joseph sat in the curtained-off section for three-quarters of an hour, his throbbing hand palm upwards on his lap. He listened to medical wooshing noises coming from the next cubicle, and someone talking in a loud, clear voice.

'WE'LL NEED TO TAKE YOUR BLOOD PRESSURE, MR CUTHBERT. IF IT'S TOO HIGH, THE DOCTOR WON'T LET YOU GO HOME.'

Mr Cuthbert said something that Joseph couldn't make out. Joseph saw shoes and grey wheels below the edge of the curtain, and Mr Cuthbert was trundled away.

He had now been in the emergency rooms for three and a quarter hours. When he moved the swab, his hand started to bleed again. Drops of deep scarlet on the floor, like a nose-bleed. The stupid shedding of romantic blood. What would Cara have said? What would she have done? Criticised him, probably, for holding the chisel wrong. The thing about Cara was that she looked romantic, but in fact she was deeply practical. She knew how to end a relationship, for instance, snapping it quickly, like a chicken's neck.

There was not much else to look at in the cubicle; just packets of *Tubigrips*, a white basin and a plastic bin which said *Property of the NHS. Sharps Only*. A small packet of waterproof plasters had been placed on the top of a hand-towel dispenser. He got up and walked towards the mirror above the basin. His eyes looked green in this light; green and slightly bloodshot. He returned to his seat, closed his eyes and listened to the buzz of the hospital. Voices and trollies.

At six-fifteen a male doctor arrived with a young woman. He sat down on the chair in front of Joseph, and the woman squatted by his side. Lovers, Joseph thought.

'So what have you been up to, Mr Turner?' the doctor asked cheerfully.

'I cut my hand with a chisel.'

'What were you doing – carving choir stalls?' the doctor brayed, glancing at the young woman for approval.

'Yes.'

The doctor looked a little irked. 'I see,' he said. He took Joseph's hand and peered at it. A very trivial injury, he looked as if he was thinking.

'OK,' he said to the young woman, 'how would you describe this? If you were telling me about it on the phone?'

The woman looked.

'A moderately deep flesh wound,' she said, 'a cut with a sharp instrument, about four centimetres long to the left of the left palm. Half-moon shape. Going up the way.'

'Going up the way,' the doctor said, 'yes. That should cover it.'

He wiped painfully at Joseph's blood with another piece of swab. 'We'll just put some sticky stitches on this, shall we?' he said.

'Sticky stitches?'

'They're, like, these little bits of tape', said the nurse. 'It's, like, much nicer than real stitches.'

I could just have stuck a plaster on myself, Joseph thought. And it wouldn't have taken me four-and-a-half hours. He watched as the doctor reached up to a shelf and took down a little sterile packet.

Walking along the green line back to reception, the smell of polish and surgical chemicals did something odd to his head. Objects in the corridor suddenly sprang up and presented themselves to him as if they were of great significance. Look at me! said the fire extinguisher, the sand bucket, the brown and white sign that said Lift to Upper Levels. Look at me! said the plant in the corner and the water cooler. Then he heard a voice; it was his own voice, low and mumbling, as he lunged his way towards a chair by the wall. He could feel sweat, cold and alarming, on his forehead. Perhaps I'm going to die, he thought, perhaps I'm going to die, broken-hearted, beside the fire extinguisher... He reached out to the chair and sat, his head bent, his mind swaying, just conscious of the enormous white plaster on his left hand. How strange: my hand is huge; it loomed up and he stared at it, absorbed, as if it was a thing of great beauty. People walked by, singly and in groups. Mr Cuthbert was wheeled past again, his leg still stuck straight out in front of him.

'Are you all right there?' a voice asked. Joseph looked up and saw a woman a long way away, almost floating, wearing a blue uniform.

'Just a bit faint,' he muttered in a thick voice that didn't sound like his.

'Can I call anyone for you, pet? Do you want me to phone your parents to come and fetch you?'

'My parents live in Dudley.'

The woman looked at him and smiled, and he could tell what she was thinking: Ah, bless. Look at his wee, dreamy face.

'I'll get you a cup of tea,' she said.

'Thank you,' Joseph replied. He paused. 'Two sugars please,' he added, as if he was in a café. As quickly as it had come, the faintness had washed over him and gone, like an ebbing sea. Now he felt OK; he just had a cold, clammy forehead and was sitting on a chair in a hospital corridor. He sat back and watched the nurse sway down the corridor and disappear beneath an archway. He looked across at a painting on the opposite wall. A picture of a vase with flowers in it, which, for some reason, made him think of Cara. A lot of things made him think of Cara. Maybe they always would. He looked at the clock on the wall. It was 6.15pm. He had been in hospital for six-and-a-half hours and now it was night-time. He had missed the whole day. If there were windows, the sky outside would be dark.

After a while there was the sound of footsteps, and the nurse in the blue uniform returned. She seemed like a figure in a dream, carrying a green china cup and a biscuit on a plate.

'There you are, pet,' she said. 'Take your time.'

'Thank you,' Joseph replied, touched by the biscuit. It had a little picture pressed into it of two stick-people playing table tennis. Sports biscuits. He remembered them from his childhood.

'I don't usually faint,' he said.

'It's always you men who faint,' the nurse replied jovially. 'People think women can't cope with the sight of blood, but it's actually the men.'

'Right,' Joseph said. He sipped his tea.

'What did you do to your hand, anyway?' the nurse asked.

'I cut it with a chisel.'

'Nasty.'

'Yes.'

He sat and thought of what he had been doing before he came into hospital. Sitting at the kitchen table, finishing the 'A' of Cara, because he had thought: What the hell? He might as well finish it. Ridiculous, to have a box that said CAR. Maybe he could give it to some other Cara one day. And then the chisel had slipped.

'I just held it wrong' said Joseph.

'That's what A&E is all about,' replied the nurse, 'people holding things wrong.'

'Yes,' he said, looking down at his hand and imagining the line of hard skin already beginning to form on his palm; a reminder that there will always be small disasters, to contradict the sweetness of life.

Balloon Shaped World

THERE WERE SO many exciting things in the party shop that she didn't know where to start. There were banners, balloons, hats, streamers and paper plates. There were monster faces, wigs, whoopee cushions and false moustaches.

'Would you like a basket?' the shop assistant asked Moira. He was wearing a badge that said *I'm 3*, and his voice did not seem to go with the shop. It was not an upbeat voice.

'OK.' Moira smiled and took one from him.

'Looking for anything particular?'

'Just stuff for a friend's birthday,' she said. 'I'm doing a surprise party.'

'Really?' said the young man gloomily. 'That sounds like fun.'

'Yes', Moira replied, losing her nerve. Maybe her friend would hate a surprise party. You always heard of people hating them. She looked down at a box full of joke Cracked Basin packets. (*Watch your friend's face fall when they think their basin's got a crack in it!*)

'He's going to be twenty-three,' she said.

'Oh'

'I don't suppose you've got any banners that say Happy 23rd Birthday?'

'No. We've got Happy 25th and Happy 21st. But no Happy 23rd.'

'Oh well. I'll just have a browse, then.'

'We've got these inflatable champagne bottles. They're fun.'

'Yes.'

'Or an inflatable birthday cake.'

'Yes. Well, I'll just have a...'

'Or dumb-bells.'

'Right.'

Moira picked up one of the Cracked Basin packets and wondered whether to put it in her basket. That was the trouble with shops like this: something happened to your sense of reality.

'Give me a shout if you need me,' the young man said, turning and plodding back to the counter. The label was sticking out of his jumper, and she felt an almost irresistible urge to tuck it back in.

She was not sure whether she was doing the right thing. But she had just been reading *In Hot Pursuit* – a book on romance which commanded the lonely reader to take the initiative. *The days of waiting to be asked out are over!* the book exclaimed in Chapter 2. *Why wait for him to pick up the phone? Times have changed! The goalposts have shifted!*

This was a typical line in the book. It was a book she despised, but still, but still... she had known this boy for nearly a year now, and there had been no romance so far.

'What's the worst that can happen?' her best friend Jo asked. 'You can just be really embarrassed for a while.'

'That's pretty bad.'

'Yes', said Jo, 'but it's not as if the world is going to explode.'

'No. Not the actual world.'

'Exactly. And I mean, nothing's happening at the moment, is it?'

'No, but maybe there's a reason for that. Maybe it's because he doesn't like me.'

'But Max is so enigmatic. You never know *what* he likes.'

'Hmm.'

Sometimes, Moira wondered if Jo was encouraging her romance because it was good entertainment. Because it was intriguing, like watching someone wading out into the cold North Sea, full of rubbish and jelly-fish, while you just stood on the shore with your arms folded.

Moira sighed, her eyes resting on a bin full of hinged, plastic snakes. She remembered owning a hinged, plastic snake when she was about eight, and the world was full of certainty.

'Excuse me,' said a girl in a red raincoat, 'can I just get to that?'

She gestured towards the bin, and Moira smiled her biggest smile and stood back. 'They're great, aren't they?' she said, as the girl picked one up and watched it curl from side to side. 'Don't they look real!'

Today she wanted to be happy. She wanted to be hopeful. But the longer she stayed in the party shop, the less she felt like giving a party. Her mind had drifted since she came in, bewildered by the streamers and banners and glitter, and she tried to focus again, homing in on the balloons. There was a huge array of them, plain, patterned, shaped, with writing, without writing. She considered getting some that said *Birthday Boy*, then imagined Max's face. Perhaps she shouldn't be doing this at all. But she had bought the pizza now, and the party compilation tape, and the dress.

She picked up ten purple balloons and took them to the counter.

'Can you fill these with helium?' she asked the young man.

Before he could reply, a bald-headed man suddenly popped up from beneath the counter, like a troll. She wasn't even aware he was in the shop. 'When's the party?' he asked.

'Tomorrow,' Moira replied, a little startled.

'It's just that, if you do it too early, love, they'll have shrivelled by the time the party starts.'

'Hmm.'

'Particularly in this cold weather. They'll shrivel. Although they will firm up again in the warmth. You just have to smooth them out again.'

'Hmm,' Moira said again, wondering if a gift for innuendo was necessary when working in a party shop.

The man looked steadily into her eyes.

'So. Shall we do it now or later?' he asked.

'I'm just wondering...' she said, holding the balloons tight in her fist and watching as the gloomy young assistant gave up on the idea of serving her and wandered away to the other side of the shop.

Maybe I'll go home and blow them up with my bicycle pump instead. Maybe helium-filled balloons are overrated. Maybe all this helium is bad for the world...

She let the balloons drop onto the counter in a little crushed heap.

'I'll pay for them now and get them blown up tomorrow,' she said. The bald-headed man sighed as if she'd made the wrong decision, and put the balloons into a paper bag that said *Party On!*

'£15 then, please,' he said, suddenly distant.

'Oh, I didn't realise... I didn't know they were so expensive.'

'The fancy ones are, darling. These are metallic. They're not like the ordinary rubber ones.'

Moira took her purse out of her bag and rummaged around in the small change section.

'I don't actually have £15 on me,' she said, watching out of the corner of her eye as the gloomy young assistant stopped at the helium machine and began inflating some pig-shaped balloons.

The man smiled, his mouth a beakish line.

'We'll just put them to one side for you then, shall we?' he said. 'You can come back.'

'Really? Are you sure?'

'No bother. Come back when you've got some money.' *In a couple of decades*, he looked as if he was thinking.

'Right. Thanks.'

And Moira left, closing the door on the sound of hissing, as if someone has just cycled over glass.

She had met Max McDonald several months earlier, at a life drawing class. He had been enigmatic from the start, drawing the model very silently and skillfully, while Moira had spent quarter of an hour setting up her easel only for it to collapse half-way through the class, slamming noisily against her head and sending her paper slapping to the ground. She had noticed Max sniggering from behind his own, expertly-arranged easel. Afterwards he had asked her where she lived, and when she said Dalry Road, he had said, 'That's my side of town,' and walked her home. Even though Dalry Road was actually a good twenty minutes away from where he lived.

This was a sign, according to Jo. Jo, the watcher from the shore. Jo, who was busy organising her wedding – to include sugared almonds and single-use cameras – to Doug, her long-term boyfriend.

'Some men just need a bit of encouragement,' said Jo. 'If he walked you home that definitely means he liked you.'

'But he only did it once. He never has again. Not since September.'

'He's waiting for you to make the next move.'

'Is he?'

'True love will wait until the end of time.'

'Mm-hmm.'

Men had always baffled her.

On her way home she stopped at the bakery and, with the remnants of her money, bought herself a *pain au raisin*. She had not eaten lunch, mainly because she could not afford it. She never met her friends for lunch, because it meant she had to watch them eating lasagne or aubergine bake with a choice of salads while she, a girl on Income Support, toyed with a cheese scone.

She had just bitten into the *pain au raisin* and was wiping crumbs and custard off her face when Max McDonald suddenly rounded the corner of the street, wearing his beautiful smile.

'Oh,' she said, blushing wildly. This was not supposed to happen. 'Hello. Still coming to the pub tomorrow?'

When she was embarrassed she always lurched precipitately into conversation. She stood and smiled at him, pastry flakes on her lips, the sun in her eyes. He was much taller than her.

'Actually,' said Max.

'Hmm?'

'I've...'

'Hmm?'

'I've got to go to Glasgow tomorrow. Our dog's died. And Mum's really down. So I'm just going home, you know, to be with her.'

'Oh no. God, that's such a shame. About the dog.'

'Yeah, thanks. She was a great dog. She was fifteen though. Had a good innings.'

'Yes. Oh, well. Maybe another time.'

'Yeah.'

He touched her elbow briefly with his left hand, smiled, said, 'See you, then,' as if she was some blokeish friend, some unromantic proposition, and walked away.

'Enjoy your bun,' he said, over his shoulder.

She watched him until he turned the corner of the street and disappeared. 'I don't know you,' she thought. 'I don't know you at all.'

And now she could hardly bear even to picture the party: the little warble of 'Surprise!' from her loyal friends; the nudges from Jo; the pizza slices; the music; the balloons, Oh God, the balloons, bulging like overtaxed hearts. How amazing, she thought, to suddenly understand something: to know that somebody is never going to love you. It didn't actually hurt quite as much as you might think. She squinted up at the yellow sun and felt almost guilty.

In the party shop, the bald man was nowhere to be seen. Maybe it was his lunch break; she imagined him hunkered down somewhere, working his way through a box of Sunblest sandwiches. The only other person in the shop was the gloomy young assistant. He was no longer wearing his *I'm 3* badge. But he was still hovering by the helium machine looking a little lost, like a balloon that someone has let go of, to drift in corners. He would be that kind of person, Moira thought; one of those men who are always only loosely tied down. Onto whom you have to hold tightly.

'Hi,' she said.

'Hi,' he replied. He was wearing the same jumper as the day before; a grey one with holes around the cuffs, as if moths had been eating it.

'I just came to say that I don't need those balloons any more,' she said.

'The party's off.'

'Oh.'

He let a big, star-shaped balloon float to the ceiling, as if it was a magic trick.

'That's a shame. What happened?'

'Someone's dog died.'

'Oh. Dear.'

And, unexpectedly, he smiled.

'Would you like one of these?' he asked, offering her a length of ribbon to which he had tied a particularly beautiful silver balloon. Plain, unadorned.

'Thanks,' she said. She couldn't remember the last time anyone had given her a balloon. It seemed like a very kind thing to do.

'It's lovely,' she said, trying of think of something else to add. 'I prefer the plain ones, really,' she said.

'The ones with writing on are overstating the point,' agreed the assistant, leaning against the counter.

Something brushed her shoulder: a strand of silver angel-hair, blowing in the breeze from the open window. Moira looked around. They were standing, she realised, in a kind of cave; a sort of glittering, twinkling, shining grotto, like Oberon and Titania.

'I think you're right,' she said. Because nobody needed writing on a balloon; nobody needed declarations. Everyone was in the party shop for the same reason.

*Magicians tend to be blasé about things materialising unexpectedly.
But when Gordon Bruce opened an old journal to discover that it
contained groundbreaking historical research on the art of conjuring, he
experienced a frisson of surprise. Curator of the Scottish Magic History
Archive, his first question was, why was the author effectively unknown
in magic circles? Here he introduces the* Textualities Book Detective
*feature, which includes his friend Bob Reid's diary notes on solving the
mystery, and Arthur Watson's original article on conjuring – which remains as fascinating as when it first appeared almost a century ago.*

Gordon Bruce

Watson Sherlocked

MY INTEREST IN the history of conjuring dates from the 1960s, when I was
a teenager, inspired by the friendship of Glasgow book collectors Tommy
Medericks and Duncan Johnstone. Reference material then was hard to
come by. Secondhand copies of desirable books such as Houdini's *Un-
masking of Robert-Houdin* were scarce, and when available were usually
beyond my price. However both these gentlemen were generous in allowing me access to their respective, and not inconsiderable libraries. High
on my wants list was a set of the *Annals of Conjuring* by Sidney Wrangel
Clarke – which, though not the first, nor complete, was and is the best
attempt at a unified history of conjuring. Clarke's story is told in *The Barrister in the Circle* (1983) by Eddie Dawes, who also gives an account of
the birth of the *Annals* in his Preface to Todd Karr's magnificent edition of
Clarke's monumental work.

A notice of Clarke's intention to publish a history of conjuring was
first announced in George Johnson's *The Magic Wand* (1919–20). Lack
of response would have left the project stillborn, had not Johnson decided
to serialise it; it ran between 1924 and 1928. Subsequently these issues
became highly sought-after and attracted a premium price.

My yearly visits to London always included a stop at Davenport's Magic Shop in Great Russell Street where Patrick Page, the manager and a fellow Scot, allowed me to sort through hundreds of secondhand magazines to add to my collection. The wily Pat usually abstracted the *Magic Wand*s with Clarke's articles – after I had done the sorting process for him. Nevertheless, over the years I accumulated some, though not all, of Clarke's history, and Duncan Johnstone allowed me to read – at his house – from one of his three complete sets of the *Annals*, none of which he would sell. As you may imagine, I read and re-read Clarke's *Magic Wand* articles and it was frustrating, whenever I came to a gap in my collection. Years later, in 1983, Magico Publishing in New York republished the entire work and I was able to have it on my shelves.

Then, one day early in 1999, I wandered in to Cooper Hay's antiquarian bookshop in Glasgow. I have known Cooper from his days in John Smith's bookshop and over the years through him I have managed to acquire some of my best loved books, including the fifth edition of Henry Dean's *Whole Art of Legerdemain* (1762), the first magic book published in Scotland, as well as the first, second and third editions of Reginald Scot's *Discoverie of Witchcraft* (1584, 1661 and 1665, respectively).

On this particular day, Cooper was browsing through a volume on his desk.

'You must be a mind reader,' he remarked. 'I was just thinking of you.'

The reason was an article by one Arthur Watson in the *Reliquary and Illustrated Archaeologist* entitled simply, 'Conjurers'. I began to read, and certain words and phrases jumped out at me. It was clear that Mr Watson had read Clarke. Some illustrations were more than familiar. Then I read a description of a Roman oil lamp, with the lamp illustrated, and I remembered this from reading the *Annals* at Duncan Johnstone's, although I did not recall Clarke having a photograph of the lamp. I turned to the title page of the *Reliquary*: publication date 1909! This was fifteen years before the *Annals* appeared in print.

Cooper offered to copy the article for me. I replied I should have to buy the volume. Bad news. It was one of a set of fifteen. However, his price was not excessive, and in the other volumes I found articles by Watson on Funambulists, Jugglers and Tumblers. Good news!

That summer the American sleight of hand expert and bibliophile Ricky Jay was in London performing his one man show: 'Ricky Jay and his 52 assistants'. I had an invitation to attend. As usual when in London, I stayed with another magician and print collector, Bob Read. I had made copies of the Watson articles for Bob, knowing he would find them very interesting.

Neither Bob nor Ricky had heard of Arthur Watson. Of course, by this time I had consulted Eddie Dawes, the foremost historian of conjuring. Again, a blank. Another friend, Persi Diaconis, Professor of Statistics at Stanford University and also a sleight of hand card expert and collector had not heard of Watson either.

Was it possible that Clarke, who makes no mention of Watson, had plagiarised these articles? Or had he unknowingly repeated the research Watson had done earlier?

After Ricky Jay's performance, Ricky, Bob and I visited the British museum where Sheila O'Connell, despite being in the middle of curating an ephemera exhibition, had searched out some early conjuring prints for us to examine – including the Baldini 'Luna' print from the *Seven Planets*. As we signed the visitors' book, I asked Sheila if they still had all the pre-war visitors' books.

'Yes,' she said.

'The First World War, I mean.'

'Yes, but they are all in storage and not on a computer.'

Arthur Watson must be in there!

Over the phone, Eddie, Bob and I drew up a profile of Arthur Watson and effectively Bob became Watson's Sherlock Holmes. It's a fascinating story. I was pleased to be present in 2005 when he gave a talk on his Watson research to the Wolverhampton Circle of Magicians, and again when he repeated it with great success later that year at the Ninth Conference on Magic History in Los Angeles (by which time we had also agreed to collaborate on an Arthur Watson feature for *Textualities*).

After the conference I returned to Scotland and Bob and his wife Pauline stayed on for an extended holiday. While in California, Bob suffered a fatal heart attack. His diary notes on the quest for Arthur Watson are reprinted here with very little alteration. They have an immediacy that conveys not only the twists and turns of the quest but also a flavour of a remarkable man whose scholarship and determination as a researcher was only exceeded by his sense of fun.

Gordon Bruce, curator of the Scottish Magic Archive, welcomes any information regarding magic performers and performances in Scotland. He may be contacted at the Scottish Magic Archive, 32 Cathkin Road Glasgow G42 9UH (visits to the archive are by appointment only).

Bob Read

Searching for Arthur Watson

BY ANY MEASURE, 1905 was a significant year. The French and the English were raising glasses and celebrating an anniversary. Unfortunately they were not celebrating the same anniversary.

The French were drinking a champagne toast on the centenary of the birth of magician Robert-Houdin. The English were swigging cider on the centenary of knocking seven bells out of the French fleet at Trafalgar.

Passing unnoticed was the death, on 17 June, of the poverty-stricken Henry Evanion, one of the early collectors of all things magical. Ten years previously, in 1895, Evanion had sold the bulk of his archive to the British Museum, now the British Library, although a substantial amount of his magic 'paper' was bought in 1904 by Harry Houdini. Unconnected to Evanion, but also in June 1905, the British Museum accepted into its collections a newly published copy of *History of Ancient Pottery* from the author H.B. Walters, their curator in the Greek and Roman Department. We must wait until 2005 to see his book assume an unexpected significance in this story.

The absence of any indigenous magical event to commemorate was perhaps not the main reason for a group of conjurers to meet in Pinoli's Soho restaurant to form what later was called The Magic Circle – the world's best-known magic club. Absent at this meeting was Arthur Watson. We can speculate on the reasons for this. He was not invited? He was not a magician? He was not hungry? What we do know is that, while the magicians were gorging at Pinoli's, Watson was sitting at a desk in the famous circular reading room at the British Library, researching the first in-depth history of early conjuring.

The Magic Circle missed this momentous fact in 1905. After all, Watson's article was not published until 1909 and he was completely unknown to the magical community. Arthur Watson was so low profile, he does not even rate a mention in the momentous 1924–28 *Annals of Conjuring* by Sidney Clarke, one-time librarian of the Magic Circle. No footnote, no end-note, no acknowledgment, no references, nothing.

This is perhaps a little surprising, considering Clarke was a barrister, trained to pay attention to detail. And even more surprising, when it can be argued that he included dozens of nuggets which were first brought into the magical spotlight through the researches of Arthur Watson.

Watson has hardly been mentioned in the magical press over the last hundred years. In 1928 there was a whole paragraph dedicated to his meticulous work in Henry Ridgely Evans' *History of Conjuring and Magic*. In 1956 he got three-lines in Kurt Volkmann's *The Oldest Deception*. Ridgely Evans was an American, Volkmann a German. Here in Britain, zilch. Not a sausage.

Watson's published work was hidden away in an obscure magazine, the *Reliquary and Illustrated Archaeologist*. There is no evidence of Watson's articles forming part of any private library of conjuring.

In 2003, four years after Watson's articles were rediscovered by Scots cardmeister Gordon Bruce, a copy of his piece on conjurers was unearthed in the dusty archives of the Magic Circle. The possibility looms large that it had lain there from 1909. Which librarian was aware of this paper? Presumably, Sidney Wrangel Clarke.

In 2005, after six years' intermittent investigation by myself and Gordon, the identity of Arthur Watson was finally pieced together. Predictably, in this centenary year: the French commemorated Robert-Houdin; the English celebrate the Battle of Trafalgar; the British Library mounted an extensive exhibition of the Evanion purchase; and the Magic Circle again missed out on revealing the incredible hidden treasures of Arthur Watson.

What has Watson to do with Magic History?

In 1999 Gordon Bruce telephoned to tell me that he had just bought a run of the *Reliquary* and that the 1909 volume contained an article titled 'Conjurers' by Arthur Watson. It was in two parts, Part I in April 1909, Part II, July 1909.

He said that it included illustrations of Cups and Balls performers. He described these and I told him they sounded like the illustrations used by Volkmann in *The Oldest Deception*. He did not have this book but would send me a copy of the article.

When I received the photocopy it was clear to me that here was a major piece of magical research. How come no-one has mentioned it before? How come I had never even heard of it? Why had no-one I asked ever heard about it?

The history of mystery is threaded with mysteries of history. Sleight-of-hand merchants have the enigmatic Charlier, who was he? Card conjurers have the anagrammatical E.W. Erdnase. Who was he? Hoaxsters are still chuckling at the tantalising half appearance of Budleigh Pepperton. Who was he? Don't ask. Digging up details is a way of life for the species of magicians described as historians. Now magical historians can claim their very own mystery man – Arthur Watson. Who was he?

New Information from Watson

Following this preamble, you will find Watson's article on conjurers and so it is unnecessary to list all the information that he brought to us for the first time, but I am particularly interested in illustrations and so I will use these to underline his importance. (The illustrations are numbered below as in the original.)

Fig 1. Lamp in Greek and Roman Life Room British Museum. Watson suggests that the raised image on the lamp could show a performance of the interlocking and releasing rings – or a jumping trick of the dog. He points out that Licetus takes the former view and cites a reference in Latin.

Fig 2. German Block-Book 1475. British Museum. Planetenbuch, Luna. He links the image on the Roman lamp, which includes an ape, with representations from the Planets series of woodcuts. This is the first time in magical literature that this series of images has been brought to our notice. Watson goes on to draw attention to Theodor Hamps' *Fahrende Leute in der Deutschen Verganenheit.*

Fig 3. Florentine Engraving ascribed to Baccio Baldini. Seven Planets. Luna. BM. Watson was the first to include this astrological engraving from 1470.

Fig 4. Hans Sebald Beham. The Seven Planets. Another Planets engraving shown for the first time.

Fig 5. Petrarch. Von der Artyney Bayder Gluck. 1532. This woodcut, he attributes to Hans Burgkmair. Later scholars suggest it is by Weiditz. Brought to light for the first time, this cut was then used by: Evans, Clarke, Volkmann, Christopher, Dawes, Read.

Fig 8. Floram Marchand. Le Grand Boyeur de Tours. I have not found this print of the famous water-spouter in any earlier work on the history of conjuring but it has been used regularly since.

Fig 9. From Hocus Pocus Junior, 1635. The first use of this woodcut although it was used simultaneously by Harry Houdini.

Fig 10. From Das Zeithurzende Lust-und Spiel-haus. This was 'photographed by Mr F.G. Francis from the writer's copy of this book'. The first time this woodcut was used – but not the last, the accreditation of this work later assumes a major importance, as we shall see.

Fig 11. Portrait of Richard Neve and illustration of conjuring trick with a bird. From a print in the British Museum. Houdini published this woodcut in 1906/7, quite independently of Watson. One can imagine a mob of magical sleuths standing in line at the BM all snapping away at this illustration – the frontispiece of *The Merry Companion* by Richard Neve. I checked the book in 2004 but the illustration was NOT in the copy I saw; however, the BM records two copies.

Fig 12. Comenius: Orbis Sensualium Pictus 1659. Another woodcut discovered by Watson in the books at the BM. Used by practically every magical scholar since 1909.

Watson's Influence

Without a doubt the earliest comprehensive history of magic is *The Annals of Conjuring* by Sidney Clarke published in instalments in the *Magic Wand* from 1924 to 1928 by George Johnson. In searching for Arthur Watson, it has become apparent that Sidney Clarke was seriously indebted to him for much of the early information in his book.

What is difficult to understand is why Clarke did not acknowledge Watson's pioneering work. This could have been simply forgetfulness or perhaps editorial pressure. I can quite understand that Johnson could hold the view that the general magic readers of his magazine would not be overly interested in the history of conjuring and certainly not to the extent of a surfeit of footnotes, citations and end-note references taking up precious space which could have been used to explain another card trick.

In fact, there are indications that Clarke deliberately obscured Watson's input. The text of the *Annals* is littered with information previously published by Watson. Some of this could have been gleaned by both authors from a third and mutually accessed source. For example, it is to be expected that both drew on *Discoverie of Witchcraft*, Scot, 1584; *Sports and Pastimes of the English People*, Strutt; *The Lives of the Conjurors*, Frost, 1886. But what are we to make of the similarity in the order of presentation? Overlaying a template of Watson's writings of 1909 on those of Clarke's allows a paragraph by paragraph comparison. Here are a few of the many examples it throws up:

The trick of swallowing a dagger or sword may be performed either by using an instrument the short blade of which recedes in the handle... *Watson*
...there is some evidence that the trick sword or dagger, in which the blade recedes into the handle, was in use in the fifth century. *Clarke*

An expression which is very commonly associated with the conjurer is 'Hocus Pocus'. An early use of the word is to be found is a disputation of *Voetius de Magia*. It is dated 1636. 'Agyrtae' the writer says, 'call this vain and idle art Okus Bokus'... *Watson*
...was a corruption of Ochus Bochus who is said to have been an ancient magician who was invoked by Italian conjurers... for Voetius in *de Magia* published in 1636, referring to conjuring, says that 'The Argyrtae call this vain and idle art Okus Bokus'... *Clarke*

Tharsander, in his Schaulpatz, 1737, quotes Hindorf. Theatr. Histor., in relating that in the year 1272, a conjurer came to Creutznach from the Netherlands, who removed the head from a boy... *Watson*
The year 1272 is given by a writer of a considerable later date as that in which a Dutch conjurer cut of a boy's head and restored the victim to life... *Clarke*

You would be amazed at just how much text is common to both papers and how they follow the same structure and logic, but the most obvious similarity is in the illustrations used. All Watson's illustrations, with the puzzling exceptions of the Planets series, are also used by Clarke. What is more, they appear in almost the same order. And here we uncover the most blatant evidence of airbrushing Watson out. Most of the illustrations accompanying Watson's 'Conjurers' originate from the British Museum. He employed a photographer, R.B. Fleming, who, records show, visited the Prints and Drawings Dept. regularly following a foray by Watson.

There is one clear exception to this. Watson included a photograph of a woodcut from *Das Zeithurtzende Lust-und Spiel-haus* (Fig 10) showing the traveling doll trick that became known as 'Hiccius Doccius'. Clarke uses exactly the same image, recaptioned 'A conjurer in 1680'. However, we read in Watson's end-notes that the photograph of this illustration, unlike the rest, was taken by Mr F.G. Francis from 'the writer's own copy of the book'.

Clarke used the same photograph. No credit to Watson. I am sure that we are all charitable enough to assume that Clarke asked permission. If that is so, why was Watson not credited?

Finally, there is another example of Watson's influence on the *Annals*. He illustrates a Roman oil lamp, the raised design of which shows an entertainer, a dog climbing a ladder, an ape and a couple of linked rings. Watson writes: 'There are shown a performing dog climbing a ladder, an ape, a cup and two rings, from which the inference might be made that the trick of interlocking and releasing rings, a common feat of conjurers at the present, was practiced by the Romans'. He cites Greek and Roman Life Room Case J. Games 277 and the *History of Pottery* by H.B. Walters.

Clarke dismisses this theory: 'It has been said that the Interlocking Rings illusion, now generally known as the Chinese Rings, was presented by Roman performers, but the evidence to support this is very slight, depending upon the existence on certain lamps and pottery of a representation of a juggler (accompanied by an ape and a dog) who holds in one hand a couple of rings.' Clarke cites Greek and Roman Life Room Case J. Games 277.

Whether the rings linked or the dog jumped through them is not the point. H.B. Walters did not mention the Interlocking Rings in his book, and he used a different photograph to that of Arthur Watson. So, who did Clarke mean when he said 'It has been said that...'? I suspect that he was referring to Watson.

Watson also influenced another methodical magical author, Dr Kurt Volkmann, whose *The Oldest Deception* focuses on the ancient Cups and Balls illusion. It is a profound work and it too was initially serialised in a magic magazine – *Die Magie*. As we have seen, Watson was the first to show us the earliest illustrations of the Cups and Balls which were included in the planets genre under 'The Children of the Moon'. Watson also drew attention to several recent books on the subject of mediaeval preoccupation with astrology which included further examples and he was meticulous in citing all his primary and secondary sources. The British Museum Prints and Drawings Department has these books, many of them published in Germany. They also hold the only known copy of a book published by the Chalcographical Society which reproduces a similar print. Volkmann cites these sources and credits Arthur Watson and his 'Conjurer' article. In terms of influence, Watson certainly influenced Clarke (uncredited) and Volkmann (credited) – and through them, every magical historian since. He has certainly influenced me.

Watson was also responsible for one of the most romantic, and ultimately wrong, magical legends. To the best of my knowledge so far, it was Arthur who was the first to draw attention to the excavations of Rosselini and the writings of Gardiner Wilkinson in which they suggested that a wall painting on a tomb in the Egyptian village of Beni Hasan could possibly depict a conjurer or thimble-rig player. Watson did not illustrate this, although he did use a picture of jugglers from the same source (*Manners and Customs of the Ancient Egyptians* 1837 and 1878) in his article 'Jugglers', 1907.

Clarke took this bait and reiterated the claims made by Watson. Furthermore, he embellished them with a line drawing of the said painting. He left out the Thimble-Rig caveat and captioned his illustration 'Cups and Balls in Ancient Egypt'. It has taken almost one hundred years to put this calumny to rest.

Other Works

For someone who showed no further interest in conjurers, Watson had dropped a pretty hefty stone in the pond of magical research. But this isn't the half of it. He also wrote an equally meticulously researched paper on tumblers, calling on the treatise by Tuccaro and the illustrations to be found on the vases and pots of Rome and Greece. He showed an interest in the history of jugglers, citing the Beni Hasan tombs again and larding the information with photographs of Greek vases. He has given us a paper about funambulists (rope walking to thee and me) and this has to be a first. He used illustrations from Roman coins, statuary and carvings. Along the way he has written of the Rebus (a loose association with puzzles and, therefore, conjuring).

Finding Arthur Watson – Time Line

1999 – *July*. Gordon Bruce telephones to advise he has found an article on 'Conjuring' written by Arthur Watson for the *Reliquary and Illustrated Archaeologist* 1909.

Invite Gordon and Ricky to the British Museum Prints and Drawing Department to see the Baldini engraving of the Planets and look at the book by Hind.

—*August*. Further visit to BM Prints and Drawings Dept. to study other examples of Planets series. During lunch break, I visit a book fair at the Russell Hotel just round the corner, and find the two 1909 volumes of the *Reliquary* with Watson's 'Conjurers' articles and the volume for 1907 with his article about jugglers. This is some stroke of luck.

To the Society of Antiquaries, Piccadilly. Locate complete run of the *Reliquary*. Perhaps the only one in captivity, as the BM doesn't have it. Order photocopies. Check member records but no sign of Watson. Looks an impossible task, finding out who he was. No photograph. No title. No middle initial. No address. No dates of birth or death. No clue to family. No age range. That evening I call Gordon to tell him of the further Watson articles. He calmly says 'I know – I bought the entire run at the sale of the library at Fort Augustus, but the balance are at the booksellers as I don't have a car to move them.'

2000. We need a loose profile of Arthur. All we have to go on are his articles. There are many clues to his research and his interests.

Facts: His papers are exceedingly well researched, full of original detail, with many sources quoted. Footnotes in Latin, Greek, French, German. Frequent references to items and literature in the British Museum. Archaeological society reports cited. Manuscripts cited that are in BM and Bodleian. He owns one magic book. No qualifications known. Used his own photographer at the BM (Fleming). Confused the Cups and Balls with the Thimble Rig. Interested in allied arts: Juggling; Tumbling; Funambulism. And puzzles and enigmas: Rebus; Tarasque. His editor was Rev. Charles Cox. Publisher was Bemrose and later Allen.

Assumptions: Classics Scholar. Possibly retired by 1909 say around 50 years old. Background in Yorkshire or Ipswich. Lincoln connection. Interested in coins. Possibly member of numismatist society and archaeological association.

Apply First Rule of Magical Research – Call Eddie. There is no doubt that I will make many wrong decisions but I can be quite confident of making a correct first one. Call Eddie. Eddie Dawes is the fount of all magical knowledge. He checks the Magic Circle membership records for me and finds no entry for Arthur Watson. Start to compare Watson material with Clarke's *Annals of Conjuring* and find many similarities.

—*June.* With Bill Kalush discuss the lack of references in Clarke's *Annals*. Consider the possibility of creating a website that everyone could use to add Clarke's sources when known. Talk about Watson discovery.

—*July.* Todd Karr calls and advises he is re-publishing *Annals* and needs extra illustrations. I tell him that he called just in time as his edition would not be complete without a mention of Watson. No one is certain if Clarke knew about these articles by Watson. Much speculation about this. Can't send Watson material as it is Gordon's story.

—*August.* Eddie collates six possible Arthur Watsons from *The Diction-ary of National Biography* 1900–1980. A promising start. The most likely candidate is Arthur George Watson 1829–1916. A First in Classics 1852. Fellow of All Souls. Assistant Master Harrow School 1854–1891. Or his son could be our man: Arthur Kenelm Watson 1867–1947 of Harrow on the Hill.

—*December.* Discover a mention in Toole-Stott of Watson's article, 'Tumblers' [the Raymond Toole-Stott comprises *c.* 1300 circus monographs].

Perform for governors of St John Beaumont's School Old Windsor. Into Cups and Balls routine and realise that to my left is Barnaby Lenon the headmaster of Harrow School. Berate him about the Arthur Watson who was a master at Harrow in the 1890s. He wisely urges me to contact archivist Rita Gibbs. I complete the show, reveal three fruit loads and we all have a good time.

2001—*March.* Todd found Watson's 'Conjurers' re-printed in *Scientific American*, 4 September 1909, with a new title: 'Hocus Pocus Mutterings', and a few mentions in Ridgely Evans' articles in *Linking Ring*. Todd also suggested Watson may be the same person who worked for York Parks Dept. and wrote a book *How York Governs Itself*, which includes a chapter on York Miracle Plays. Kalush maintains Clarke could not possibly have used Watson because of the important material Clarke left out. It is a pretty powerful argument. Gordon Bruce contacts the Yorkshire Archaeo-logical Society.

I attack the 1901 census, published on-line in January 2001. It crashes for over a year through weight of traffic. (I find out in 2003 that comput-ing work was given to the prison service. They gave the 'old lags' the job of transcribing the information. The inmates substituted their own job descriptions. Prison Warder became Screw. It didn't help.)

—*April.* Write a chapter on the Watson material for Todd Karr's new edi-tion of *Annals.* It transpires after umpteen telephone and email conversa-tions that Todd's discovery of the *Scientific American* two-part article is actually only one part of the original which has been divided again. So he hasn't seen the entire feature. It would be tragic if it wasn't so funny.

Kalush emails information abstracted from Periodicals Contents Index Web. Humanities and Social Sciences. Chadwyck-Healy. Bell and Howell Information and Learning http://pci.chadwyck.com. Several articles by an Arthur Watson published in 1938, 1947. Kalush reckons it could be the same man. I think not, as the gap between what is known (1898) and the last date (1947) is pretty wide.

Visit Harrow School and see archivist Rita Gibbs. The lead is Arthur 'Vanities' Watson, Classics master. Strong candidate for our Arthur. Check the school papers and the *Harrovian*. He died in 1916. This could be the man, but we need more evidence.

—*May.* Mark Mittons contacts Jacob Lasky at the *Scientific American* offices in NY to ask what info they have on Watson. A long shot but they may still have records – where did they send the cheque? Henry Ridgely Evans was somehow associated with this and with Hopkins' *Magic*, which was referred to by Watson in his article. What was the Ridgely Evans-Hopkins-Watson-*Scientific American* connection?

The *Scientific American* enquiry meets a brick wall. Get a call from Kalush. 'Clarke definitely knew Watson's material.' I ask, 'What on earth has changed your mind? You were adamant.' He tells me that he checked the *Bibliography of Conjuring and Kindred Deceptions*, 1920, by Clarke and Blind, and Watson's article on Conjurers is listed there. This is the Blind leading the blind. Gordon does not have a copy of Volkmann's *The Oldest Deception* and so cannot compare the images. I do not have a copy of the Clarke-Blind bibliography so cannot check it. Kalush does not have a copy of the Watson material. Karr is sent a copy of Watson by Gordon but it is sent sea mail and never arrives. How difficult can we make this?

—*December.* I read 'The Department of Prints and Drawings' in the *British Museum Users Guide*, 1987, Antony Griffiths. Among the list of collections are the visitors' books 1867–present. That's it. 'Eu-bloody-reka,' as Art would maybe say. He must have been in the Print and Drawings Dept. when he visited the library. His papers are littered with print images. I wonder if I can find out exactly when he visited? And where he lived? From 1890 all visitors were recorded by staff, but from 3 February 1900 visitors themselves wrote their names and address on entering the Print Room.

Deliver a copy of Clarke/Karr *Annals of Conjuring* to Sheila O'Connell at the BM with thanks for her help. I ask to check the visitors' books for 1908. They are not there. I make an appointment to go to Olympia the following day.

Visit British Museum outstation in Blythe Road Olympia. It is open by appointment one day a week between 10am and 1pm. My friend, Blue Badge Guide Stephie, jumps at the chance to come along. Lifts out of action. We meet David Rhodes of the BM and walk up to the fourth floor. We choose the 1904–1905 and 1908 visitors' books. Total number of names for 1904 = 8385. We get through about 4000. Suddenly there it is: *Feb 22*

1908. A Watson 24 Gordon Street. WC1. At last we have an address.

More good fortune. I arrive home to find a message from Eddie. Peter Lane has discovered the Watson article on Conjurers in a cardboard box in the Magic Circle Library. The box has been stored away for years and has just come to light. So we now know that the Watson material was sitting in the Magic Circle. Wonder if it arrived before, during or after Clarke's incumbency. I check out 24 Gordon Street in the *A–Z*. Strikes me as funny that it is practically opposite the current HQ of the Magic Circle. I take a trip to see what it is now. It appears to have been absorbed into the University of London buildings.

2002—February. Mark Mitton is in town. He jumps at the chance to accompany me and trawl through the Holborn Local Studies Library. We go through street maps, electoral registers, plans; Post Office street directories, *Kelly's* directories, County Council and Parochial Electors registers; census returns on microfilm for 1901. Exhausting work. No Arthur Watson is listed at 24 Gordon Street. It was a 'Lodging House'. A bloody boarding house. Dead end.

Peter gives me more information about the Watson articles found at the MC. Written on the box was 'Articles on Conjuring'. Eddie shot down from Hull to inspect the box and recognised the handwriting as that of – Sidney Clarke. So, it transpires that Sidney definitely read Watson's work and he certainly used it in the *Annals*. Why did he not credit Watson? It looks suspiciously as though he deliberately omitted Watson's name but incorporated his findings, even down to using Watson's own illustration from his own magic book.

– March. Email from Eddie with details of Rev. Charles Cox, editor of the *Reliquary*. Member of many archaeological associations and British Numismatic Society. Vicar of St Albans, Sydenham.

I track down contact number for St Albans, Sydenham and email them. I pick the wrong contact number. They write back: 'Wrong church – wrong faith. Try the other lot.'

– December. Visit the Magic Circle Library. Check several books by Henry Ridgely Evans for mentions of Arthur Watson. Evans quotes Watson in *Adventures in Magic*, 1927. He also includes the woodcut from Petrach which Watson first brought to light. In *History of Conjuring and Magic* he also mentions Watson. Bob Loomis downloads other brief Watson references from the *Linking Ring*, 1937.

2003—April. Bob Loomis sends me a copy of the *Sphinx*, April 1919. In it is an article by Henry Ridgely Evans, who cites Watson. I am becoming convinced that HRE corresponded with Watson, although there is no evidence for this. Someone (Eddie?) told me that George Daley has researched Evans – I will get around to asking George if he came across letters from Watson.

—*July.* Visit Chicago to give a talk to a history conference. Take a side trip to Lund Museum of Magic, Michigan. Bob Lund created files on every know magician. I spend an afternoon checking letters of Henry Ridgely Evans. No sign in them of any correspondence to or from Watson.

At last, I can get on to the 1901 census. It has been down for over a year. I look for Arthur Watson and stab a guess at age. 50 +/– 5 years. Thirty candidates come up. Start again. Eliminate the Domestic Groom, Blacksmith, Stuff Presser (what?), Fishmonger, Slater of House, Sadler, Horse Keeper Groom, Cab Driver Groom and Ironstone Miner Below Ground – I figure the Latin and Greek would be of no use to any of them. Draw up a shortlist which includes a barrister, a JP and a reverend.

Hook up with funny man Bob Sheets from the USA. We visit Lambeth Palace to check the clerical records and find out more about a Rev. Arthur Watson born in Lancing, Sussex, who moved to the Isle of Wight. Check Crockford's *Clerical Directory.* The people at Lambeth Palace are very helpful and suggest a talk with the Winchester Diocese office, which includes Isle of Wight.

—*August.* Telephone Isle of Wight archives and they suggest I write to a Mr Smout, the County Archivist, to ask where I can get info on a Rev. Arthur Watson, who lived there around 1901.

2004—*April.* Download info from *Cricket Archive.* Arthur Lacon Watson played for Hampshire and Cambridge 1885 and 1888. Batting right hand, Bowling right arm fast-medium. b. 27 Aug 1866 Cowes I of W. d. 28 June 1955 Westwood I of W. This is more than even I need to know about Arthur Lacon Watson. His dad was Rev. Arthur Watson. Was either of them our man?

Decide to try some of the associations to which Arthur could have belonged. Get a reply from British Numismatic Society – signed by a Mr Charles Farthing. Farthing of the Numismatic Society, to phrase a coin. Such pleasures warm the heart. Worth savouring – Farthing of the Numismatic Society. Heads I lose. 'Unfortunately, etc...'

—*December.* Goof around at the International Day of Magic. Having a drink with a group that includes clever magician Chris Power – works at British Museum. He introduces me to a charming young lady, Lesley Fitton. She seems perfectly intelligent and profoundly sane and I wonder what the hell she is doing at the International Day of Magic. I ask her what she does. Get this – she is a curator in the BM Greek and Roman department. Can't believe my ears. Synchronicity or what? I ask, 'What do you know about Arthur Watson?' If there is a Latin phrase for 'Bugger All', I think she would have used it. I arrange to call her in a few days.

A couple of weeks later, I drop the volumes of the *Reliquary* off at the BM Print and Drawings Dept. to be passed down to Lesley Fitton in the Greek and Roman Dept.

2005—January. Lesley confirms she has received the *Reliquary* volumes. Mitton calls – he is in town. Last Sunday I took him to see Methley Street, where Evanion and Chaplin lived. Today I am due to see Lesley the curator Greek and Roman at the BM and I invite Mitton. What a thrill. A personal tour backstage by Lesley. We have a great time and see the Roman oil lamp that Arthur had photographed for his article on Jugglers.

Almost as an afterthought, Lesley remarks that they have a correspondence folder of the curator H.B. Walters. Arthur Watson cites his book *History of Ancient Pottery.* I ask, given Watson or Fleming would have had to ask permission to photograph items, would this be in the correspondence? She tells us that she will look through it. F.G. Francis took the photograph of the page from Watson's book. R.B. Fleming took the photographs at the BM. This suggests that Francis lived close to Watson and Fleming lived close to the BM.

All this adds up if our Arthur is the Rev. from I of W. He comes to London. Stays at the Gordon Street boarding house. Arranges with Fleming to take pics at the BM. If Walters was curator at the BM, maybe his letter file would shed light on Arthur?

It also occurs to me that Watson was visiting the BM at the same time as Henry Evanion and possibly Harry Houdini. What a turn up. And they were all photographing the Richard Neve frontispiece of *The Merry Companion.*

It must be the Rev. Have not heard from Mr Smout, so I write to Pip Orchard. 'Have you heard of a Rev. Watson on the island around 1909?' He emails me to say he doesn't know anything about a Rev. Watson, but he knows a bloke that will. Bernard Taylor – another magician. We are cooking. Bernard sends a photo of Rev. Watson bearing his autograph, and a photo of his son, Arthur Lacon Watson. We are getting somewhere. I can compare signatures in the BM visitor's book.

Unpack the digital camera I bought. A complete bloody mystery to me. Fix up an appointment with Sheila O'Connell for Tuesday at Blythe Road.

Hotfoot to BM archives in Blythe Road. Only open two hours on a Tuesday. Meet the mega-helpful Sheila O'Connell and get to check the 1908 visitors' book again. I compare the signature on the photograph of the Rev. Arthur Watson with the BM signature. It is nothing like it. Not even close.

So, I'm staring disconsolately at Arthur's signature and address and it dawns on me that when Steph and I found this signature the first time, we were tight on time and left it at that. I later checked the address 24 Gordon Street. But what if there are more entries? This time around I had a little more time. I start from the 22 February 1908 entry, looking for Watson's photographer, R.B. Fleming.

June 9 R.B. Fleming, Hillingdon Heath. I note that on this day the curator was Hind. Hind wrote a book on woodcuts and I think the Planet Series that Watson (and Kurt Volkmann) consulted. I start to make a note of the duty curators. *July 9. R.B. Fleming. (Hind). Aug 13. R.B. Fleming. (Hind). Aug 17. R.B. Fleming. (Hind).*

Then another breakthrough. Another entry for Arthur Watson. Different signature style to the entry Feb 22, 1908. *A. Watson, 24 Gordon Street, WC1* – undoubtedly by the same hand.

Sept 11, 1908. Arthur Watson Ty dol Cunningham Park. Wealdstone. (Hind). This is a completely new address. Could I establish a geographical link between Watson's address and Fleming's?

Oct 16, 1908. R.B. Fleming Hillingdon Heath. (Dodgson). Nov 14. A. Watson, back at *24 Gordon Street WC1. (Hind). Dec 3. R.B. Fleming Hillingdon Heath. (Dodgson). Dec 7. R.B. Fleming Hillingdon Heath. (Dodgson).*

Then another break: *Mon Dec 28, 1908. R.B. Fleming, 111 Vaughan Road, Harrow*(!!!) Does all this lead back to Arthur Kenelm Watson, son of 'Vanities' Watson, the schoolmaster from Harrow School? The Harrow connection points this way. I live in Harrow so I can follow this up easily.

I am trying to learn how to use the digital camera. I ask permission to photograph the signature. How the hell do you get this thing to work without setting off the flash? Also, how do you take macro photographs? Not easy. I take a couple of lousy shots. I think of R.B. Fleming – he would have had to lug a Daguere and a flash pot set-up with him to the BM. That is why they called photographers 'Smudge'.

Leave at 1pm with Sheila and her colleague and take the tube to Russell Square. They go off to the BM and give me directions to the Warburg. Been meaning to visit the Warburg for four years. I called once to try to get a handle on what they did. I was no wiser after they explained.

I always discounted the articles written by an A.Watson in 1938 and 1947. Surely not our man who was writing in 1898. In the Warburg I photocopy a couple of these articles and speak with the librarian. He puts me on the internal phone to the archivist Claudia Wedepohl and I ask if she has any information about Arthur. She tells me that she will check and get back to me a couple of days.

I notice that Anthony Blunt has written a few articles for the *Warburg Institute Journal*. Bet they were a bit surprised when it was revealed that he was a Russian spy, along with Kim Philby, Donald Maclean and George Blake. I get home and check the *A–Z* for Vaughan Road and Cunningham Park, Harrow. They are within walking distance of each other and not too far from where I live. Full circle, back to Harrow School. Don't tell me Arthur Kenelm Watson is back in the frame? We start again.

Check out Harrow Local Studies Library and *A–Zs* and Electoral Registers and *Kelly's* directories and street directories and Ordnance Survey maps for 1904 and 1911. The place was very different then, rural, but the train was running out past Harrow and I expect it ran on time. There were also two pockets of housing, the Cunningham Road area and the Vaughan Road area. Whadya know?

Email Claudia Wedepohl for info on Arthur. Drive around Harrow and photograph properties in Cunningham Road and Vaughan Road. Quite different styles. Cunningham Road all large houses, mostly with names – I can see a schoolmaster living here. I walk up one side and down the other, see all eighty houses, and only ten have numbers. *Ty dol* is not named so it is likely that it used to be one of the ten that are now numbered. But I do meet Sarah, the young lady moving in to no. 80, and she offers to check her deeds. My researches of the electoral roll and street directories indicate it was owned by a dentist, A. Sowden Hills. I make a note of all the occupants of the numbered houses in 1915–1918 *Kelly's*. When I get home I find an email from the Warburg.

Claudia Wedepohl. 'The name Arthur Watson appears frequently between 1928 when KBW, the private library of Aby Warburg, was still in Hamburg, and 1938. Watson's address in 1929 was 12 Cedar Court, Brent Village Finchley. You will need to get permission from director Prof Charles Hope with letter of recommendation.' I have already asked Eddie to write such a letter and it is in hand.

Sheila O'Connell emails with the contact details for the BM Archivist. I dash off a request to Gary Thorn. Return a couple of days later to take photographs. I photograph 111 but *Kelly's* in the Harrow Local History archives does not show a 111 Vaughan Road. It jumps from 109 to 113. How crazy is that? – yet another dead end. In 1915 at 1 Cornwall Road, Headstone Pinner, lived a Richard Baldwin Fleming. I bet he is our photographer. He moves about a bit. One day I will get around to checking if he ever snapped our Arthur.

On the way back from visiting Lesley Press I detour to locate the Watson address, 12 Cedar Court. Brent Village. Raining buckets and I conclude that his house is buried under the motorway and Brent Cross Shopping Centre. Download list of Watson articles held by Warburg Institute. I notice that the Warburg Institute is part of the University of London. Warburg have fifteen Watson articles. See list. Bloody funny this is. The Magic Circle is using facilities at London University for its Heritage day in July 2005. Can hardly believe how Watson has dogged the MC.

—*February*. Armed with letter from Eddie dated 28 January, I visit the Warburg to meet Dr Dorothea McEwen and Claudia Wedepohl in the archives. Very helpful archivists. I have already been in touch with Claudia and so know they have letters from Arthur. But I have no idea how many. I have a choice between systematically browsing their electronic archives, where Watson is simply mentioned in other letters, or checking the letter folders. The Warburg index system is incredible. They could pin-point the first letters in the folder for 1929. I go for this as I want to compare the signature with that of the BM Prints and Drawings visitors' book (1908).

I open the folder; pull out the letter dated 1 January 1929. BINGO. The signature is a perfect match.

Year-by-year, folder-by-folder, I read all of Watson's letters and the replies. Over fifty items in all. I reach 1947 and remember one contender was Arthur Watson – son of Arthur 'Vanities' Watson – who died in January 1947. A scribbled line in a letter dated 21 February 1947 from our Arthur to the Warburg tells us pitifully, 'It is very cold'. The winter of 1946/47 was the coldest winter since records began. It was bloody freezing. It certainly did for Kenelm.

It is 4.30pm. I had intended to go to Waterloo Station to book my ticket to Paris next week. To hell with it, Waterloo and Paris can wait. This is far more important. I feel so close. Pulling folder after folder, I eventually come to the last Watson correspondence. The very last letter is not by Watson at all. Dated 3 February 1954, it is from Shaen Roscoe & Co, solicitors. It advises the Warburg that Dr Arthur Watson died on 15 January 1954. He bequeathed to Warburg his collection of notes and photographs. I have never been so happy to see a death notice.

And a *Dr* Watson at that. Sherlock would have been pleased.

In 1990 I jointly set up a PR company, the last offices of which were in Ridgmount Street. Looking for Arthur Watson, I set off westward and travelled as far as Michigan, USA – some 6000 miles.

Had I turned eastward and walked just two blocks, I would have stumbled over the Warburg Institute, situated in Woburn Square, where Watson's letters lay hidden; or down two blocks to the British Museum where his reader's ticket application can be retrieved in three minutes flat. And so we learn.

There is so much more to find out about the life of Dr Arthur Watson. What did he do between 1909 and 1929? Where did he work? What was his musical input? What did he look like? There are now a goodly number of leads in all that has been uncovered so far. It could be another interesting journey.

But, to tidy up a few loose ends, I was now in a position to check his date of birth.

When I get home I find an email from the BM archivist Gary Thorn. Fantastic news. The card index reading room records brought up six Arthur Watsons. Our man is Arthur Watson. Ticket A40969 first admitted to reading room 19 June 1890. Address 6 Church Row, Hampstead NW. Signing the signature book as living at 6 Gayton Road Hampstead. Renewed his ticket continuously until December 1944. At various times he lived also at: (1897) Holly Bank Potters Bar; (1898) 24 Gordon Street, London WC; 1925 – 12 Cedar Court, Brent Village, Finchley.

His application (1890) describes his profession as 'Music'. He was 27 and had a BA from University of London.

I email a few interested parties. 'ABANDON SEARCH – WATSON FOUND – HOLMES.'

Visit the BL Newspaper Library Colindale. Check *The Times* microfilm for 1954 death notices. There it is: 'On January 15 1954 at his home, 12 Cedar Court, Finchley, N3 Arthur Watson Phd FSA aged 91 years, son of the late Thomas and Ann Watson of Lincoln, and last brother of the late Foster Watson. Cremation at Golders Green Crematorium on Thursday Jan 21 at 11.45am. Inquiries and flowers to Kelly & Co 269 Regents Park Road Finchley N3. Finchley 1148.'

Email Eddie. Suggest that now Watson's identity has been established he may wish to use this story in the Magic History Collectors' day at the Magic Circle Centenary, which is to take place in London University, where Arthur was educated, on the site of his one-time home, and within a block of the Warburg Institute, with which he was associated for twenty-five years. Receive a letter from Eddie dated 24 February. No room at the MC Collectors day for Arthur Watson story. Sorry Arthur, you seemed to be doomed to oblivion.

To Newspaper Library Colindale to check *Hendon Times* for Arthur's funeral. Not even mentioned. It's a bloody conspiracy.

– *March*. To Warburg. Check library codes for Watson articles and visit fourth floor library to read two of these – 'Knives with Music Inscribed' and 'Music Galleries'. Both published in *Musical News*. Edited by Lea Southgate.

Another trip to Blythe Road. Little time to check the visitors' books for 1905. R.B. Fleming makes many appearances from different addresses.

In the afternoon I nip in to see Gary Thorn in the BM archives. Courtesy and helpful in the tradition of all the curators that I have met. I turn up Evanion's reader application 2584.67 dated 18 April 1867 and his renewals over the next ten years. When he first applied he lived at 221 Kennington Road SE. Purely on the off-chance I look for James Sevren, another mysterious magical collector. He sold a bunch of magic paper to Evanion, who later sold it to Handcuff Harry. And there it is. James Sevren, 15 Drury Court, Strand. 4 July 1872. Ticket 2370. Independence day if ever there was. It is now only a matter of time before we get a fix on Sevren. I bet it was the site of his barber shop.

Can't turn up Harry in the reader application records; not under Houdini or Wiess. This may be because he had a temporary ticket – or maybe he used an alias, or maybe Evanion did the work or maybe that is what Richter was up to...

Drive over to the Barnett Heritage Office. Meet Hugh Petrie and pinpoint Cedar Court on the grounds of what was Brent Lodge. So, it wasn't buried after all. I scan through a few St Mary's parish newsletter. No sign of Watson but the hospital he was in around 1940 is advertising as is Kelly's funeral directors. We are getting closer Arthur. Then I drive over to find the house. Built in 1912, it is a delightful Art Nouveau style building split into about fifteen flats. Nobody in at number 12 but I can come back.Later I talk by telephone to Maggie Ferguson, custodian of the archives of the Finchley Society. She will keep a look out for anything to do with Watson in the clippings folders. Watson's letters indicate an involvement in the honours ceremonies of London University held at the Albert Hall. He also knows a one-time principal, Prof. Cunstable. He probably worked there. Will check this out. He mentions the young Mr Wormald a few times – I reckon Wormald worked at the BM. In 1941 Watson had a spell in Finchley Memorial Hospital – maybe they had a patients' party and a group photograph. The quest goes on.

Articles by Arthur Watson

1898. 'Glimpses of the Anglo Saxon Boy'. *Educational Review.* Warb. DCA 130. I suspect that this tear sheet ended up in the Warburg as part of Watson's bequest.

1898. Dec. 'The Rebus'. *Antiquary.* (Source Periodicals Content Chadwyk-Healy. Kalush)

?date. An article about a crane, title and date not noted. *Reliquary and Illustrated* Archaeologist. Seen by BR at Society of Antiquaries, 2000.

1900. 'Music Galleries'. *Musical News.* Warb. Tear sheet likely from Watson's bequest. It includes about 8 photographs of church music galleries. Seen by RGR Feb 2005.

1901. 'The Tarasque'. *Antiquary.* Vol. 38 no. 140. Aug. Warb. (Source Periodicals Content Chadwyk-Healy. Kalush). DCB, 2000.

1903. 'Tumblers'. *Reliquary and Illustrated Archaeologist.* July. Warb. See Society of Antiquaries, 2000.

Sciopedes Warb. Date to check *Reliquary and Illustrated Archaeologist* Seen by BR at Society of Antiquaries, 2000.

1904 (Oct). 'The Funambulist'. *Reliquary and Illustrated Archaeologist.* Warb. (Source Periodicals Content Chadwyk-Healy. Kalush). Seen by BR at Society of Antiquaries, 2000.

1907 (Jan). 'Jugglers'. *Reliquary and Illustrated Archaeologist.* (Source Periodicals Content Chadwyk-Healy. Kalush). Seen by BR at Society of Antiquaries, 2000.

1909 (Apr). 'Conjurers' Pt I. *Reliquary and Illustrated Archaeologist.* Warb. Society of Antiquities, seen 2000. (Source Periodicals Content Chadwyk-Healy. Kalush.)

1909 (Jul). 'Conjurers' Pt II. (Periodicals Content Chadwyk-Healy. Kalush). Seen by BR at Society of Antiquaries.

1910. 'Knives with Music Inscribed'. T. Lea Southgate and Arthur Watson. *Musical News* Warb. Line drawings of knives from V&A Museum. Warb. DBF 120. Seen Feb 2005.

1928. 'The Speculum Virginum with special reference to The Tree of Jesse'. *Speculum 3.* Warb. database. Seen Feb 2005. Catalogue-shelf CHE 290.

1934. 'The Early Iconography of the Tree of Jesse'. London University Press. Warb. COK 177.

The remaining articles were identified by Bill Kalush through Chadwyck-Healey Periodicals Content, but discounted by myself until 2005:

1938. 'Mary in the Burning Bush'. *Warburg Institute Journal* 2. 1938/1939. Warb. (Source Periodicals Content Chadwyk-Healy. Kalush.)

1947. 'Saligia'. *Warburg and Courtauld Institutes, Journal* 10. (Source Periodicals Content Chadwyk-Healy. Kalush.) Seen 2005. Warb. COF 200. Tear sheet possibly Watson Bequest.

1947. 'A Manuscript of the Speculum Virginum of the Walters Art Gallery'. *Walters Art Gallery Journal* 10. (Source Periodicals Content Chadwyk-Healy. Kalush.) In Warburg Institute. Seen Feb 2005.

1953. 'Catalogue of Trees of Jesse in the XIII and XIV Centuries'. Typescript Mss. Warb. database. Seen Feb 2005.

Acknowledgments

This has been a fun puzzle to solve and it could not have been accomplished without the enthusiastic help of all the following experts and friends: Gordon Bruce, who found the original articles; Edwin 'Eddie' Dawes. The researcher's researcher; Lesley Fitton, curator, Greel and British Museum; Rita Gibbs, archivist, Harrow School; Lynn Healy, IT whiz Kid who tamed the online 1901 census for me; Peter Lane, librarian at the Magic Circle; William 'Bill' Kalush, meticulous researcher and devil's advocate; Todd Karr, publisher and researcher; Wendy Laney, Internet genealogist; Bob Loomis, indefatigable magic historian and *Linking Ring* watcher; Dorothea McEwan, archivist, Warburg Institute; Mark Mitton, magician and collector of cerebral curiosities; Sheila O'Connell, curator, Prints and Drawings Dept. British Museum; Pip Orchard, magician and one laid-back cookie; Hugh Petrie, archivist, Barnet Heritage Office; Bernard Taylor, magician and Isle of Wight historian; Stephie Tickner, London Blue Badge guide and top-line inquisitor; Garry Thorn, archivist at the British Museum. To have contacted Gary first would have saved five years work; Pauline 'Divito' Read. Forever understanding; Claudia Wederpohl, archivist, Warburg Institute. Institutions: Holborn Local Studies Library, Lambeth Palace, Harrow Local Studies Library, Newspaper Library Colindale, British Museum, Warburg Institute, Museum of Magic (Lund) Michigan, Barnet Heritage Office.

Arthur Watson

Conjurers

Finis hujus maglae non est ut simpliciter res fiat,
sed similitudinem rerum oculis proponat.
Boissardus: *De Divinatione et Magicis Praestigiis*

THE WONDERFUL OF one age becomes the commonplace of the next. Never were more wonderful feats accomplished than are performed at the present time, but so complete has become, with the majority of men, the reaction against the admission of the miraculous, that the effort is made to account for all miracles, to explain, e.g., telepathy and psychic phenomena. If no explanation which is satisfactory is forthcoming, our attitude is none the less sceptical as to there being any element of magic involved. We regard the matter not as one for which there is no explanation, but merely as one not yet explained. Up to about the end of the sixteenth century, the wonderful was by preference regarded as magical – as the work of supernatural powers, good or bad, but mostly bad. A puzzling phenomenon, the explanation of which was not obvious, was generally regarded as due to the invocation of powers above the natural. Many of the feats ascribed to demoniacal or divine aid are such as we know to be similar to the tricks included in the conjurer's repertory. The performers who knew the *modus operandi* endeavoured to keep the secrets of their marvels, as modern conjurers are in some cases able to do, though with greater difficulty, and those who could explain had every reason not to do so. It answered their purpose, as a rule, to preserve a monopoly and, in many cases, to retain the reputation of possessing supernatural power, even when their tricks depended merely on some special apparatus, some more or less simple sleight of hand, or some mere trick of confederation.

The Egyptian, Roman, and Greek priests kept in their hands the knowledge of physics and mechanics, and devoted their skill to the construction of ingenious automata which impressed the uninitiated with a feeling of awe and mystery. Probably a small percentage of people now understand the workings of a penny-in-the-slot-machine, but it inspires no awe. Everyone knows that, although he does not understand its working, it could easily be explained to him if he had time to listen to the explanation. In point of fact, so satisfied is the modern man that explanation is possible, that in many cases he shows a certain callousness. This fact the chemist knows all about, that the physicist, that the engineer; it is in safe hands, and life is too short to understand it even in a rudimentary way. We understand things by proxy.

But just as now there are devotees of occultism and those who hold by planetary influence, so, in times when natural phenomena whose explanation was not known were generally ascribed to supernatural agency, there were men in advance of their time who fought against popular superstition, and admitted the naturalness of apparent wonders, and helped to destroy the belief in magic in part or in whole.

Origen, in his *Tractatus sup. Matth.*, says: 'Magic art does not seem to me to be a term for anything still existing, but even if it is, it does not stand for evil work nor for anything which we should hold in contempt.'

The idea that the tricks of conjurers may be admitted as deceptions, although we may not know the means by which they are performed, is expressed by Sextus Empiricus who lived in the second century. He says in his chapter *De Sophismatibus*, 'For just as we do not allow that the things which conjurers do are real, but know that they deceive us, although we are ignorant how they deceive us, so we do not trust false arguments which only have a show of being sound, although we cannot exactly say where the catch is.'

Again, Roger Bacon, in his epistle *De secretis operibus artis et naturae et de nullitate magiae*, says: 'Whatever is beyond the ordinary course of nature or art is either superhuman or a pretence and full of fraud, for there are men who create illusions by the rapidity of the movements of their hands, or by the assumption of various voices, or by ingenious apparatus, or by performing in the dark, or by means of confederacy show to men many wonderful things which do not exist. Anyone who investigates the matter will find the world full of such things, for jugglers perform many deceptive feats by the dexterity of their hands.' Bacon, without denying the existence of superhuman intervention, recognised that many phenomena which are commonly ascribed to it were merely the working of natural laws or the work of clever conjurers. There were many things, he knew, which were held as miraculous by the majority, not only of laymen but even of clerics, which could be explained by natural philosophy.

In describing how Peter de Maharncuria, the only man of whom he knew anything praiseworthy in experimental research, gathered his knowledge from various sources, he tells us that he enquired, among other things, into the illusions of conjurers, so that he might know all which was worth knowing, and that, as far as possible, he might be able to reject whatever was false and to be attributed to magic.

Mathematicians, he says, sometimes are fraudulent in their circles, in their empty signs and foolish incantations which have no real value, and with the credulous they ascribe to the stars things in respect of which they have no power. Bacon does not deny the existence of magic, but he endeavours to expose the false ascription to it of natural phenomena, and he asserts that tricks of legerdemain or confederacy were ascribed to the influence of the heavens, whereas they were entirely independent of it. It is the function of science to determine what can be done by natural means and what not, to discover all pretence in making invocations and incantations; the madness of magicians is to be exposed by experimental science just as sophistry is to be exposed by logic.

Joh. Chr. Frommann, in his *Tractatus de Fascinatione novus et singularis*, 1675, says, quoting Cardanus, 'that conjurers so completely dazzle the eyes of beholders, that those who are without philosophy regard them as magicians'. Giovanni Battista Porta, in his *Natural Magic*, 1658, has a chapter entitled 'To discover Frauds whereby Imposters working by Natural means pretend that they do them by Conjuration.' Again, in a book published 1735–42, entitled *Schau-Platz vieler ungereimten Meynungen und Erzehlungen*, by F. G. Wilhelm Wegener, under the pseudonym Tharsander, it is asserted that there were in the roll of magicians many conjurers and jugglers who professed to perform their tricks by the aid of a spirit, and were, in consequence, held as practisers of the black art. This opinion is backed by reference to Francis Hutchinson's *Historical Essay concerning Witchcraft*, 1718, and Becker's *Die bezuberte Welt*.

On the other hand, some men, according to Bodin, included among their tricks some one trick which was a feat of legerdemain, so that it might appear that all the other tricks were only exhibitions of dexterity when, in reality, they were magical, just as Satan provokes men to laughter that he may lead them on to wickedness, and Del Rio believed that natural magic was not harmful so long as it did not lead men to believe that it was the work of demons.

Conjurers, then, were, in some cases, led to seek the reputation of performing by magical arts. Del Rio says that the Devil's art disguises itself as either natural art or skill; conjurers desired to be regarded with awe, even at the expense of being thought in league with evil powers, and at the risk of their own safety. The idea that all wonderful things may have some explanation which would reveal the *modus operandi* without reference to the superhuman is, for the most part, modern. Writers who knew that many tricks were merely feats of legerdemain, or performed with special apparatus, or accomplished by means of confederacy, yet retained the belief that many other wonders were the work of the Devil. Frommann says in his *Tractatus de Fascinatione Novus et Singularis*, 1675:

> But if conjurers (cauculatores) without the art of magic can perform feats which almost exceed belief by their great agility, by the help of little cups, little balls, string, and similar things, and deceive the eyes of beholders, how much more can the Devil, who is master of a thousand arts [*Tausendkünstler* – in round numbers to indicate his consummate knowledge and countless ways of deceiving], dazzle the eyes – who is not only agile and swift, but also invisible himself, who holds the power of moving himself and of moving other things, has many allies, can command the elements, can draw and repel huge bodies, bring together things which are apart and disperse those which are together; can hide the seen, arrange various objects... and is skilful in many other ways of deceiving.

Ludovicus Vives, too, did not wonder that demons could perform wonders, since conjurers could make such shows that they would be counted by some as miracles if they were done by other persons. 'Indeed,' he goes on to say, 'there are some who believe that all these wonders are done by the Devil's aid.' From this view he dissents, and says that their art is so practised that with their swift movements they elude the observer's eye. As instances he enumerates some of their feats, such as eating bread and bringing flour from the mouth, drinking wind and bringing it out from the forehead or the throat, swallowing swords, etc.

Reginald Scot, in his *Discoverie of Witchcraft*, 1584, set out with the purpose of revealing the mysteries of so-called witchcraft. 'Now, therefore,' he says, 'my meaning is in words as plaine as I can, to rip up certeine proper tricks of that art; whereof some are pleasant and delectable, other some dreadfull and desperate, and all but meere delusions, or counterfet actions, as you shall soone see by due observation of everie knacke by me hereafter deciphered.' He adds that he could 'show so much that Bodin,

Spinaeus, and Vairus would swear he was a witch.'

The publication of Reginald Scot's book marks a great advance in the abandonment of the attribution to magic or supernatural aid of feats which appear wonderful. Scot himself does not disbelieve in supernatural power or the devil's, but he shows the way in which a number of conjurer's tricks were performed. He is not antagonistic to the performance of conjuring tricks, which, exhibited in the proper spirit, are 'neither impious nor altogether unlawfull if they are done for mirth and recreation, and not to the hurt of our neighbour.' In another chapter Scot says that 'the doings of conjurers are not only tolerable but greatly commendable, so that they abuse not the name of God, nor make the people attribute unto them His power; but alwayes acknowledge wherein the art consisted, so as thereby the other unlawful and impious arts may be by them the rather detected and bewraied.' His sympathy with conjurers is shown by his regret that it fell to his lot to reveal their secrets, and so make it more difficult for them to earn a living.

Even in the eighteenth century the existence of 'unlawful and detestable means' was thought to be common, for Richard Neve, in his *Merry Companion*, 1716, states that too many employed such means in his day. 'The end of legerdemain is,' he says, 'either good or bad, according as it is us'd; good and lawful when it is used at Festivals and Merry Meetings, only to procure innocent mirth, especially if it be used without desire of being esteemed above what we are, bad and altogether unlawful when 'tis us'd on purpose to cozen and deceive, or for vain glory, to be esteemed above what is meet and honest.'

It is not surprising to find in books on Magic records of feats which have a more or less striking resemblance to the work of the conjurer, and to find the miracles which we know now, and he knew then, to be clever deceptions solemnly accounted for by reference to devils. From books on Magic, then, some materials may be found relating to the various conjuring tricks known in the past. Other sources are incidental references in books not primarily dealing with any matters cognate with conjuring, similes, vocabulatioes, and representations. Lastly, from the sixteenth century onwards, are books dealing either in part or in whole with what is specifically conjuring or legerdemain. The most important of these books, printed before the end of the seventeenth century, are Reginald Scot's *Discoverie of Witchcraft*, 1584, *Hocus Pocus Junior*, 1635, and Thomas Ady's *A Candle in the Dark*, 1656. In the following pages an attempt is made to present from contemporary sources, evidences of the prevalence of conjuring tricks, some of them not very different from those offered for the amusement of spectators at fairs or music halls in the present day.

The quick movement of balls or pebbles from under cups is one of the commonest tricks. Such a trick, it has been thought, is represented in Rosellini's, and in the reproduction of the same subject in Wilkinson's *Manners of the Ancient Egyptians*, 1878, vol. ii., p. 70. Tricks with cups and balls were practised by the Greeks, and were doubtless included in the recreations accompanying their feasts. References are found in Suidas to conjuring tricks – apparently to tricks with cups and balls, for in explaining the word ψηφολογοι, he likens them to conjurers who deceive the eyes by their quickness in changing the places of pebbles.

Again, Stephanus, in quoting Budaeus, explains the word as the equivalent of circulator, so called, he says, because of his quickness in moving pebbles. A slightly more detailed description is given by Pollux, who, under the word ψηφοπαικτέω, refers to hiding pebbles and making them appear in various places, not by some simple trick, but with deep cunning. Again, Stepnaus and Casaubon quote Sextus Empiricus, as follows – 'The ψηφοπαίκται cheat the eyes of the beholders by the swiftness of their hands.' Casaubon further quotes St. Gregory Nazianzen in the same sense, adding the note of the of the scholiast, 'like conjurers, who deceiving the beholders and cheating their eyes by the nimbleness of their hands, and by the quickness of the bendings of their fingers.'

An account is given by Athenaeus in his *Deipnosophistae* of a conjurer with cups and balls whom he saw in the theatre, as follows:

One thing I remember, and I gape with astonishment at it now, and am almost struck dumb. A certain man stepped into the midst, and placed on a three-legged table three small cups, under which he concealed some little white round pebbles such as are found on the banks of rivers; these he placed one by one under the cups, and then, I don't know how, made them appear under another cup and showed them in his mouth. Then, when he had swallowed them, he brought one from the nose, another from the ear, and another from the head of those standing near him; last, he made them disappear from before the eyes of all. That man is a most mysterious performer, and could beat Eurybates of Oechalia, of whom we have heard.

Athenaeus also makes mention of three other conjurers, viz. Scymnus of Tarentum, Philistides of Syracuse, and Heraclius of Mitylene.

In a passage of Seneca (Epistle 45, to Lucilius) a tricks of oratory are likened to the performances of conjurers. 'Moreover,' he says, 'if a man is asked whether he has horns he is not so foolish as to feel his forehead, and again, he is not so silly or dull of wit as not to know when you are trying to talk him over by a clever trick; so such things are innocent deceptions like the cups and balls of conjurers, in which the very trickery is pleasing. If I get to know how a trick is done I lose my interest in it. It is just the same with tricks of speech, which cannot be called by a better name than sophisms: they are harmless to those who do not know them, and they are without interest to those who do.'

A representation of conjuring is given in Licetus, *De Lucernis Antiquorum*. There are shown a performing dog climbing a ladder, an ape, a cup and two rings, from which the inference might be made that the trick of interlocking and releasing rings, a common feat of ocnjurers at the present day, was practised by the Romans, or they may have only referred to a jumping trick of the dog. Licetus takes the former view.[13] In Daremberg and Saglio's *Dictionnaire* it is suggested, as also by Licetus, that the object at the bottom of the illustration represents the *acetabulum* of the conjurer. A lamp with the same subject may be seen in the British Museum, in the Greek and Roman Life Room, Case J (Games), No. 277 (see fig. I), which is represented in H.B. Walters' *History of Pottery*, 1905.

In a *Verzeichniss der Antikensammulung der Universität* (Würzburg), by L. Urlichs, published in 1865, is the following description of a Roman

lamp, which is evidently of the same type as that in the British Museum: 'A juggler (praestigiator), clad with the *exomis*, squats on the ground and looks round at an ape placing its left arm on his right arm which he rests on a little round vessel. On the ground to his left is a cup, a sponge, and two little vessels. On one side is an upright ladder, which a dog is mounting; on its head are two interlocked rings.' It may be noted, in passing, that the ape, as accompanying a conjurer, is again

Fig 1. Lamp in Greek and Roman Life Room, BM

Fig 2. German
Block-Book, 1475.
Planetenbuch, Luna

found in some representations of Luna under the Seven Planets.

In the Middle Ages conjuring formed one of the accomplishments of
the lower kinds of minstrels and jugglers, and cup and ball tricks are referred to in an old fabliaux, where two minstrels relate what they are able
to perform. The second of the two minstrels has included in his repertory
some feats of conjuring, among which is included a cup and ball trick.
'Well know I,' says one of the two – 'Well know I the cork ball, and to
make the beetle come alive and dancing on the table; and so I know many
a fair table game the result of dexterity and magic – I know how to play
with the cudgels, and so I know how to play with the cutlasses, and with
the cord and the rope.'

Again, that tricks with cups and balls were practised is evidenced by
other representations which have come down to us. In Fig 2 is shown a
conjurer at a table. One of the bystanders appears to be venturing his
opinion as to which of the cups the ball is under, and the practitioner
holds the fingers of his left hand delicately on the cup as if to show there
is no deception, and that it is a fair game. The illustration is taken from a
Planetenbuch, a block-book of 1475, in the British Museum. Representations which have a family likeness to this are shown in Theodor Hampes'
Fahrende Leute in der deutschen Vergangenheit. That opposite page 28 of
the book quoted is a representation from a block-book dated 1470, in the
Cabinet of Engravings in the Berlin Museum, and represents the 'Wirkung
der Planeten.' Another, opposite page 36, is a representation from a pen-

and-ink drawing in the Housebook of Prince Waldburg-Wolfegg, and dates from the fifteenth century. In this example the conjurer's table is outside a show, from which projects a sign bearing representations of feats of tumbling and balancing. The conjurer may be supposed to be taking one of the pebbles from the mouth of a bystander after the manner described centuries earlier by Athenaeus. Other examples are given at the end of this article in the list of representations of Luna as one of the Seven Planets. From the fact that this subject is included in a type of representation, we might assume, even in the absence of other evidence, that conjuring with cups and balls and thimble-rigging was an established practice (Figs 3 and 4). One of the poems of Walther von der Vogelweide (thirteenth century) describes a conjurer performing a trick, not with cups and balls, but a trick of a similar kind, viz., making objects appear mysteriously from a hat. Here we are given the very talk of the conjurer: 'So many men,' runs the poem, 'one sees are like jugglers, adroit and practised in trickery and deception. Thus one says, Look! What is under this hat? Now take it up – there is a hawk with defiant spirit. Take it up again, and you will see a proud peacock. Once more take it up, and you will have a monster of the sea!' A hat trick is also referred to in Lercheimer von Steinfelden's *Christlich bedenken und erjnnerung von Zauberey*, printed in 1585.

A cup and ball trick is shown in a woodcut by Hans Burgkmair, from an edition in German of Petrarch's *De remediis utriusque fortunae*, published in Augsburg in 1532, though the plates used date from about 1520 (see Fig 5). A company is seated round a table, the performer being at

the head. Here we may suppose he is taking a ball or pebble from the mouth or nose of one of those present in the way recorded by Athenaeus, and described by Reginald Scot in later times. The snake on the table may be taken to indicate that the performer, in some cases, combined with his tricks of legerdemain the charming of snakes as the Hindu and Cingalese conjurers do at the present day. (With regard to 'handling snakes,' Reginald Scot, in *The Discoverie of Witchcraft*, says, 'Marie with a woollen rag they pull out

Fig 3. Florentine engraving ascribed to Baccio Baldini

their teeth beforehand, as some men saie; but as truth is, they wearie them, and that is of certeinte. And surelie this is a kind of witchcraft which I term private confederacie.')

A cup and ball trick is shown in a book entitled *Hocus Pocus Junior,* published in 1635, with some indication of the way in which a ball lies concealed between two cups, one of which fits into the other. A similar representation is given in a German book of pastimes entitled *Das Zeitkurtzende Lust und Spiel Hauss.*

Reginald Scot says, in his *Discoverie of Witchcraft,* 'The True art (therefore) of juggling consisteth in legierdemaine, to wit, the nimble conveyance of the hand, which is especiallie performed three waies. The first and principall consisteth in hiding and canveing of balls' (Chapter XXII), and in the next chapter he sums up the manner of legerdemain with the ball by saying – 'Concerning the ball, the plaies and devises thereof are infinite, in so much as if you can by use handle them well, you may shewe therewith a hundreth feats; but whether you seeme to throw the ball into your left hand, or into your mouth, or into a pot, or up into the aier, and it is to be kept still in your hand.' He further describes ways of hiding balls in the palm and between the fingers, and under candlesticks, bottles, saltcellars, and saltcellar covers.

Casaubon, in a note on Athenaeus, says that he found in Plutarch mention of men who pretended to swallow swords, and he refers to an illusion to the conjurer's art, in the saying of a Greek poet, that a man ate catapults and swords; and Gregorius Palmas, Archbishop of Thessalonica, writes that conjurers were accustomed to swallow small stones and knives. Apuleius, again, in his *Metamorphoseon,* says that he saw at Athens before the *Stoa poecile,* or Painted Colonnade, a juggler on horseback devour a sharp two-edged sword. Sword-swallowing is referred to by Ludovicus Vives in his *Comment. on Augustin de C.D. lib.* 10, cap. 16, who says of conjurers (*circulators*) that, 'to the great fear and horror spectators, they swallow swords

Fig 4. Hans Sebald Behan. *The Seven Planet,* Luna

Fig 5. Petrarch. *Von der Artyney Bayder Gluck,* 1532

and vomit forth a power of needles, girdles, and coins'; and Lercheimer, his *Christlich bedenken und erjnnerung von Zauberey*, says that jugglers walk on a sharp sword with bare feet, or swallow it.

The trick of swallowing a dagger or sword may be performed either by using an instrument the short blade of which recedes in the handle, or, after patient practice, by actually forcing a long sword down the throat. Such accounts as the foregoing are not; therefore, to be discredited as impossible. In modern times it has become possible to swallow four swords at a time by the use of a sheath inserted in the throat. In like manner walking on swords, referred to in the passage quoted above, may be accomplished by a process of hardening the feet, a form of trick in existence in modern times being the mounting of a ladder of which the rungs are sharp swords. These sword tricks are explained in detail in a book on Magic (New York, 1901), by Albert A. Hopkins.

Many tricks of swallowing have been invented by conjurers. A very incredible one is that related to Zeito in the fourteenth century, who, in contest with another conjurer, is said to have swallowed him, boots excepted; the swallowed mman, however, shortly afterwards re-appeared. A Jew, Zedekiah by name, who lived in the ninth century, did what was even more wonderful, viz. swallowed a horse soldier and a chariot laden with grain!

Other tricks appearing to be full of danger were performed with knives.

116

Wier, in *De Praestigiis*, 1566, says that every day jugglers might be seen piercing their cheeks and arms with daggers and bodkins without drawing blood. Strutt quotes, in his *Sports and Pastimes*, from a morality written by Thomas Ingeland, entitled 'The Disobedient Child,' a servant's description of his master's wedding:

What juggling was there upon the boards!
What thrusting of knyves through many a nose!
What bearynge of formes – what holdings of swords!
What puttyhnge of botkynes through legge and hose!

Scot gives trickes of this kind, as 'to thrust a bodkin into your head without hurt', 'to thrust a bodkin through your toong, and a knife through your arme; a pittifull sight, without hurt or danger,' 'to cut half your nose asunder, and to heal it again presently without any salve.'

In one such trick a juggler, who had not taken any proper precautions, killed himself in very deed at a tavern in Cheapside, and died in St. Paul's Churchyard. Some instruments for knife tricks are represented by Scot, and are reproduced from the 1584 edition of his *Discoverie of Witchcraft*, in fig. 6. The original contains a marginal note calling attention to the difference between the knife for 'shew' and the 'knives of devise'.

The trick calculated to produce the greatest sense of danger to the spectators is that of decapitation. It is possibly some juggler's trick which Johannes Trithemius relates from previous writers. He says that a certain Jew, Zedekiah, a doctor by profession, appeared to men to cut of heads, hands, and feet openly, place them dripping with blood in a basin, and

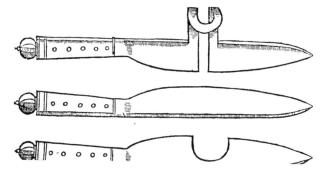

Fig 6. 'To thruste a knife through your arme, and to cut halfe your nose asunder &c.'
Reginald Scot: *The Discoverie of Witchcraft*, 1584

immediately restore them to their proper places, leaving the men none the worse for it. Another story about the same Jew is told by Francisci in his *New-polirter Geschicht-Kunst und Sitten-Spiegel*, 1670. He says that there was in the time of Louis the Gentle a Jew, named Zedekiah, who used to cast a man, limb by limb, into the air, and then put the parts together again. Such a thing, he adds, was only a bewitching of the eyes, but that even such bewitching could not have been caused without the Devil's help no intelligent person could readily be induced to admit, though he admits that conjurers and men acquainted with the secrets of nature do things which are taken for the work of the Black Art, whereas they are only natural phenomena.

Tharsander, in his *Schauplatz*, 1737, quotes *Hindorf. Theatr. Histor.*, in relating that, in the year 1272, a conjurer came to Creutznach from the Netherlands, who removed the head from a boy, and, leavingt the body for half an hour on the ground, put it on again. The same writer says that certain Turkish magicians could cut children in two, and put them together again.

Camerarius relates a story which he had heard of a man going to a fish market pretending that he wanted to buy fish. When he had made his choice, then he began to pretend that he had left his purse at home, and to say that he would send money for the fish immediately. The little woman who had the fish for sale would not agree to this, because she was afraid he would deceive her. 'But,' said the juggler, 'I will leave you my head in pledge,' and, putting down his head, he went off with his trunk only. The terrified woman begged that he would take the fish if only he would put his head on again.

Lercheimer says that sometimes one man cuts off the head of another and puts it on again, and then the blood-thirsty spirit wishes for nothing better than that, once the head is completely severed, it may not be replaced. He goes on to say: 'I remember a terrible story which I must relate. I have it on credible authority than in H. there was a nobleman named A. v. Th., who was able to cut off heads and put them on again. The man who had made up his mind not to continue his traffic in such deadly practices, but, being in the company of a set of good fellows, he allowed himself to be persuaded to give them some delight for the very last time; but no one, as might be supposed, was ready to lend him his head for this purpose. At last a serving boy was made use of, being assured by the conjurer that he would put his head on again. The conjurer cut off the head, but could not manage to restore it. Then A. said to the company that there was some one present who was preventing him, and that he wished to warn that person not to do so; then he tried again, but without success. A second time he warned and threatened him against preventing him. As that did no good, and he could not set the head on again, he made a lily grow on the table, then he lifted up the head and the flower. Immediately one of the company fell backward from his seat, and his head was separated from his body. This man was the magician who had prevented him; after this the conjurer was able to restore the head to the boy. Lercheimer goes on to say that this exemplifies how the magician, who has the weaker spirit in his service, must give way to the one who has the stronger.

The conjurer escaped out of the country until the affair had blown over, and he had received pardon. The great power residing in the miraculously produced lily is shown in the case of certain conjurers who are said to have performed a decapitation trick before Faust at Frankfort; these conjurers cut off one another's heads and replaced them. They made use of an elixir of life which was potent to bring into full bloom a lily-bud placed in it only a few moments. When Faust broke off the flower from the stalk of the lily the charm ceased, and the conjurers were unable to replace the head (Frost: *Lives of the Conjurors*). In both these accounts we have two well-known tricks, viz., that of decapitation and that of the miraculous growth of flowers.

Richard Johnson in his voyages describes a feat of decapitation which he saw, in which the victim's head, being severed by drawing a cord tight, fell into a kettle of hot water. The story bears the mark of the relation of a conjurer's performance, inasmuch as when Johnson expressed a wish to see the head, they told him that if they should see it with their bodily eyes they should live no more. That the decapitation trick is best performed at some little distance will appear from Reginald Scot's account, which

The forme of ye planks.

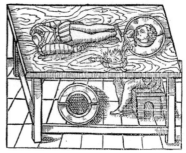

Fig 7. 'To cut off one's head, and to laie it in a platter which the jugglers call the decollation of John Baptist.' *The Discoverie of Witchcraft*

reveals the mechanism by which it could be produced. It is as follows:

To cut off one's head, and to laie it in a platter, etc., which the jug-glers call the decollation of John Baptist.

To shew a most notable execution by this art, you must cause a board, a cloth, and a platter to be purposelie made, and in each of them holes fit for a boie's necke. The boarde must be made of two planks, the longer and broader the better; there must be left within halfe a yard of the end of each planke helfe a hole, so as both plankes being thrust together there may remaine two holes, like to the holes in a pair of stocks. There must be made likewise a hole in the table-cloth or carpet. A platter must also be set directlie over or upon one of them, having a hole in the middle thereof of the like quantitie, and also a piece cut out of the same so big as his necke, through which his head may be conveied into the middest of the platter, and then, sitting or kneeling under the board, let the head only remain upon the board in the same. Then (to make the sight more dreadfull) put a little brimstone into a chaffing dish of coles, setting it before the head of the boie, who must gaspe two or three times so as the smoke enter a little into his nostrels and mouth (which is not wholesome), and the head will appear presentlie starke dead, if the boie set his countenance accordinglie; now if a little blood be sprinkled on his face the sight will be the stranger.

This is commonlie practised with a boie instructed for that pur-pose, who, being familiar and conversant with the commpanie, may be knowne as well by his face as by his apparel.

In the other end of the table, where the like hole is made, another boie of the bigness of the knowne boie must be placed, having upon him his usuall apparel. He must lean or lie upon the board, and must put his head under the board through the said hole, so as his bodie shall seeme to lie on the one end of the board, and his head shall lie in a platter on the other end.

Miraculous appearances or disappearances have been, and still are, effects much valued by conjurers. When science was restricted to the priests it would appear that they used it in ways akin to those in which the modern conjurer conducts his performances. The visions and magical appearances of deities such as those related by Pliny and Iamblicus were probably pro-duced by means of plane or concave mirrors. The images were sometimes thrown on to a cloud of smoke, which increased the mystical effect, and rendered them more generally visible.

Salverte gives the following passage from Damascius: 'There appeared on the wall of the temple a mass of light, which at first appeared to be very remote; it transformed itself, in coming nearer, into a face evidently divine and supernatural, of a severe aspect, but mixed with gentleness and extremely beautiful. According to the institutions of a mysterious religion the Alexandrians honoured it as Adonis.'

Mediaeval accounts of miraculous appearances and disappearances are related with credulity, and it seems as if the recorder, having witnessed some sight which aroused his wonder, allowed himself to put the interpretation on it which the creator desired – as if the spectator at the theatre should affirm that he saw in reality the objects which are painted on a scene. Possibly it is due to such ready credulity that the conjuring effects of Albert Bishop of Regensberg are related by Johannes Beka (*Fontes*). The story is as follows:

Albert of Regensberg invited King William of Holland in Epiphany, 1247, to a banquet. The bishop led the King from the dining room into his garden, where servants of wondrous beauty were preparing everything for a jovial meal. It was winter time, the whole surface of the earth was thickly covered with snow, and the nobles who accompanied the King began to grumble at being expected to sit down to meat in a garden and without a stove when the weather was so bitterly cold; but when the Bishop sat down with the King, and the guests, each according to his rank, had taken their seats and were awaiting the dishes, the huge mass of snow and ice vanished in a moment, the heat increased under the beams of the sun, the grass sprang up, and flowers of extraordinary beauty blossomed. Every tree was covered with green leaves, and brought forth ripe fruit. The vine-trees blossomed, and brought forth fresh grapes in abundance; the birds twittered and sang. The summer heat was so powerful that the guests had to take off some of their clothes, and they sought the shade under the thick foliage of the trees. After the banquet was over, in a moment the servants, birds' song, the foliage vanished – the snow returned, the guests put on their coats, and returned shivering to the fire in the dining-room.

Again, according to the story given by Martin del Rio in his *Disqui-*

sitionum Magicarum, Cologne, 1657, Zedekiah, a Jew, in the ninth century, in the time of the Emperor Louis, suddenly produced in the midst of winter a most pleasant garden in the palace of the Emperor, with trees, flowers, grass, the songs of birds.

The sudden appearance of the vine around a dinner table is included among the wonders which may be performed through magic by Vives, in his *Comment. ad Augustum de C.D.*, lib. 10, cap. 16, when he says that books have been written about such things which are easy to do.

Wier, in *de Praestigiis*, 1566, tells of an illusion, related also by Lercheimer, about a conjurer in Magdeburg, who complained that his performance brought him in so little money that he wanted to mount to heaven. Accordingly he threw his pony's bridle up in the air, the pony followed, and the conjurer hung on to its tail; thereupon his wife caught hold of his coat, and the maid followed. The bystanders saw this with astonishment, when a man came up and asked what was the matter. They replied that the conjurer and his pony had ascended to heaven, whereupon the man said that he had seen the conjurer enter an inn, and when the people found that they had been the subjects of an illusion they went away. Possibly this was some optical illusion credulously accepted as being real in the first place by spectators unused to such sights.

A certain fascination attaches to fire-tricks, and the modern fire-king has many precursors. Simon Magus was supposed to have been impervious to fire. Pyrrhus, according to Plutarch, had a great toe which fire would not burn, and Athenaeus writes of a conjurer named Xenophon, having as his disciple and successor Cratisthenes, who brought fire from all parts of his body. Reginald Scot says:

> Others likewise have (as they say) a *Katherine* wheel upon their bodies, and they saie they are kin to St Katherine, and that they can carry burning colds in their bare hands and dip their said hands in hot scalding liquor, and also go into hot ovens. Whereof, thought the last be but a bare jet, and to be done by anie that will prove (as a bad fellow in London had need to doo making no variance at all therein), yet there is a show made of the other, as though it were certeine and undoubted; by anointing the hands with the juice of mellowes, mercurie, etc., which for a little time are defensatives against the scalding liquors and scortching fiers.

Frommann, in his *Tractatus de Fascinatione Novus et Singularis*, 1675, says that the skin may be so hardened by magic art that it does not feel the fury of fire, as in the case of Simon Magus, who, when placed in the flames, did not burn, and was proof against hard and sharp objects, and against all arms and balls shot from bombards. This art, he says, was called dei Passauer-Kunst, because it first became known when the army collected around Passau, which afterwards, in 1611, burst into Bohemia and occupied Prague. (Senertius, lib. 5, *Princ. Med.*, page 521.)

Antonio Paullini, writing about 1717, says that, forty years before that time, a French fire-swallower was seen in many parts of Germany, who had by him a vessel full of glowing coals, from which he kept on putting them into his mouth, first with one hand and then with the other, and then chewed and swallowed them. He took a piece of meat and put it on the hot coals in his mouth, and there cooked it, and ate it as if it were a delicacy. He set light to sulphur and pitch, and swallowed them with their blue flames in his throat, so that a hissing sound was produced. He would take a glowing piece of iron and lick it with his tongue so that it hissed, or he would take it between his teeth, and carry it for a time around the theatre. Paullini also describes Jean Royer's performance of lighting brandy in his mouth, and petroleum which burned without wick.

Martin del Rio, quoting Thomas Farellus, deca. 2 *rerum Sicularum*, lib. 5, cap. 2, says that Eunus, while speaking, sent forth flames from his mouth, which was not to be attributed to Devil's magic but to the fact that he had hidden in his mouth a nut full of sulphur and fire, by which he gave forth flames by breathing lightly on it. Del Rio also states that Farellus refers to a certain Diodorus doing the same thing (cap. 1, lib. 3, deca. 1).

Similarly, as St. Jerome says, Barchochebas, who put himself at the head of the Jews in their revolt against Hadrian, made them believe that he was the Messiah by vomiting flames from his mouth, Modern conjurers put a ball of tow in their mouths, let it burn out almost entirely, and add fresh pieces to revive the fire. The sparks are too feeble to injure them, provided that they breathe the air through their nose.

Records remain of two conjurers before the end of the seventeenth century who have performed tricks with water, viz., Manfred of Malta and Jean Royer of Lyons. The former is represented in an engraving of the seventeenth century in the Germanische Museum at Nuremburg.[22] Here he appears sending forth three separate streams from his mouth before a company of spectators; there are also represented nine vessels, doubtless for the reception of liquids of different colours which he miraculously produced. Between an angel and the sun are the words *Solus sicut sol,* and beneath the angel the words *Fama volat*. Another angel offers him a wreath, which is the *proemium virtutis*. In the Nuremberg Museum is also an advertisement of his performance headed *Rfama volat*, setting forth that Manfred, in addition to his water tricks, would lift a stone weighing 700 lbs. by the hair of his head, would fly down a rope from the height of a house, &c.

Abraham a Sancta Clara says of this performer's water tricks that he could perform them four times a day. He had a vessel full of lukewarm water brought and fifteen or twenty glasses. First he opened his mouth in order to show that he had nothing between his teeth, then from his mouth came red wine, water, brandy, rosewater, orange water, white wine, and the like, which could all be recognised by the taste; but it was noticed that on every occasion he began with red wine. Sometimes, after taking water to the extent of twenty glasses, he would squirt it aloft from his mouth like a fountain. Cardinal Richelieu imprisoned this Manfred, and threatened to hang him if he did not prove that his tricks were performed by natural means and not by magic. Manfred revealed the *modus operandi* in secret, and was set free.

Scotus has given an account of the means of production of different coloured liquids in his *Natural Magic*. When he was in Rome he was invited, together with Kircher, to the house of a certain antiquarian. The latter produced a roughly-carved cup, of which he wished to know the use. Kircher asked for water, and found that the cup, which was made of light wood from Mexico, changed the colour of the water which was poured into it, and that various colours could be shown by varying the light and shade, and by placing it against various coloured pieces of cloth. At first the water poured into the cup became pure blue – the longer it stood the deeper it became. If the water was poured into a glass bowl and placed in the light all trace of the blue colour vanished; but if the bowl was placed in the shade the water took a beautiful green tine; it became red, and afterwards it assumed the colour of various coloured clothes placed against it (Scotus, *Magia Naturalis*).

The second of the two conjurers referred to above was celebrated for his fountain tricks. Jean Royer of Lyons could send forth from his mouth, according to the account given of him by Abraham a Sancta Clara, twelve or fifteen different coloured liquids, leaves and flowers; also he exhibited a fountain playing high from his mouth, and for as long as it would take a man to say twice over the fifty-first Psalm. (The duration of the operation of this mouth fountain is estimated in Paullini's *Curieuses Cabinet* as the time it takes to cover two hundred paces.)

Royer, like Manfred, was said to have aroused suspicion that his performances were practised by Devil's aid, and to have saved himself by revealing the tricks to Scotus and Kircher, who accepted his explanation and undertook to keep the secret during Royer's lifetime. After a time Scotus appeared to have too hastily concluded that, as he had heard, Royer was dead, and to have revealed the trick while Royer was still living.

An explanation of Royer's trick is given in the *Zeikurtzende Lust-und Spiel-Haus*, the performer being sup-

Fig 8. Floram Marchand,
Le Grand Boyeur de Tours

posed to take on an empty stomach water coloured with certain substances which, being diluted with the varying quantities of water which he drank, produced liquids like in colour to varying kinds of wine. Vinegar, lemon-juice, and brandy were added to give a flavouring.

Another performance of the same kind as those of Manfred of Malta and Jean Royer of Lyons is described in what appears to have been a book-leaf preserved amongst the prints in the British Museum (see fig. 8). It is a portrait of Floram Marchand, who is styled Le Grand Boyeur de Tours, and beneath is printed: See here the pourtrait of this man of Tours, /His art and reasons here are published. /What makes this glass look white and that so red: /And all the progress of the works displaid – /The whole deceit is here now open laid.

The book, or pamphlet, dated 1650, is by Mr. Thomas Peedle and Mr. Thomas Cozbie, who brought the conjurer 'into England from Tours, in France; and after Wednesday next, being the 26th of this present June, will be constantly ready every afternoon, if desired, in their own persons to work an experimental proof of what is here declared.'

Wier, in *De Praestigiis*, says, 'the many feats which minstrels and jugglers perform every day by agility and swiftness of hand seem to those who are skilless to be miracles, and we are lost in admiration of them.' Pomponatius states that at Manutua and Padua he saw a man of this kind, called Reatius, who did incredible things which seemed to the vulgar to be performed by the aid of demons; accordingly he was given over to the authorities on a charge of heresy, and showed in secret that his actions were only illusions, and were either tricks of legerdemain or carried through by secret confederacy with many other persons. Reginald Scot divides confederacy into two kinds – private and public, the private being some pre-arrangement and, further, when another person or other persons are in league with the performer. As an example of private confederacy he gives a card trick. The 'conjurer will show you a card or any other like thing, and will saie further unto you, Behold, and see what a marke it hath, and then burneth it; and nevertheless fetcheth another like card so marked out of some bodies pocket, or out of some corner where he himself before had placed it, to the wonder and astonishment of simple beholders, which conceive not the kind of illusion but expect miracles and strange works.'

A trick of public confederacy is such as telling 'whether one cast crosse or pile by the ringing' of a coin. This is done by the form of questions asked by the confederate; according as the question is, 'What is it?' or 'what is't?' the performer knows which way the coin has fallen. Another confederacy trick mentioned by Scot is 'How to tell where a stollen horse is become.' To perform this it was necessary to get a confederate to steal the horse first, and the conjurer knew then where it could be found.

The conjurer of the present day usually attempts to interest his spectators, not merely by the tricks which he performs, which in many cases would speak for themselves, but also by his accompanying remarks. There is often very little need for his explanation, and conjuring may be effective without speech. The employment of patter may to some extent be regarded as a survival from times when words were used to impress beholders with a sense of mystery, and to lead them to suppose that the conjurer was associated with spirits or demons, by whose aid the trick was thought to be effected. In the description given by Walther von der Vogelweide (see page 93), the speech of the conjurer is limited to a statement of the trick which he is performing; but in a number of cases we find instances of the actual use of mysterious words which were used as though they had some inherent power, or, on the other hand, as a kind of fluent talk employed for the purpose of heightening the effect or of diverting the attention of the beholders at that moment when the sleight is performed. St. Gregory Nazianzen uses the expression λογοι ψηφολόγικοι, which may be taken to mean words such as the *acetabularius* would use. Roger Bacom has several references to the charms used by conjurers who make use of *circulos et characters vanissimos et carmina stultissima et orations stultissimas.* It may be noted in passing that, although Bacon disapproves of the use of charms and enchantments when they are inefficacious and used merely for display, yet he admits that there are certain genuine *deprecations* instituted by men of truth or ordained by God and angels as, for instance, those used in ordeals over the white hot iron or the waters of a stream, and in other ways by which men are shown to be either innocent or guilty.

Again, in his *Opus Majus* (vol. i., page 399), in speaking of the power of words, he says that they have the greatest efficacy of all things, and that almost all miracles which have been performed by holy men from the beginning of the world have been done by the virtue of words. Further, he admits their use as justifiable in medicine, and quotes Constantine as approving of them, not because they have any real physical value, but because they render the patient more ready to take his medicine, and give him a more abundant hope of recovery, inasmuch as the mind has great power over the body.

Frommann, in his *Tractatus de Fascinatione novus et singularis*, 1675, quotes Riolanus Pater as stating that he had often found epileptics rise if the following lines were whispered thrice: *Gaspar fert myrrham, thus Melchior, Balthasar aurum, /Haec tria qui secum portabit nominee Regum /Solvitur a morbo Christi pietate caduco*, and Weir, in *de Praestigiis*, gives the following against toothache: *Galbes galbat, galdes, galdat.*

Fretagus writes, 'It is said that toothache can be stopped if during the sacred offices the teeth are made to meet, and meantime these words are muttered: *Os non conminuetis ex illo*, or if this ridiculous phrase is hung round the neck: *Strigiles falcesque dentatae, dentibus dolorum persanate.*

Against the bite of a mad dog the following was supposed to have efficacy: *Irioni Khirioni effera, Khuder fera*: and *Hax pax max Deus adimax.*

Casaubon, in a note in his *Animadversiones in Athenaei Deipnosoph.*, describes the *joueurs de goubelets* of his time as performing in such a way that the beholders, not knowing how the tricks were done, thought that they were achieved by virtue of the words which the conjurers poured forth or by some other magic power.

Scot, in his *Discoverie of Witchcraft*, gives as an example of words which may be used in a trick with balls the following: *Hey, fortuna, furie, nunquam credo, passé, passé, when come you, sirra?* and the 'excellent feat to make a two penie piece lie plaine in the palme of your hand, and to be passed from thence when you list,' he suggests might be accomplished by such words as: *Ailif, casyl, zaza, hit mel meldat: Saturnus,*

Jupiter, Mars, Sol, Venus, Mercurie, Luna or in transforming or altering the colour of one's cap or hat: -*Droch myroch, & senaroth betu baroch asmaroth, rousee farounsee, hey passe passe.*

Neve, in the *Merry Companion*, gives as the fourth of the requirements of a conjurer the following: 'He must also have his terms of art, namely, certain strange terms and emphatical words to grace and adorn his actions, and to astonish the beholders; and these odd kind of speeches must be various, according to the action he undertakes.'

An expression which is very commonly associated with the conjurer is 'Hocus Pocus.' An early use of the word is to be found in a disputation of Voetius *De Magia*. It is dated 1636. 'Agyrtae,' the writer says, 'call this vain and idle art *Okos Bokos*, words taken from the real or imaginary name of an Italian priest or mystagogue, or from some other source.'[32] Nares confirms this as the source, saying that their origin seems to be rightly drawn from the Italian jugglers, who said Ochus Bochus in reference to a famous magician of those names, and in a German book, *Etwas für alle*, by Abraham a S. Clara, it is said that the conjurer was formerly called *Okos Bokos*, the real or assumed name of an Italian who must have been an extraordinary master of this art. It may be noted that foreign writers in various instances have used the expression in forms which are further removed from that form which has been the basis of the supposed derivation as a corruption of *hoc est corpus*. (The date of the sermon of Tillot-

son, in which he says that in all probability these juggling words are nothing else but a corruption of the words used by the priests of the Church of Rome in their tricks of Transubstantiation, is 1694. This derivation appears to be a quite gratuitous invention.)

In a book entitled *Seltzame Gerichtshandel*, by Matth. Abele, 1635, the author, in drawing a comparison between conjuring and the law, says that he has found, after industrious enquiry, that a certain Zoilus had likened the 'Hogges und Pogges' of the conjurer to

Fig 9. From *Hocus Pocus Junior*, 1635

the 'distorted and ambiguous speech of the lawyer.'

Joachim Rachel, in his *Neu-Verbesserte Teutsche und Satyrische Gedichte*, has the following: *Was mit der langenzeit sol wachsen und bestehen,/Das muss nicht okes bokes wie aus der Taschen gehn.*

Again, J.B. Shuppe, in his *Schriften*, 1660, says that men who prefer vain and idle speculation and disputation are like rope-walkers and jugglers. It is an art of walking on the rope; it is an art of playing various tricks, such as Joan Pottage or Ockes Bockes of Amsterdam used to perform.

The second edition of *Hocus Pocus Junior* (the earliest in the British Museum) was published in 1635. That the expression was no doubt in existence be-

Fig 10. From *Das Zeitkurtzende Lust-Und Spiel-Haus*

fore that time may be argued from the facts – (1) that it was the second edition which was published in 1635, and (2) that the word 'junior' implies a predecessor who was senior, and indeed, the writer, in describing one of his tricks, refers to his 'bonus genius' or 'nuntius invisibilis' or 'hiccius doccius' 'as my senior calls it.' Again, Ady, writing in 1656, speaks of 'one man more excelling in that craft (conjuring) than others that went about in King James's time, and long since, who called himself the King's most excellent Hocus Pocus; and so was he called because, at playing every trick, he used to say '*Hocus Pocus, tontus talontus, vade celeriter jubeo.*" This, if it may be accepted, takes back the expression at least a further ten years.

Further, Ben Jonson, in 'Magnetic Lady,' acted in 1632, uses the expression Hokos Pokos in the following passage from the chorus at the end of the first act:

BOY: Do they think this pen can juggle? I would we had Hokos Pokos for 'em then, your people, or Travitanto Tudesco.
DAMPLAY: Who's that, boy?
BOY: Another juggler with a long name.

Here it may be noted that Hokos Pokos is coupled with an Italian name, and, further, that it is in form near to that given by Voetius.

The foregoing references lead one to suppose that Hocus Pocus was an expression in varying forms which was generally known in the middle of the seventeenth century, not only in England but abroad, and there is evidence of a kind that it was known at least as early as 1625. It would not be surprising to find the words in use at an earlier date. THe earliest suggestion of a derivation, viz., that referred to as given in Voetius under the date 1636, is that Italy is the source of the expression, and that it was probably the assumed name of a man.

As derivations have been suggested the Welsh *hoced* – a cheat, and *bwg*, or *pwca*, a hobgoblin, and the French *hocher* – to stake, and *pocher* – to poke; but these derivations are not to be taken seriously. Further, the second word 'pocus' is almost without doubt a reduplicated form of the first, and for quite analogous reduplications may be quoted 'higgledy-piggledy,' 'hurly-burly,' 'hickery-pickery,' and 'hokey pokey.' Analogous to the reduplication in 'hiccius doctius' may be mentioned 'handy-dandy,' 'hoity-toity,' 'humpty-dumpty,' 'hoddy-doddy,' and 'hickery-dickery.'

The little wooden man used in a vanishing trick is called 'Hiccius Doctius.' The trick is represented in the *Hocus Pocus Junior*, and in the frontispiece to the 'Hocus Pocus,' which forms part of a German book entitled *Das Zeitkurtzende Lust-und Spielhaus* (see fig. 10), where the trick is fully described, the conjurer saying: 'Look, gentlemen, this man I call Bonus Genius, or Hiccius Doctius,' and at the end he says, 'Hei genius meus velocissimus ubi.'

Fig 12. Portrait of Richard Neve and illustration of conjuring trick with a bird

Fig 12. Comenius:
*Orbis Sensualum
Pictus*, 1659

Hiccius Docius is in the frontispiece of the second edition of *Hocus
Pocus Junior, or the Anatomie of Legerdemain*, and is referred to in the
preface to that book as follows:

> Courteous Reader, doe you not wonder? If you doe not, well you
> may, to see so slight a pamphlet so quickly spent; but lightly come
> and lightly goe, it's a Jugler's terme, and it well befits the subject.
> Would you know whence it first came? Why, from Bartholomew
> Fayre. Would you know whither it's bent? – For the Fayre again: it's
> a stragler, a wanderer, and, as I said, as it lightly comes, so it lightly
> goes; for it meanes to see not onely Bartholomew's Fayre, but all
> the Fayres int eh Kingdome also, and therefore in the front. Hiccius
> Doccius is the postmaster, and what he wants there I'le give him
> here – a word or two of command, a terme of art not so much sub-
> stantiall as circumstantiall, Celeriter, vade, over hedges and ditches,
> thorow thicke and thin, to come to your Fayres.

In this preface we may suppose that the author is writing with the same
kind of inconsequence as the conjurer speaks at the fair. The expression
Hiccius Doctius is said to be a corruption of *hic est doctus*.

Various aspects of conjuring have been emphasised in the different
names attached in different languages to the performer of tricks of legerdemain. The Greeks called him the ψηφοπαικτης from the pebbles which
he used. Similarly the Romans styled him the *calcularius*, or *acetabularius*,

(an analogous denomination is the English 'thimble-rigger') from the little stones and cups respectively. In French he is the *joueur de goubelets*, and the French *escamoteur* comes from *escamot*, a cork ball, and has reference to the cup and ball trick. Again, he was the *saccularius*, or bag-man, just as in German he is the *Taschenspieler*, so called from his way of hiding objects in his pocket or bag. Similarly in Italian he is the *bossoletino*, or purse-man, and Voetius, in his disputation *de Magia* gives us the Flemish for conjuring *uyt den aessack spleen*. In French he is the *prestidigitateur*, from the readiness or quickness of his fingers. In English *conjurer* refers to the calling of spirits to his aid, and *juggler*, which is often used for conjurer, is derived from the latin *joculator*, which is in Italian *gioculatore*, and in French *jongleur*. Another German word, *Tausendkünstler*, refers to the variety of his tricks, while the English *tregitour* originally refers to the mechanical contrivances used by the conjurer, though this original meaning is not evident in the following passage from Lydgate's *Dance of Macabre*, where the word is equivalent to conjurer:

> *Maister John Rykell*, sometime tregitour of noble Henri,
> Kinge of England,
> And of France the mighty conqueror;
> For all the sleightes and turnyng of thyne honde,
> Thou must come nere this dance to understonde.
> Nought may avail all thy conclusions
> For deth shortly, nother on see nor londe,
> Is not dyseeyved by noon illusions.

Arthur Watson's article on conjuring ends here. In this reprint his note on 'Representations of feats of conjuring in Book-Illustrations or Prints' has been omitted since this information is provided in the text. His end-notes have also been omitted since these were largely quotes from the Latin; those in English have been incorporated into his article.

CASINOS, CLUBS & CO.

Linocuts by Paul Ballingall

© PAUL BALLINGALL

MYSTERY PANTS © PAUL BALLINGALL

© PAUL BALLINGALL

BONGO CLUB © PAUL BALLINGALL

GAMBLERS © PAUL BALLINGALL

DRINKER © PAUL BALLINGALL

© PAUL BALLINGALL

MR & MRS NOAH © PAUL BALLINGALL

THE CONSPIRATORS © PAUL BALLINGALL

THE OPENING © PAUL BALLINGALL

Tom Leonard

Epithalamium

For Stephen and Lucy

Let me not to the marriage of true minds admit impediment
Shakespeare says – and maybe it is something to do with minds.
Or there again, something to do with everything else
you can think of; going to the shops, sitting in a bus together,
who you want to waken up beside in the morning,
And who you want to go to bed with – for the rest of your life.
Who you're going to have your most important rows with
who you want to share your silences, who you want to share
your money with, if you have any. Who you want to share
your poverty with, if you don't. Who you can share your poverty with,
and still get on when there's no fancy stuff to occupy your minds.
It's maybe being thirty with somebody, being forty with somebody,
being fifty, being sixty, getting used to ways of doing things
with the same person, getting used to not doing things with them
when you have to go your separate ways to raise the dough

for a house. 'The trouble with marriage,' I used to say,
'is you have to stop living with each other.' All this up at
the crack of dawn stuff, out to your separate jobs,
who's first home at night, who makes the dinner, if anybody
makes it. And all the account business, joint or separate. And the
usual list as to who does what, ironing, hoovering, washing
the clothes. Who does what. Who's got lousy habits. Who thinks
their farts are funny. Who's the most incomprehensible, opaque,
wrongheaded pain in the arse you could ever find, and you've
found them living with you. But give it an hour. Or a day.
And watch out for the wisecracks. There's Chekhov:
'If you can't stand loneliness don't get married' – and there's
no shortage of busted-up couples out there who won't bust
a gut with grief if you join them. You stick your own way. To
hell with them. It's not a sentimental thing, it's a serious thing
the most serious thing you'll ever do, if you're doing it properly
as you are. Saying it to others, before others, this is who I want,
this is where it ends and begins with me. And uniquely so.
So here's to you, Stephen and Lucy, standing at that old portal:
here's to a good road before you, and a long one,
and the two of you walking together happily, down it.

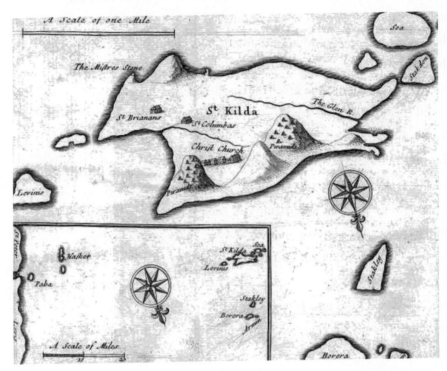

A Late Voyage to St Kilda, the remotest of all the Hebrides, or the Western Isles of Scotland, Martin Martin. London: D. Brown and T. Goodwin, 1698, from the collection of early travel writing at the Mitchell Library, Glasgow.
(The Mitchell Library)

Zsuzsanna Varga

Be There Dragons?
Early Travel Writing at the Mitchell Library

It is an excellent Countrey for a despairing Lover: for every corner affords him Willow to make a Garland on; but if Justice doom him to be hang'd on any other Tree, he may in sight of the sentence live long and confident. If he had rather quench his spirits than suffocate them, so rather chuse to feed Lobsters then Crows; 'tis but leaping from his window, and lights in a River or Sea; for most of their dwellings stand like Privies in moted-houses, hanging still over the water. If none of these cure him, keep him but a Winter in a house without a Stove that shall cool him.

THIS IS HOW Owen Feltham (1602–68), a religious writer of some repute, described the Dutch in his *A Brief Character of the Lowe-Countreys Under the States. Being Three Weeks Observation of the Vices and Vertues of the Inhabitants* (London: Rich. Lowndes, 1671). Feltham does not confine himself to criticising the country for its geography and climate, he also condemns it for the unreliable character of its inhabitants, for its dearth of culture and lack of respect for Duty and Authority. His emotional, sometimes venomous language, results in an animated, highly charged account.

This volume is one of many examples of seventeenth-century travel writing being made available at the Mitchell Library in Glasgow through the Britain in Print Project, funded by the Lottery Heritage Fund and led by Edinburgh University Library. The project is designed to unearth and electronically catalogue those pre-1700 books printed in Britain in a variety of languages that have so far, in terms of electronic catalogue access, remained outside the public domain. Sixteen libraries are participating, led by Edinburgh University Library on behalf of CURL, the Consortium of Research Libraries in the British Isles; and public libraries such as Birmingham Public Library, Edinburgh City Library and the Mitchell Library, Glasgow.

The Mitchell Library's pre-1700 collection amounts to about 4500 printed titles – monographs, pamphlets, and periodicals – some of which have been untouched since the opening of the present building in 1911. Now that it is becoming possible to request them through the electronic catalogue, they will enable research on many different subjects, including the Civil War and the Union of the Crowns.

A significant theme of the collection is the history and diversity of mankind, social development and civil society at home and abroad. I found myself particularly fascinated by the way these preoccupations were expressed in some of the history travel narratives. One example is German historian Samuel Puffendorf's *An Introduction to the History of the Principal Kingdoms and States of Europe* (London: Gilliflower, 1697), in J. Crull's translation. The volume covers the history of Europe from the Assyrian empire until 1679, discussing Poland and Russia in addition to the Western core countries. Puffendorf originated the contention that the development of human civilization is a historical process – a progressive refinement of social courtesies and an increasing cultivation of the arts and sciences. This perspective had an enormous impact upon Scottish conjectural historians.

Hedged between the great discoveries of Columbus and Francis Drake, and the early sentimental journeys of Addison, whose *Remarks on several parts of Italy* was published in 1705, the travel texts show a shift from dry, factual records towards accounts of subjective experience. The collection also reflects a typical spread between translations and indigenous British writing. Translations dominated the market, amounting to about forty per cent of travel writing published in English before 1700. 'Written in French and faithfully Englished' is a recurrent term on title pages, especially of those works that describe distant parts of the world. Some are now classic texts, including the Portuguese Jeronymo Lobo's *A Short Relation of the River Nile* (London: John Martin, 1673), *The travels of Sir John Chardin into Persia and the East Indies*, published in English and French concurrently in 1686, and Villault's *A Voyage to Guinee* (London, 1670). Indigenous travel writing covers the emerging colonies, mainland Europe (whose northern and eastern borders were seriously debated), and England, Scotland and Ireland.

In the second half of the seventeenth century, more and more expeditions had scientific purposes. The Royal Society for the Improvement of Natural Knowledge, set up in 1660 played a central role in commissioning and publishing original work and translations; the Society was also strongly committed to the scientific exploration of the British Isles. In 1665–66, its *Philosophical Transactions* included a 'Catalogue of Directions for Travellers', with notes on natural history by the chemist Robert Boyle. The Mitchell Library's little volume *A Direction for the English Traveller: To Enable him to Coast about England* (n.d. London, John Garrett), takes a scientific approach to domestic travel, and provides charts of distances between different localities in England, divided up by shires and countries.

Lobo's *A Short Relation of the River Nile* is an interesting example of a missionary text. Lobo, a Portuguese missionary, enjoyed a considerable reputation in his time, and his *Voyage to Abyssinia* was translated by Dr Johnson from the French. In the foreword to *A Short Relation*, translator Peter Wyche identifies the source of Lobo's narrative as being Robert Southwell, who is said to have obtained it from 'an inquisite and observing Jesuite at Lisbon.' Lobo's trip was undertaken to investigate the source of the Nile. Embedded in classical knowledge, his text is full of quotes from ancient authors, including their descriptions of floods of the Nile in summer months. His observations are interspersed with fantastical sequences. Lobo retells the story of Prester John, the mythical saviour-emperor of Christianity, refers to Abyssinia as the land of the unicorn, and tells of the fabulous pelican who feeds its own blood to its young.

Turning to another little volume about distant lands, Edmund Hickeringhill's *Jamaica Viewed* (London: John Williams, 1661) provides an insight into the relationship between travel writing and the colonising project. While warning of dangers, it was primarily intended to tempt possible emigrants. Jamaica, first colonised by Spain in 1494, was taken over by Britain in 1655 in a campaign led by Admirals Penn and Venables. Hickeringhill, who had followed the English troops to the Caribbean, explicitly serves the colonising agenda. His introduction defends the reputation of Jamaica, which was seen rather as 'Grave then Granary'. argues that its natural resources and climate make the island very suitable for plantation: it has rich soil, and some of the fruit and vegetables grown there are 'more rare and not to be found in any other of the English colonies in America'. He even insists that the country suits the English complexion. This book is a real rarity – only Cambridge, Oxford and Leeds Universities, the National

From *The History of Lapland, Wherein are Shewed the Original Manners, Habits, Marriages, Conjurations etc of That People* by Johannes Scheffer. Oxford: George West and Amos Curtein, 1674.

Library of Scotland and the British Library hold copies.

The Mitchell has a number of volumes produced by John Starkey, one of the leading disseminators of travel writing. Active as a bookseller in London between 1658 and 1689, as well as being the publisher of Milton's *Paradise Regained*, he brought out a considerable number of travel texts, such as *The Voyages and Travels of the Duke of Holsteins; The Present state of the Ottoman Empire; The History of Barbado's [sic]; A Relation of Three Embassies, from his Majesty Charles the Second, to the Great Duke of Muscowy, the King of Sweden, and the King of Denmark, Performed by the Right Honourable Earl of Carlisle, in the years 1663 and 1664*; and *Il Nipotismo di Roma* (Englished by the fellow of the Royal Society). In the publisher's catalogue, they are listed alongside chemistry books and legal volumes: they served as practical reference books for expeditions and colonisation projects.

Travel books about Europe could be of considerable use to the military, and were used by government. Nicolas Besongne's *The Present State of France: Conteining The Orders, the Dignities and Charges of that Kingdom* provides a detailed description of the state organisation of the kingdom of France, including the court, the structures of jurisdiction, the bishoprics, universities and the embassies. Another volume from the same series concerns *The Present State of the United Provinces of the Low-Countries as to the Governments, Laws, Forces, Riches, Manners, Customes, Revenue, and Territory of the Dutch, in Three Books* (London, 1669). The people of the Netherlands are said to have rendered themselves 'conspicuous and considerable'; the author contemplates the 'rise, growth and grandeur of States and empires', which he attributes to 'human wisdom and industry as well as divine providence'. The work is mainly concerned with the history and the government of the Low Countries, but the third volume provides a description of morals, manners and customs. The Dutch nation is presented as 'subtil and understanding', a model of commerce and of public and private virtue. 'Women and maids are fair and chaste', and are said to have as much liberty as their husbands. This idealisation of the benefits of commerce is partly intended as an affirmation of the benefits of the emergence of Britain as a commercial power.

The mapping of European frontiers is a central preoccupation of the author of *The History of Lapland, Wherein are Shewed the Original Manners, Habits, Marriages, Conjurations etc of That People* (Oxford: George West and Amos Curtein, 1674). The Swedish humanist Johannes Scheffer here discusses the geography, history and climate of Lapland, and the

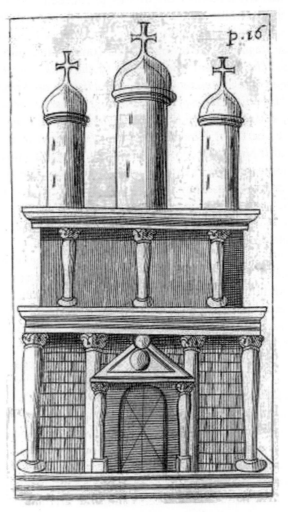

A plate from *The Present State of Russia*, in a Letter to a Friend
in London, a series of letters by Samuel Collins Robert Boyle.
London: John Winter, 1671. (The Mitchell Library)

origin of the language, which he correctly relates to Finnish. He says of the Laplanders, that the cold climate 'prevents their growing tall, dries up likewise their moisture'. They display 'veneration and due esteem to marriage' but, despite the Christianising efforts of the Swedish monarch Gustavus Adolphus, they are morally backward, much given to superstition, 'beyond all imagination fearfull and mean spirited, being frightened at the very sight of a strange man... above all things dreading war'.

The Present State of Russia, in a Letter to a Friend in London (London: John Winter, 1671) is a jewel. It consists of a series of personal letters to the scientist Robert Boyle from Samuel Collins, who worked for many years as the court physician to Tzar Aleksei Mikhailovich. Collins was not subject to the tight restrictions usually imposed on diplomats and other visitors. He therefore had a unique insight into everyday life in the imperial household and more freedom to observe Russian society, which strikes him are very backward, exotic and strange – he even has the Russians whistling and spitting differently from the English. Witchcraft, drunkenness and wife beating are represented as reprehensibly commonplace, and Collins delivers a scathing critique of a political culture driven by deceit and secrecy. Although he writes about the imperial family with affection, political surveillance extended to every level of society:

In the night season the Czar will go about and visit his Chancellors Desks, and see what Decrees are pass'd, and what Petitions are unanswer'd. He has his spyes in every corner, and nothing is done or said at any Feast, publick Meeting, Burial or Wedding but he knows it. He has spyes also attending his Armies to watch their motions, and give a true account of their actions: These Spyes are Gentlemen of small fortunes, who depend on the Emperours' favour, and are sent into Armies, and along with Embassadors, and are present on all publick occasions.

Working among the early travel texts at the Mitchell is a joy. They not only contain some wonderfully idiosyncratic and vivid writing, they are important historical documents and it is wonderful that the Britain in Print project is bringing information on them into the public domain. They show the development of travel writing in its infancy, from factual descriptions to lively personal accounts. The pre-1700 books now being made more accessible in libraries around the country will undoubtedly enrich the research of future generations of political, constitutional and social historians.

Julia Rampen

'Oma'

In my grandfather's memories
she has assumed the Madonna.
Cacao hair, pupils charring,
eyelashes like shivers of espresso.

An ocean, a war, between them.
Secreting the voices of resistance
in a satchel, he cycled streets
walked by skeletons.

They locked her in the schoolhouse.
Jade and turquoise trees waxing
heat. Perspiring jewels. Flaming
roses smouldered, devoured walls.

Left to die in a burning heart, in turn
she imprisoned her purse. In cobbled,
ribbon city exile, she kept coins
like suns enchained to an aging bag.

Only occasionally spending
the blue knit patterns of love.

Beach Secrets

It was just a hole.
A secret four foot darkness lodged inside
earthy loaves of rock. A winding wormhole where
night from another century
had collected and sandstone shrugged dust.
We became ants, nudging knees,
torch racing madly from wall to wall.
A trail of nightlights
unknown eyes in our wake

Looking back, the trace of the day
had been knocked out and we were
standing in the past. Murky shaft brooding our
presence;
an ancient stairway spiralling
into hewn rock, and through a forgotten window
something glimmered. Another tunnel and
forgotten sea water slinking in the dark.
I wondered when it was caught.

On the way back to the present, we brushed ghosts
with finger-tips and nightlights
flickered in the remains belonging
to nobody,

to smuggler's dreams.

Hunter's Point

We, the Litter Moon sisters, pulling up on the shore
in crescents fished from the sea, found a boathouse
crushed by a giant foot; the roof sprawling
in the sand. And a meadow burning with the hum
of crickets, a demented house that fell from the sky.

I wandered through an insane mind. In rooms
buckling with neglect, we kicked cluttered decades
to shadows, climbed a stair that fell up a floor
and reached our phantom hosts. Bed still made,
a pair of trousers strangled in dust, the ace of clubs.

Sketchy. As if someone took a pen, constructed
vague walls and doors, half crumpled it, gave up.
We stood in a mirage; the sun whipping windows
that winter fell through, and heard the rats scuffing
their empire, itching the side of our world.

One liquid summer's day

We were clambering rocks like candle wax,
absorbing rotted colours; rusting, crusting.
The waves were boxing indigo, and the wind
rattled like lost harmonics in our eardrums.
Shrunk down to our real size,
we clutched at our senses, my sister, mother,
brother on the pungent rocks. Salt eyes stared;
tilting pupils on a many headed oyster.

You could salt and shake the whole day
in a glass – gulls bickering for whiteness, the squall
shoplifting conversations from other places,
foreign star-steamed shores.
Weeds grappling like iron, and rocks that socket
into cups of hands, polished by the oozing grease
of time. The ocean hammering at your skin, sun
lifting hair, or dripping myriads of rock pools,
all secreting the ambition to be seas.

 I saw them camped in a tent of shadows,
two teenagers, boy and girl, summed up
in a pocket of caves, the ocean bashing at their feet.
Unreachable. His brass ring a satire of sunlight;
the magpie-girls hair shredding in the wind.
Above them, gulls like sodden toilet paper chalked
the blackboard sky. The elements buffeting
a tiny black privacy, their thoughts burying eyes.

Tim West

William's New Friend

IN THE LITTLE town of Stonehaven, in the north east of Scotland, there lived a young man named William. William was nine years old, of a pleasant demeanour, and had few friends. Sometimes William would get very sad and lonely because of this, but most of the time he just shrugged his shoulders at the world and thought: 'Well, who needs friends anyway?' William was a young man possessed of a quite lively imagination and was perfectly capable of having fun by himself.

Once William had had a good friend – his parents had bought him for his seventh birthday a little rabbit, which he called Bugs. (Although his imagination was, as we say, lively, this applied only when it came to constructing castles in the sky, and he was never much good at thinking up names. Besides, at seven, his mental faculties were not yet fully developed). William loved Bugs dearly, felt him the very best of friends, talked incessantly to him about his passions, his excitements, his fears, his regrets, for about three weeks. Then he forgot to feed Bugs for several days. They buried him under the compost heap.

But on the day of our story, when we first encounter the pleasant young William as he tramps downstairs in his mud-spackled Wellingtons, Bugs was but a little-recalled memory to him, and he was intent upon other things.

'I'm going out!' William bellowed to the house at large as he fixed his heavy rain coat.

'Where you going?' came the reply.

'Out!' he roared, and banged the back door closed behind him. He tramped, as only young men of nine years can tramp, down to the woods.

The Dunnottar Woods were a refuge for William, where he would hide from all the demands of modern life – school, homework, the pressure to fit in. The woods were peaceful, free of stress, and rather beautiful, particularly at this time of year, when the amber leaves had scattered from their trees and strewn themselves about the paths, when the air was crisp and clear and the branches well-defined spider shapes against the grey-blue sky. In another couple of weeks it would be cold enough that you could see your breath condense as you exhaled – a small magic, William thought. Although the woods were in fact rather small – a man and his dog could easily circle them in under an hour – they were quite large enough for William, who anyway knew all their secret ways. They were largely empty, and if he did come across a dog walker or a young couple or – worst of all – a pack of children from his school, he would simply take another path to avoid them or hide behind a tree until they went away.

William valued his solitude and hated to have his woods defiled by the presence of others. Once an old woman had spotted him and tried to talk to him, but he threw stones and bits of twig at her until she gave up and went away. He would only tolerate the presence of birds, indeed he loved to have their company, and would stand motionless and stare at them for as long as they would allow him. He found them beautiful, but they valued their solitude too and he had to sneak up on them or they would swiftly fly away. Sometimes he saw kestrels, and once a kingfisher. There were no animals to be seen except rabbits, which bored him now.

He made his way down the hill, across the road, on up to the top of the next hill, where the air crackled and the view was one of rustic beauty – across a barren, auburn field to the stark white trees of the far side of the woods, the sky a muted, cloudless blue behind them. Around the field, across the old quarry, past a dazed rabbit lying in the open upon the dead grass, its eyes a glaze of myxomatosis, its back leg half chewed by some dog earlier in the day, on past the old stone wall of the nursery, and up the slick, sludgy slope of Gallow Hill, at the summit of which it is now said that the town's executions did not in fact take place.

On the cairn atop the hill – a burial site of some sort, for Picts or Celts or Gaels or whoever it was that had died and needed lodging at this spot – there sat a gnome or a goblin, or perhaps a pixie. William could not tell; he was not too well versed in the biological sciences, and what little he did know at nine was rooted in genotype rather than phenotype analysis – his forward thinking educators concerning themselves with teaching children to run before they could walk. In any case the creature was certainly not a fairy – he could tell that, because it was far from beautiful.

'Hello,' said William, startling the goblin, who had her back to him. She jumped to her feet, span to face him, and put her hand to her chest in a state of shock, trying to steady her breathing.

'Hullo,' said the goblin. 'You gave me the fright of my life.'

'Sorry,' William replied. 'I didn't mean to sneak up on you. I...'

'Not at all,' the goblin said to him. 'I was away in my own little world, that's all. I should have heard you tramping up the hill. Sometimes I just get caught up in a thought, sit puzzling over something tricky, or play a make believe in my head, and completely forget where I am. I once spent a whole afternoon lost in contemplation of a pretty leaf, and forgot to eat my dinner at six. It was only the sound of my tummy gurgling that woke me or I might still be sat there now. My name's Thimble, by the way.'

'William,' said William. 'Pleased to meet you.' He added this as he was a well brought up young man and, whereas he would have run and hidden from a human interloper, he was quite content to be civil to one of the wee folk. Besides, he was the interloper here.

'And you,' said Thimble with a smile. 'William's a pretty name. I once knew a mouse called William, though he preferred Bill. I've always thought Bill dreadfully abrupt, and Billy is frankly awful. Silly Billy and what have you. But William's nice, and it suits you. Poor Bill Mouse couldn't live up to his name, and ended up being known as Myrtle. I forget why. Tell me something, William, how is it that you can see me?'

'What?' asked William bluntly, good manners forgotten for a moment in the surprise of being asked a question about the operation of his eyes atop an exposed hilltop on a cold autumn day. 'I mean, pardon me?'

'Most humans can't, that's all,' Thimble explained. 'They can't hear animals speak either, though they can see them well enough. I've never been quite sure why that should be the case, to be honest. I suppose I'm not furry enough, or something like that, though neither's a frog and people can see them, can't they? Or can't they?' There was something vaguely amphibious about Thimble's looks, now she mentioned it. Perhaps she was related to frogs in some way – she didn't say, however, and this is not the place for such idle speculation. 'Anyhow, it's a bit funny that you should be able to see me, that's all I mean. Have you ever heard an animal speak by any chance?'

'No,' William mused, 'and I once owned a rabbit for a few weeks, and he never said nothing.'

'Anything,' Thimble corrected him absent-mindedly. 'Rabbits are terribly boring creatures, I expect he wouldn't have said much even if you could have understood him. Well, there you are, another little mystery for me to ponder. I'll add it to the list and have a good think about it sometime. Why should William, alone of all humans I've ever seen so far in my thirty-six years of life, possess the ability to see me?'

'Well, I do have a quite lively imagination...'

'I hope you're not implying you've simply imagined me,' said Thimble, shocked. 'But how dreadful! Any minute you might give up your game and I'd cease to exist. And me halfway through a book, too.'

'I'll keep on imagining you then, if you want,' William said.

'No good, no good. It only takes a moment's lapse and I'm gone, with no appeal. You could try thinking about me again later, I suppose, but it might not be quite the same me, if you see what I mean. It'd be new, or slightly different, or perhaps I'd revert to the me you first imagined, just before you startled me out of my daydreams. Then I'd have no memory of this conversation, or anything that's happened since it began. That'd be a pity – the most beautiful little robin just flew by.'

'I'm sorry,' said William, close to tears. 'I didn't mean to imagine you, it just sort of happened.'

'Oh, it's not your fault, William,' said Thimble with a reassuring smile. 'It'd be a real shame if you stopped imagining things – dreams are such wonderful escapes. Besides, I'd much rather have lived for just half an hour on this beautiful day with this lovely view than never have lived at all. I'm merely saying that, given the choice, I'd prefer not to fade back to nothingness as soon as you're distracted by something more interesting than me, or the minute you drift off to sleep.'

'I'm sorry,' William said again, his eyes red, his hands trembling.

'Now, now. Let's have none of that,' said the goblin. 'Seeing as I am here, and this may be my last day on earth – as well as my first – how about we go for a nice walk?'

So William and his new friend went for a stroll around the woods, and William showed Thimble all the secret paths, all the nooks and crannies and magical spots where he sought refuge from a stressful life of early bed times and school assemblies. He took her to the rope swing over the river, the little hut made of spindly sticks bound together by green garden string, the hollow tree you could sit inside, the spot where the sun made the world golden at about four o'clock. Last he showed her the Dragon Rock, and they sat atop it, side by side, eating ham sandwiches.

'Poor thing,' Thimble said, 'I wonder what happened to him.'

'Yes,' said William. 'I've never quite decided whether it should be a dead dragon or just a sleeping one. I think I'd prefer it's asleep, because that way sometimes I can make it wake up and eat people and stuff.'

'You mean this is another of your imaginations, William?' asked Thimble.

'Yup.'

'But it doesn't stop existing when you forget to imagine it?'

'No. It's just a rock, then.'

'Well maybe there's hope for me after all. Do you suppose I'll become a rock when you forget about me? And come back to life when you remember again?'

'Dunno,' said William. 'You don't look much like a rock. You look more like a frog to me.'

'Even better,' said Thimble. 'That way I can hop around and catch flies when you're away. Although flies aren't nearly so nice as ham sandwiches... Are there any lily pads around here, by any chance?'

'Don't think so. I've shown you everywhere I know in the woods.'

'Yes, you have, you've shown me all of your secret places, haven't you? If we're going to be friends then I ought to tell you a secret in return...' Thimble sat stroking her chin thoughtfully for a while, not sure if she had any secrets to rival a hollow tree or a golden afternoon sun. At last she remembered one that was quite good, though not so pretty, and she explained to William a procedure for constructing a perpetual motion device from simple household goods. 'It's fun to watch for a while,' she said, 'but it becomes monotonous after not very long. Still, it's the best I can think of.'

In later years William made his fortune through constructing such a device as his new friend had described, to the general betterment of mankind, and he was able to lead a life of idle richness, living on a remote country estate where people couldn't come to pester him. He spent his days in making up stories for himself and staring at birds for hours on end.

But the day after meeting his new friend on Gallow Hill he went back to the woods to look for her and discovered that the little frog called Thimble, much to his disappointment, had hopped off somewhere. He never saw her again.

Gwen Suominen

You think it's crazy here, wait till you get out there

I'm so confused
but who wouldn't be
in a world where
God doesn't know
whether he is his own father
or his own son
and geniuses walk the wavy line of insanity.
Mary stays a virgin in our minds.
We keep her like that.
We cherish her like that.
Of course this is part of a religion
no proof is needed
by believers
of the One God.
But there are other One Gods
& other virgin births
often with awful outcomes
for the male child in question.
You wouldn't want to know.
Just believe.
Take it as a gift.
It may come in ever so handy
in this difficult world.
But there are other worlds?

So we look for another world
but always some of the same rules apply
in case we ruin this one by accident
or because we thought 'have Dominion over'
meant we could do what we liked to it.
But it always gets scary
things always get out of control
we get mangled
'cause we're still alive
believing God will go ahead of us
point out the way
through the three-dimensional star map.
'Home sweet Home.'
'But it might be a bit muddy.'
Could we still play football?
Will there still be a mall?
Will it take us all
on the bus for poor people?
Will all the gay people have to stay behind?
Well I would come of course but I'm gay now today.

Would there be just one great big space ship. Multicultural?
All our eggs in one basket.
Or a little fleet
tapdancing its way to insanity
with the terrorists & such round the outside
in big aggressive space ships
that can kick ass.
And hospital ones in the middle.
Would all the politicians be together?
Would all the terrorists get on
bouncing off the walls on their way to insanity?
But they are already, aren't they?
Who isn't?
Politicians have fine minds, that's why they can write The Constitution.
Ministers have fine minds, that's why they're so good at burials.
Surgeons have fine minds, that's why they do what they do.
Who wants to know the details.
Ah sweet insanity. Try thinking of fuck all.

What would the bankers do?
Who would have money any more?
Would we all go running on the spot
& swimming and diving off cliffs?
I'd like a DVD of waves please. Just waves.
Of rain please, all kinds & wind.
The garden ships & fields of gold.
Are deserts any good at all?
Icebergs anyone?
Would the blue whales still sing
when we were all gone?
& who would have the maps?
Map room of the future. Can we have one now please?
I need to do my homework so I can look out of the window
on my way home & recognise that falling star.
That Temple in the future's going to get a bit muddled, architecturally.
Who would lock the door?

Lighthouse, anyone, with crashing waves all around?

And don't forget the elephants
& the zebras and the fishes with nice fabric prints on them.
Are mosquitos any good at all?
And school ships
& tennis courts & ski slopes.
Would we all have the same luggage?
The laundry rooms
names on our clothing in case we get the wrong pants.
The Tesco ship & the corner shop ship
The coffee shop ship
& the drugs. Who would have the drugs?
Is cannabis any good at all? 'You don't look Dutch to me.'
Try getting a beer
Try calling in sick
I was writing this under the covers
on my shared computer just to say
I'm sick. Go away.
& the game shows. *Today you have won*
A pair of binoculars.

Then there's the building & construction
of the Space Fleet for Interstellar Relocation.
Would Russia & Japan build the American space ships
& America build one for Japan?
Would Germany build one for Britain & vice versa?
But that's out of date now, isn't it,
there's no bad feelings any more.
Would the Buddhist ship be conceptual and spacious?
Would the Japanese one fold up in your pocket?
Would the Russians form a queue, again,
and take winter clothing?
Would the Arabic one face East, or is it West?
Who would lead the way to insanity?
Could George Bush take his dogs?

All the prison ships and hospital ships
& ships of fools
& wheat of chickens.

The Sea of Eternity.
The seat of paternity.
The role of women.
Horse racing, anyone?
A picture of mountains please & snow falling on trees
a succession of important dates
every day a holiday on the Universal Calendar.
If I sign up as Miss Congeniality
Do I get all the holidays
& can I borrow the credit for the present & pay it back later?
Can I say goodbye to myself on a DVD when I die
in case the prayers are wrong?
Can I wear what I want to float around in Space forever as cosmic dust?
Do I get to know where I am going?
Does anyone?
What if I quit?
What if I want to emigrate?
would I fit in?
Would I make new friends?
What if I don't want to go at all?
What if I think it sounds crap?
Would I get a weapon
survival training
a pension
any chance at all?
You'd want to be crazy to stay behind that long day,
crazier still want to go.
The smoking ship.
The sinking ship.
The isolation unit.
The experimental, radioactive, nuclear power plant ships.
Radio 'Out Here' –

Could I turn it off?
Could I make it dark when I wanted?
If I cried would it be on the news?
Would I go unnoticed for a month if I died?
Would I call the policemen 'Harry'?
Tea Harry? Make that two. I hear you have a clone.

This is what I thought about when
I went crazy.
They locked me up.
So in case anyone is looking for me
I'll just leave a note
so they can't find me anywhere in Edinburgh.
'Gone for a Shit in the Woods'.
Trouble is with my luck
I'd probably find one.

Dilys Rose

Obituary

her name was whatever you fancied

her eyebrows a twin-peaked cliché

her irises had seen it all before

her mouth was a magnet

her tongue swung between sweet chariot and Uzi

her throat was a tool of the trade

her clavicle the wishbone of a swan

her shoulders tear-proof pillows

her scapulae rose-wood boomerangs

her vertebrae were an interlocking puzzle

her breasts were a challenge to gravity

her nipples cogs in a well-oiled machine

her cleavage a gap in the market

her lungs plump grouse trying to fly

her spleen was reserved for cheapskates

her heart was not always a vale of tears

her belly was a slow cooker

her navel was only gazed at by others

her liver worked overtime and unsociable hours

her buttocks were proving loaves

her pelvis was a yoke

her hips pistons

her vagina was pay-as-you-go

her womb was an empty nest

her thighs were a plough

her knees knew various forms of worship

her feet had a going rate all of their own

her toenails were never ever naked

her psyche was a hot and sour conundrum

her religion was take it or leave it

her morality was a closed book

her affections were here today, gone tomorrow

her philosophy was buried in Rousseau's garden

her self-image on good days was Botticelli's Venus

her sense of humour was after the watershed

her smile was impenetrable

her laughter was a forest catching fire

her theme tunes were *Simply the Best* and *Don't Explain*

her standards were not to be sneezed at

her diet was not always of worms

her tastes were mostly beyond her means

her memory was a glory-hole

her fears were rarely groundless

her dreams were not all bad

the love of her life is none of your business

Maeve's Hair

is hot, heavy, hard work
alarmingly expansive.
It has its own agenda,
more bad days than good.

Maeve's hair   stands up for itself
at every opportunity,
requires expert handling
though the expert has yet to be found.

Maeve's hair   needs optimum conditions:
no rain, wind, humidity,
only a modicum of sun,
precious few nights on the town –
ditto for pawing boyfriends
and shampoo ads featuring Jennifer Aniston.

Maeve's hair   was once – but heaven be praised
is no longer – a haven for nits.
It drapes itself over the shower head,
clogs up the plughole – so often!

Maeve's hair   is gold-fingered in summer
leaf brown in autumn
mud brown in winter
shoots up with the snowdrops in spring.

Maeve's hair   dances to its own tune
prefers tango to two-step
flies in the face of everything.

Hilda's Aura

Hilda has been seeing things
which aren't there and don't quite fit
the space they occupy,
which overrun the plain solidity
of rules and reasons: the table
won't stay flat, the wallpaper
pattern jangles, dining chairs
evolve into bucking steers.

Hilda has been seeing things:
shrinking cats and jigsaw dolls,
daytime stars which swarm, darken,
sink like oil slicks into boiling hills.
Sometimes too, there's sound:
the feathered breath of angels.
Her fingers tingle. She's a sorcerer,
casting spells upon herself.

Hilda has been seeing things
which stop her in her tracks,
while off to the side a little,
beyond the scintillating scotomata,
a grown-up voice is asking:
What are you looking at?
Though usually a truthful child
she always answers: Nothing.

Hilda has been seeing things
which aren't there, objectively.
She knows that what she sees
is never make-believe, pretend,
knows too that no-one else has access
to the pulsing hum of her universe;
that brief glimpse of heaven
before the sickness and the pain set in.

Peter's Shadow

His wasn't the first to go missing.
Others traded their shadows for gold,
for everlasting life, or sent them off
into the world on solo expeditions.
If they returned to their owners,
they came back changed. Dangerous.
Peter's shadow was nothing special:
a thin thing, caught like a shirt tail
when Mrs Darling leaned into the night
to close the nursery window.

Why did she store a folded shadow
in a drawer? Why encourage a boy
with wings to come back at all?
Unless Wendy wasn't the first to visit
Neverland. Unless, when she was a girl,
Mrs Darling herself had pricked the soles
of the feet of the boy who wouldn't grow up,
saying: Hold still Peter. See how neat
my stitches are. This won't hurt a bit.
Why else would anyone save a shadow?

Michael Brown

Dalguise

The April of my first glasses caught
spring in sharp focus. Sometimes I snapshot
pheasant's gilt and crimson in dull grass,
brown hare silhouetted on snow mass,
snowdrops bunched in the green glen,
frost hunched among wet edges,
but no longer chickadees chipping in hedges
the nuthatch hidden away from the lichen.

I would like to study how sheep move,
trace the oystercatcher's cry above
flecks of foam on the river Tay,
wait to see molehills become that way,
but I am in my late Monet excess,
when Birnam Wood screens old oaks,
flowers swirl in green brush strokes,
as if he were painting blindness.

The little boy who looked after the sheep
sees them most clearly in his sleep,
failing sight become his common fear,
vague spring not a season, but a year.

Lawrence Krauser

Puppet Theory
(*excerpts*)

'WOKE UP' TODAY – don't know why, never learned how – on the bench, didn't know why. Arnold's face inches above me scrunched and peering. One of my eyelids had ceased to move, if I'm to believe his mutterings. I had no idea, I see fine.

My eyes are made of the two halves of the same obsidian sphere, ocean pearls embedded in their convexities. Whether these superb ingredients have anything to do with my optic intelligence I cannot say. I rather doubt it. As far as I remember I don't have ears, and yet I seem to hear OK. I have been conscious a good eighty years and have never seen much connection between this souped-up jumble of blocks and the nest of thoughts I consider my 'self.' If I am placed on my shelf upside-down, this makes no difference to me. Decapitation does not affect my lucidity. Air is not an issue. If I ask myself whether it is in any way better (more 'pleasurable'/meeting higher standards/toward some larger good) to be out on this shelf rather than in the claustrum of my box, I answer: I couldn't care less!

Perk of a puppet, that. Not a bad nonexistence. Do mostly matinees – did one today, in fact. I was human all afternoon. Nothing new there, I am frequently called upon to impersonate all kinds. And I would like to be clear: I have nothing against the self-animated. Wouldn't wanna live there, is all. True, I used to 'dream' of movement by my own volition. No more. Or rather: I have a different dream. So goes desire.

Sometimes after a gig, if it's late or Arnold is otherwise irritated, he will leave me in my box or chuck me back on the shelf with my face twisted to the wall. But most days I look outward, splayed for evaluation by potential renters, and I have a superb view of the television set over the workbench. This very evening I watched the Thrilling Conclusion to a national crisis. (By 'national' I mean pertaining to that group of viewers able to walk, drive, dial, or otherwise motion to obtain the shampoo or policy advertised.) In brief: two borders bumped, aggressions ensued, differences were defused, heroes have been reunited with loved ones and are now deservedly resting at home. And indeed they did function beyond expectation in the practice of their 'selfless' trade. Kudos!

And shrugs. Alas or hallelujah, as a thing I am indifferent to all things. Makes no difference if it's 'real' or 'fiction,' all simply stories told at the shop. I used to prefer breaking news because it appeared to be more spontaneously photographed; times change.

Today, as a human, I reached a critical point, acted, and failed in my aim. Intermission followed. In the second act I reached the same juncture, behaved the same way, and this time succeeded. But, as with many puppet shows, the script was simplistic and afforded no reason for the difference in outcomes. It was all up to the puppeteer to lend credence. Mine, alas, was a hardcore techie, all rote and rigor, no feel for psychokinetics – people like that should be in robotics.

When I say 'robotics,' I mean that field in which mannequins are deployed for practical rather than theatrical purposes. I'm sure the profession has its poets. It is true that I would be more inclined to 'identify' with a robot than with a human, puppets and robots and statues and dolls all being obvious kin. To simplify (a habit which runs in the familia): Robots replace humans in work. Dolls replace them in play. Statues suggest what they can never be. Puppets show them who they are. That's the spectrum, more are less – obviously there's a good deal of overlap in the How & Why departments. Some might call a puppet a public doll, a doll a social statue, a statue a spiritual robot, a robot a blue-collar puppet, etc. I myself am inclined to regard all simulcra as puppets of varying degrees of accomplishment, and my personal lexicosmos usually requires no more than humans and puppets, not that I would wish to hold a press conference on the subject. It would seem self-evident that puppets and humans are different matters entirely, and I point out the distinction only because there seems to be a chronic strain of confusion running through both groups. But between them lies a Great Divide that turns abysmal when denied. So I strive to keep things clear: I am humanesque, yes. But there was no doctrine for my form. I was part of a forest until swiped by some fleshpot who hewed me in his image to stand for him in his theatre; I owe my career to him, not to nature; my substance and structure remain strangers.

This mind of mine is a separate riddle, but to believe it could have been conjured by the voodoo of congruence is to succumb to extra-arboreal reasoning. Who's to say there's not some similar thoughtfulness residing in all matter, of every shape – fully functional but without consequence?

My Laodicean glaze notwithstanding, I like to think I exist in a state of perfect 'love' with all things. Devoid as I am of any actual need (and thus sans prompt to wish or judge), my general acceptance of everything I know grows exponentially with each passing moment. Every day, for example, I strive to be less interested in which channel's on. At the same time I acknowledge that neutrality is foiled by the very thinking of anything. Agape, that point of supreme knowing, is likely a blooming idiot.

Anyway it was a quick operation, painless as always, and now I have new eyelids. My flaking oyster shells have been replaced with fortified porcelain.

Ah, showbiz.

*

Of all the words I know, 'Pinocchio' is the only obscenity. To me the syllables of this word are like the venom on the fangs of a diamondback rattler, or the barbed hair on a tarantula's legs that detach and enter the orifices of the enemy and cause an intolerable burning sensation therein. Both of these predators I observed this morning in their respective natural habitats on what appeared to be an extremely well-funded documentary. In fact my sighting of these dastardly characters was the immediate cause of my thinking of Pinocchio, which word, prior to this program's airing, was as far from my thoughts as breakfast.

As I have said, I am nothing if not indifferent, so if then I reveal that there is something by which I am disgusted and outraged, my opinion will perhaps carry more weight on the scales of judgment than those of they who blush and flinch regularly.

You forget what happened this afternoon.
Not that I expect to be judged.

You were on the bench...
I am pure math: exempt!

Arnold was working on you...

You forget: I don't forget.

DO YOU REMEMBER WHAT HE SAID?
You're a bit of slow!

WHAT DO YOU THINK OF WHAT HE SAID?
It wasn't this afternoon, it was this morning.

'MY LITTLE PINOCCHIO.'
Stop! What's it to you? Exhibit A: Pinocchio, if he ever existed at all, certainly does not live here. I mean, there might be a longnosed puppet in the shop, I've heard talk of us casting productions, but I've never seen him. Arnold's addressing me by that horrible name belies a screwy, pathetic nostalgia. Disney's gone to his head, as it has to everyone's.

LET'S SAY, IF YOU WERE HUMAN –
Oh please, I hate that game.

FOR ARGUMENT'S SAKE, IF ARNOLD –
I would have socked him one. Besides being utterly offensive, the notion is ridiculous in every way. I'm not anywhere near as thin as that sticky brute, I have a bulbous nose that has never grown, I have neither pretensions nor a stomach to be sick to, though sometimes the latter I'd like, like right now just thinking about this, plus I never open my mouth myself so how could I lie? I hate to think that in your mind, Arnold's I mean, this nickname is some sort of ultimate compliment. It's true I'm our leading he-puppet, being the simplest in the shop, the most changeable, but one would hope for a bit more compassion from one's keeper, or at least a little tact. The marionette which bore that name was never a puppet worth the word to begin with, he was born speaking, nastily at that, he was hungry before nightfall and never knew immobility. He put his maker in jail and murdered his first friend. Some puppet!

To tell the truth, I'm not really sure why Arnold's in this business, I don't believe he's ever been a puppeteer himself.

*

PUPPET IS INTELLIGENT AND ARTICULATE. I SHALL REFER TO HIM WITH A MASCULINE PRONOUN, FOR THIS IS HOW HE THINKS OF HIMSELF, BUT

HIS GENDER SELF-IDENTITY IS CLEARLY A DELUSIVE REFLEX ARISING FROM PROTRACTED INVOLVEMENT IN THE THEATRE. HE INSISTS HE HAS NO INTEREST IN BECOMING HUMAN, AND CLAIMS WITH PARADOXICAL ADAMANCE TO HAVE NO FEELINGS. HE HAS A LIVELY IF ECCENTRIC SENSE OF HUMOR AND A TENDENCY TO DIGRESS, PARTICULARLY WHEN HIS THOUGHTS LEAD HIM TO PINOCCHIO, UPON WHOM HE IS CLEARLY FIXATED. OEDIPAL? PURSUE.

Rented today by a puppet hater. She clearly wished she had 'real' actors – humans – which fesses a shortage in herself, I fear, and we, her cast, were the casualties – though it's our audience I pity. I did like the script, which featured myself as a generic Continental, a royal with a castle and servants who bring me cigars on purple pillows – Napoleonic bearing, a shot of gangsta, I think this was her intention. But instead of mixing in Mussolini like I want to, I think it's sweet for the part, I feel my blocks going that way, she doesn't let me let her go there. I can feel her uptightness through the strings, I'm not wanted, which affects things; as a puppet, I'm totally contingent upon her zeal.

In the course of the show I choose a bride from a mail order catalog, write to her, pour out my soul on paper, send photos of myself (frank poses in my swimsuit, lotta wood), she accepts my proposal, I fly her in from the New World and she turns out to be quite the fatale grifter – a fun setup but the whole show's been contaminated by this apathy from above, not pleasant. I'm bellowing silently up to the rafters, It's up to you, sister!

Of course, being a puppet, I don't want to meet my bride. Even if I did I certainly couldn't express it, but my puppeteer refuses to see or acknowledge this and fights against puppet nature, thinking of human actors, lapsing into frustration – she stiffs the show.

Thank the Stringsmith just a one-day gig. The puppeteer returns us, me and a few others, to Rent-a-Puppet, leaves unhappy, complaining to Arnold we're not well-lubricated. He knows better, knows a customer like that will never be satisfied, we all take it in stride. (Arnold is – generally – quite sensitive to what he imagines are our feelings. He never overbooks us. He'd never sell us.) She'll go home and turn on the TV and see real people and weep. Or maybe, and I hope this is the case, she'll go out on the town and dance her crass off and fall asleep enlightened. If the media follows, we'll all know tomorrow.

And if not? Shivers!

Ah, humans. Your need precedes you, walking backward, beckoning.

Or not. The language I speak you invented. If anyone knows, it's you.

I must be honest. I have a soft spot for Mussolini – the tyrant who ended up the marionette next-door. As he himself put it thirteen years earlier, Everybody dies the death that corresponds to his character. Italy, there's your masterpiece, and he was flesh and blood straight out of the gate –

And what a race! All wars make good viewing, but that one was out to beat the band. It's my favorite by far. Not only did I participate directly, but it is the best documented epic I know, with never a shortage of new drams, docs, docu-drams, always a new facet to be polished or revealed. Fascism was so contagious a genre that even the Allied leadership was A-List. (Not like today, when it's all about the trappings. Glamour is the poor man's charisma, fine for the peacetime democracy whose top dog is ideally the people's puppet, displayed in reflected, not projectile, light – but these are not peaceful times.) And while I fear those days are gone forever, the history of war is the history of past tactics applied to present conflicts and updated only at the last second, so for now my nostalgia continues to be validated by TV. Sadly, most of the po-mo schedule is kidstuff in comparison, and the smorgasbord's crammed to stymie all coherence. Superfluity not only poisons product, it confounds the shape of appetite; for a proper showdown there needs to be some real consensus, but we'll never get off the ground with everyone who can afford a videophone mounting their own offensive. Granted, some of the kids, some of the most rambunctious, have very wealthy parents – and any theatre operator will confirm that bankrolled bellicosity upstages subtle craft – so we'll see...so far nobody's that rich. Stay tuned, puppet!

As if we had a choice.

*

'WE,' DID YOU SAY? FOR A MIND WITH NO SUBCONSCIOUS, YOURS CERTAINLY SLIPS ENOUGH.
Those of us in the theatre often mirthfully deploy the royal 'we' in our private conversation. A king or queen speaks for the many there are. We speak for the many we have been.

STILL, WHY DO YOU INSIST YOU HAVE NO SUBCONSCIOUS?
My parents were trees, I have no feelings, no contact with others, I cannot lust or defecate – what do I need a closet for? My thoughts are to me as so many game pieces positioned on a field under my whole and continual scrutiny. Oh, I suppose a Pinocchian might say that, 'unable' as I appear to

be to hoist my mind into 'action,' I am as good as eternal sleep. To which I reply: Whatever! I'm a billion times as integrated as any stratified human. Having been so many for so long, I am already more actualized than any one of them could ever be. 'I' as I know me would not survive the contortions of a single self's upkeep, which I imagine must be something like being granted custody of one raindrop for the duration of monsoon season.

Not that sometimes I don't wish I had a subconscious. For instance, what I saw on TV this morning – did you see that?

I'M NOT SURE WHAT YOU MEAN.
Yes you saw it, I know you saw it, well lucky for you if you didn't. If I had a subconscious I'd have stuffed it in the back of my mind so fast I'd have barely noticed – ah, I wish I had been out on a gig, facing the wall, any dumbshow of denial. And my first impulse –

YES?
No... it's silly.

SLOW DOWN. IT WAS JUST AN IMPULSE, IT HAS IMMUNITY. WHAT YOU DO IS ANOTHER STORY, BUT YOU NEVER DO ANYTHING SO THERE'S NOTHING TO WORRY ABOUT.
Well, I thought – I wondered – maybe there was – is – something I *could* do. Can you believe that? I actually thought – just for a second – If I were only human, I would – then I caught myself...

WHAT WAS IT YOU SAW ON TV EXACTLY?
It was the ultimate trespass of humanity on puppetry. Briefly, I wanted to retaliate. Treason is contagious, I guess...

TREASON?
Betrayal of one's kind. I saw humans act like puppets and in turn I nearly reacted with humanity. In the end I just sat there, of course.

AND IF YOU WERE HUMAN? WHAT WOULD YOU DO: A SINGLE FLESHY VIEWER AMONG BILLIONS?
I'd just sit there. I'd pretend I was a puppet.

YOU CONTRADICT YOURSELF.
I do not contradict myself. When a puppet wreaks havoc in order to turn

human, I am critical; but when a puppet is cast in a show and imitates life, I applaud. Similarly, I resent the chaos wrought by humans who treat others as puppets, or who aspire to be puppets. But I'm all for the theatre. The Great Divide must be examined, understood...

I swear I thought I knew tears in my eyes today. Not literally, of course; but I wasn't 'imagining' them – or well of course I was, but in that part of the imagination that receives, not devises. The sensation was there. A hallucination, perhaps: but appropriate to the circumstances, a veritable idea.

Still with me, this condition. Hours later in the night on the shelf, here I am experiencing an unprecedented blinking sensation due to a tearlike conception. Odd. It usually takes no effort at all to remain uninvolved. According to some, empathy is a late-season flower; have I played too many people in my time?

By the way, are you familiar with Mussolini's production of Pinocchio?

I NEVER HEARD OF ANY SUCH THING.

*

Advice to those caught in a web, from one who was born there: Hear ye, flapping futiles! Cease struggle, be still! Learn the silk stranded around you; this, like the bandages of the Invisible Man, will show you your true form. Next, attune to the tugs at attachment points where you are linked by filaments to the controlling world, whose movements, sensed across radii, pluck your possibility. Perhaps you have less than you thought, than you wished. But a true view is of more use than flails in space. Know the world through the strings, and so learn yourself.

*

Grandfather never could resist a bet – this was back when he was just a cuckoo clock – used to bet on his own second-hand. No wound-up wooden clock is ever 100 percent metronomic, there are always slight tips toward either way of the beat, and Grandfather, who hears so much (though I've never detected any evidence that he hears a word I think – implacable furniture, Gramps), used to bet on how much off-center the next tick or tock would be, used to bet himself – and always lost! Never won once, didn't have the calculus, but he got such a kick out of whatever happened compared to what he wagered, the weird juxtaposition of guess and verdict, that on each occasion he would quiver with amusement which would escalate, feed on itself until he was rippling, shaking with laughter, great pendulous heaves, on and on, great laughter – and this laughing, you see, would take a toll on his timekeeping, throw it off even more – in some ways delightful to him, the joker, but after all he's only a mechanism. He's been on the bench a number of times. Arnold always does right by him, could've been a great clocksmith but I guess that's personality for you. Still ticking great though, Gramps, and still betting.

Or so I imagine of that clock there.

In truth I have no idea whether any of my comrades think at all. Alone in kind, or kinned, I? Wood, tin, plaster of Paris, none of us can move or speak, how could I ever know? My thoughts wander, and bounce off each other, but have never bumped into those of another – not even Arnold's, and from what I understand of humans, he must be thinking. He turns the TV on. He occasionally prefers one channel over another. He pays the electricity bill.

I wonder about the finger puppets, they're the shelf under me, maybe half a thousand packed tight all the way to the windowed wall. I wonder, if they do think, do they think as one? Usually I imagine a cacophonous chorus of hundreds of pipsqueak voices, although I suppose there's no reason they might not sport thundering deep voices. I also wonder whether being constantly referred to as 'finger puppets' has at all affected the way these particular puppets think or behave or think of themselves. Almost always they are hired out in large groups to represent a simple collective idea, crowds and choirs. In every show I've done with them they've been eloquent and true to a T, excellent puppets. But conscious? I have no idea. I'm just a soul whose dimensions are wood –

Cogito ergo squat.

Lawrence Krauser Interview

Lawrence Krauser in conversation with Jennie Renton, discussing his novel Lemon, *about a man who falls in love with the eponymous citrus fruit.*

You have described Lemon *as a Rorschach block, saying that everyone can make what they want of it. What meaning do you put into that Rorschach yourself?*
You don't want to know too much about that!

When did you first get the idea for the novel?
In college I'd written a story, a short story about an old man, a widower. He doesn't fall in love with a lemon; he just has this lemon that he has with him.

But why a lemon? Did it just come up from your subconscious?
My then girlfriend read that models drink water with lemon, and suddenly we were drinking water with lemon all the time.

To clear your complexions?
Looks good if you're caught by the paparazzi.

There's a Fritz Lang film with an office where the walls are closing in... was it Metropolis? *Anyway, there's a claustrophobic, surreal office scenario in* Lemon. *Don't you like offices?*
Well, publishing is relatively civilised and it attracts folk who have a genuine love of books. But it's still lots of people in a tight space. I don't like rectangles very much and I don't like politeness, and offices absolutely depend on politeness.

What do you mean by office politeness?
I like to feel free and in any office there's a narrowed spectrum of accept-able discourse. When I'm there, my personality tends to be strictly on guard against my instincts. The situation demands formality... And then, there's being an author and working in the trenches of publishing, which creates its own schizoid dynamic.

There's this terrible thing about publishers' rejection letters, that they al-ways say 'How wonderful this book is, it just doesn't fit our list.' And what they're really saying is, 'Don't come back. Don't ask. Go away.'
That's not always so – from working in publishing as an editor my-self, I know that what these letters say can be literally true. A book really might not fit a list. There are templates.

And you must have realised that Lemon *isn't likely template material.*
Well, no. And so I sent a couple of chapters to Dave Eggers at McSweeney's. He had just published the first issue of *McSweeney's Magazine*, a great literary magazine. And he took it on.

At times Lemon *made me think of* Eraserhead, *the David Lynch film.*
I can see that when you say it, especially when he goes back home to in-troduce the lemon to his parents and they're asking, 'Are you having sex with this lemon?'

Tell me about where you spent your childhood.
New Jersey, over the George Washington Bridge, north of Manhattan.

When did you start writing?
I wrote a play when I was eight or nine but I was mostly a musician. Then in college, after I left music school, I fell in with the English depart-ment. I had some excellent professors, very nurturing people who made me feel that writing was something that would be possible for me to do, even though the act of putting something into language is something I find difficult.

That's interesting in itself, given that you've written a novel and plays, when music comes more readily – you must want to push yourself as a writer.
Music, jazz in particular, is a nod to the transient nature of thought. But if I say something to you about what I was thinking when I wrote

Lemon, in five minutes I'll have a different idea about that. Tomorrow I'll hate what I said. Language is illusory but because it has grammatical structure and it's in print, it seems it must be true – this must be what a person believes, must be an accurate map. So for someone like me who is more temperamentally suited to an abstract form like music, writing becomes an interesting puzzle. The challenge is, 'Can I put words together in a way that I can live with tomorrow?' I always hate hearing myself talk and so writing dialogue, putting words in someone else's mouth, is somehow easier to live with.

I heard you hand-drew every cover for Lemon. *What was the print run?*
Ten thousand.

You really hand-drew ten thousand covers?
There was also a Dutch translation in an edition of a thousand, and I drew those covers too.

When you started off, what do you have on the cover?
Just a blank panel.

Why did you do that? It seems very territorial.
Very territorial? Interesting.

OK. Generous, too.
It was great fun. I love to draw, so it allowed me to doodle to my heart's content.

You know how in Lemon *you talk about humans sharing so much DNA with grass and lemons and so on – when I heard about the covers I thought, that's it! These books, they're covered in Lawrence Krauser DNA!*
I think I must have an exhibitionist streak.

Have you?
Sure.

Do you like doing readings?
I went to twenty-one cities with *Lemon*. It's unheard of for a small eccentric novel to do that kind of book tour. McSweeney's events tend to be lively, and most of them turned into elaborate variety shows with people

joining in, actors and musicians, whoever was in town.

I hear that you accompany your piano playing with readings... or is it the other way round?
I play piano whenever I can.

I like your descriptions of the sea shore as a sort of living museum. And I imagine you beachcombing...
Well, when I decided to write *Lemon* it was a February and I went to a New Jersey beach town that I probably wouldn't have wanted to visit in season. Off-season it was kind of magical, and totally deserted. I was there alone for a month and there are things in the book that come directly from that experience. One was when I was stopped by the police for crossing the parking lot and they brought me in for questioning. 'What are you doing here?' they asked, so I told them: 'I'm writing a book.' 'What's your book about?' they wanted to know. 'It's about a man who falls in love with a lemon...' They didn't like me at first but by the end they were kind of amused. All that stuff went straight into the novel.

Yes, you strike me as a natural beachcomber, not just as writer.
Well, that's true. I have things in my bag right there, shells and things, that I picked up at North Berwick. And also a little bit of a thigh bone that I found on the river below Hawthornden Castle in Roslin Glen, near the spot where I saw a kingfisher.

Kingfishers are so lovely.
Oh yeah!

Lemon is published by McSweeney's ISBN 0970335512 and can be ordered through bookshops and online through Amazon. McSweeney's Internet Tendency is at www.mcsweeneys.net.

Shampa Ray

Sushi

I once ate Sushi at Roslin Glen
straddled the low branches of a cedar
your last Marks and Spencer
five pound voucher, I
tore and gobbled into history
each parcel arrived
like a wedding gift
horseradish
fish
rice held back
my dirty teeth ate old money
until the dimpled
black plastic tray
lay surrounded by the ancients

Russian Doll

After dinner I would empty that doll
She was dark papier maché
Solid and fat
Cracked her open
And so I continued
The whole brood
A lineage of smiling women
Snapped apart around the middle
Until the birds wing beat in me
For the little one that did not break

This is just to let you know

The gas is off
The candles safely snuffed
The door locked
The cat fed
The spirit elevated
The socks doubled up and matching
The decisions made correctly
The effort valiant and just
The near future certain
The will to live never so alive
The conscience clear
The distance between us appropriate
The ceiling of possibility high
The mentality calm and balanced
The hope always greater than the fear
The memories ordered into chapters
The friends trustworthy
The lovers generous
And the floor is clean
So I've closed up that box of yours
Let peace come now
Let peace come dropping slow

After reading John Clare

In the end the cure
was not a thought or a flag
nor searching
for what can be learned by itself
but more of a spider
that has crept under the windowsill
to notice the blessed
ordinary thing
to be arrested by it, to remember
the names like flower, light, holy
to be like this quiet man
praising his fields
and in every last line
'I love'.

Poetry

This morning I hear it again
Water singing under my bed
A hand to the mouth and lip
As I fish for my own voice

Walking Out

the dandelion clock has
soared above the roof
and I am walking out

two things to take
my cat and my heart
with me walking out

never lonely here
my mind spreads out in fields
green arms walking out

thistledown eyes are shut
sacrum to the ground
my sorrow is walking out

of me, inch by inch
like beetle tracks
a life sentence walking out

this game show of right life
people in their proper place
me simply walking out

wet sounds over the hill
I know my river
gushing still, walking out

Valerie Lawson

Whisper

Secrets embalmed in horsehair plaster
and parlor cushions, rooms to arrange the dead
gather odd angles of light along the edges
of bevelled glass whisper made flesh
layer whalebone and lace under linen
cotton wool rows of buttons that require
other hands to undo fear a wedge
that splits the tongue loops endlessly
in the black box of throat, lost echo
chamber bounces on brain-washed
tympani whisper a scream in a pinch
trapped in sucking chest wound
small in something large wide-eyed necessary
things that dance in the dark revel in least chance
whisper stands on whisper shoulders
whisper the sound of water on rock
whisper *en masse* a murmur
murmur on murmur a roar
whisper heard if you listen
sometimes history disappears

Resolution

Innocent mouth before the taste hits
water doesn't wash away
but spreads fire, theater without
extinguisher, playbill missing
a page or worse, containing
a blank one. The lopsided
wheel, uncompensated shaft,
the turn and turn and turn,
spinning gravel. Not a getaway
this after beginning, gear box
with no reverse, birthday present
in Christmas wrap. The almost,
almost point of an eraser, the black
smudge, the hole left in the paper
on the way to tearing the ink out.
Cannot unwind this, crosstitching
must be picked at patiently
to undo the threads, catgut
mixed with silk, no one noticed
until it rained. It rained for days
in the minutes at the stove
bacon out of the pan, rendered oil
in a mug on the sink, bread sopping up egg.
What do I do with this hatbox?
This balloon and pin?

Susie Maguire

Fragments

THE MUSEUM SHOP was closed. Only a panting, bowlegged French dog roamed the Place du Grand Fauconnier, under the scrutiny of the gargoyles. Ah oui, Le Lunch Hour, I should have remembered. My climb up the steep cobbled streets in midday heat had been a misuse of time. I'd have been better packing, eating leftovers, scribbling the last few duty postcards. Thinking how I'd deal with my life when I got home. Not that I needed to think any more, only take action.

I looked again at the information sheet fixed to the massive oak door: closed between 12 and 2. My wristwatch read 1 o'clock, but the Roman numerals on the church tower across the square insisted that it was, and ever would be, 5.30.

I was wondering lazily about ascending the narrow church tower for a final bird's eye view of Cordes-sur-Ciel, as a way of passing time, when my attention was caught by a figure at the top of the tower; a green shirt, white-blond hair rippling in the breeze. A woman. There was something about her which kept me watching: the only other human in sight, maybe it was that, or the slightly hesitant way she moved. Her features were a blur, but the set of her head suggested tension, or possibly fear.

The woman paused for a moment. She seemed to be focusing on something below her, and I found myself looking around to see what it might be, but there was nothing, the streets were still deserted. She looked odd up there alone, out of place, like a modern actor in a costume drama, Rapunzel dressed by Gap.

She took something from a pocket, and leaned across the parapet, scattering a tiny white snowstorm onto the red-tiled spine of roofs below. Far

194

below, and she was leaning rather dangerously. She wore shorts, and the pale backs of her thighs rose into view until she was practically lying along the coping. I began to wonder about her intentions, and her common sense, whether she had any understanding of what hot summers and cold winters do to sandstone over several hundred years. Sweat trickled down my ribs, and my neck began to hurt, as I continued to look upwards.

White fragments drifted out from her fluttering hands in slow motion. The faintest of breezes caught and cushioned the paper petals, waltzing them in every direction until they clung where they could, spreading about the square in a confetti of fallen blossom. A scrap floated down a few feet from me and became trapped in the heavy steel mesh covering of Simon de Montfort's favourite well. The bizarre tourist attraction had been a place of violent death for the unlucky Cathars of the region, circa 1306. Yesterday I'd pressed a coin into a slot and peered down at the briefly illuminated depths, read the historical details on a trilingual plaque, wondered at the savagery and certitude of those domestic crusaders. Now I thought of the well only as a dark, deep mouth ready to devour this strange manna, the hiding place for another mystery. Abandoning my visual fix on the figure still perched hazardously on the tower, I walked quickly over to the well and reached for the fragment of paper. It tore as I wiggled it loose from the wire, and I ended up with a piece the size of a bus ticket.

White paper, black ink, from a broad-nibbed pen. It appeared to be part of a letter, though written in such haste or anger the hand was hard to decipher, but, I thought, written in English. I shaded my eyes and craned back to look up at her. She was gone. Where?

I watched steadily for a few minutes, in case she'd stepped behind the very top of the tower, hoping she'd emerge.

No, she'll be alright, I told myself, muttering under my breath, come on, come on.

But there was no flash of green shirt or blond hair on the tower, and at its foot, the heavy church door stood ajar in the silent heat, proclaiming the emptiness within.

I stuffed the paper scrap into my pocket as I ran across the square, sandals slapping the paving, scattering the doves in alarm, theirs and mine. The cool, dark interior of the church was a shock after the light, but I stumbled left, as my eyes adjusted, to where I knew the door to the tower stair stood open. I grasped the handrail, listened, heard nothing, and started to climb. With each step, and I took them in pairs, my leg muscles protested and my mind was seized by images of what might be at the end of my climb – a body lying broken down below, a hand clinging to the stonework ? Don't think, just get there.

My throat ached and my breath came rapidly as I reached the top. The little door stood open, and when I paused, with the sky in sight, to get my balance, a strange sense of déja vu swept over me like a fever chill, and the thick stone walls swam before me. I pushed my face into my cupped hands, and bent into them, breathing deeply, slower, slowly. Then I stepped out.

At once I was arrested by the panoramic view, the patchwork jumble of roof shapes and, below, the hidden green of gardens, the flag-lines of washing discreetly floating in courtyards. The sun beat down with a white glare but the air was cool and scented. And I was glad to be up there.

Far down to the right I saw the Porte de l'Horloge, and, counting along, identified the gable end of my cousin's house by the bold, deep blue of its shutters. I turned left, and began edging clockwise round the little parapet, crumbs of stonework crunching like muesli under my feet. In some areas I had to step over fist-sized chunks which had fallen inward from the lichen-covered coping. I called out – hello? – my voice sounding foolishly polite, but the only response was a distant cracked bell, chiming the quarter.

My rapid search found no one, and no other way of descent. So, where was she? Who was she?

The scrap in my pocket was crumpled. I smoothed it between my fingers, conscious of a reluctance to read it, propriety battling curiosity. But when I did, the forceful pen marks resolved into words with perfect clarity. It read '...tomorrow is the last...' Last what? Last day? Last chance? I wanted to find the woman and ask what she planned for tomorrow, and the day after that.

For a few minutes I just stood there, gazing down across the valley, letting my eye follow the line of poplars bordering the slim, grey ribbon of the road south to Toulouse. Then, as I turned to start back to earth, I glanced down to where I had been standing, as I watched her, in front of the Museum. And there she was, looking at a notice on the studded oak door. When she turned, my white-blond hair blew around her face like a veil, and she pulled the green shirt away from her body in a familiar gesture. She looked up. Her mouth opened, as if she might call out.

The bowlegged dog padded by, nose down, and the gargoyles laughed quietly. I took the last letter from Tom out of my shorts pocket and began to shred it into tiny snowflakes.

SPACE BOOKED

Photographs by Ariadne Xenou
Four Edinburgh secondhand bookshops

A portrait is of a person and the space they inhabit helps to say something about that person. I was looking at bookshops... specifically bookshops full of old books. They are very special and like the shops themselves the people who work in them are all very different. That's interesting for a photographer, and challenging.

SABIEN VAN CRAENENDONCK, ARMCHAIR BOOKS, 72/74 WEST PORT
© ARIADNE XENOU 2006

When I was growing up in Athens I was in awe of the fact that my mother had so many books – and the fact that she had read them all, and kept getting more. She started giving me books from a very young age. I was fourteen when she gave me Süskind's *Perfume*, which is still my favourite book because it talks about smells so intensely and analytically – but it's only writing, there are no smells, you make them up. That book makes you make up all those smells.

DOREEN DALLAS, WEST PORT BOOKS, 147 WEST PORT
© ARIADNE XENOU 2006

A good book gives me really strong visual stimulation. If that happens, I use my camera to recreate it. I enjoy bringing people together, creating a set, a little play just for one moment. It's all linked, books and theatre and people and photography are all joined together.

RON WILSON, THE OLD TOWN BOOKSHOP, 8 VICTORIA STREET
© ARIADNE XENOU 2006

There's something very tactile about these box-shaped things with stories in them. The internet is huge but it's not tactile. To me it's important to be able to touch and smell. Books smell. The older the book, the more its smell has to tell. I can smell a book and it will take me to a specific image. I'm there – and all from this one little tickle.

RICHARD BROWNE, MAIN POINT BOOKS, 8 LAURISTON STREET
© ARIADNE XENOU 2006

Janis Mackay

Hogmanay

Our slapping steps suck kisses out of the boggy ground.
Round the mossy headland now
where lichen-hoared Oaks score the sky.

Like the wee-folks we walk from bound minutes and hours
into the story place swollen with ballads and loss
when the wet day opens west, to

once a village, now ghost stones, pilfered dykes
and over this rent history
the drow of the sea, and us.

Not just; on a turn eyes catch the flash
of a calloused hand form in the air hawling rope,
the broad grasp of a woman's palm,

silver gleam of knife, muckle wrist
fish gut. Centuries collapse
with a boy at her feet. Trust

imagination to find key-holes
faith of sorts a key, put
over us gliding horses. They gather white again

as the old year breaks on the rocks
and in the wall at the world's end
a door's ajar. Just.

Gerry Cambridge

Young Snow

I remember the three feet drifts
Of the Overtoun Road,
Black scribble of twigs for miles
Balancing the thin white walls
In the fresh-squeezed light. Seven below.
I would live forever. Not in love
Nor wished to be,
That day I saw poems everywhere,
Blood-faced, stamping through
That creaking dazzle and that rare blue,
Laughed at the stains of steaming yellow
Where the bellowing bullocks huffily
Peed and butted and munched their hay.
In the Springside shop, hunched old ladies
In extraordinary hats,
Clutching their wire-mesh baskets,
Muttered, outraged, 'Is this no' awfy, son?'
    And I agreed.

Robert Alan Jamieson

Perfiekt Sjætlin

Though we speak it perfectly well,

> I imna
> We irna
> Du isna
> Ju irna
> Shö isna
> He isna
> Dæ irna

spækin Eng-gliesh.

> We kan, bit sanna.

We winna.

Perfect Shetlandic

We kan spaek it perfiektlie wiel bit

I am not
We are not
You (singular) are not
You (plural) are not
He is not
She is not
They are not

speaking English.

We can, but shan't.

We won't.

Da Veksaesjin a Nemin

to Tom Leonard

At da awpin waek
  T'seliebraet da daeth a'Sjætlin
  Twa oda paal-baerirs got up dir birss.

 Da first, a pojit, roars 'Laamint
 da fyn aald lied'at we ir lost.
 Jun Norrin wirds, jun quhaentist grammir.
 Dis is a dae a'aafil draama.'

 Da sekint, a lingwiest snurtin, sez
 'Du's gien klien gyt. Quhyl I
idmit hit is a loss, hit wis a dyalikt
at best. I doot'at hit wisna a
 langwiech, hed neddir wirds nor vynd
fir toght a'oght bit aertlie maettirs.'

Quhan in kums da grejiev-dellir,
  Shaakin da møld fae his haands,
  Quha looks at da baeth an saes:

   'That's her in the ground then, boys.
   A messy business I've had with her.'

A Problem of Definition
ta Tom Leonard

At the public wake to celebrate
        the death of the Shetlandic tongue
        two of the pall-bearers came to blows.

    The first, a poet, cries 'Lament
    the fine old language we have lost,
    Those Norn words, that quaintest grammar.
    This is a day of deepest drama.'

    The second, a linguist snorting, says
    'Cease your histrionics. While I
    agree it is a loss, It was a dialect
at best. I can't agree it was a
    language, had no capacity at all
for abstract thought of fine expression.'

When in walks the gravedigger
        wiping soil from his hands,
        who looks at both and says:

                'Jun's hir itida grund dan, bojies.
                A gjiurm A'm hed wie'ir.'

Elizabeth Burns

Scribe

They say the world's our parchment:
we mark it with the furrows of the plough,

the wake of ships, the paths we trample
over woods and hills. We set our lives out:

build a hamlet or an abbey, a manor house,
a hut. We clear the forests, sow the fields

with corn or barley. The candle of the sun
shows us the way. God watches –

sees the footprints that we leave, the way
our lives are written, tiny as silverings

of snails, ink marks of a pen. The world
is endless pictures. The page I dwell on

shows our abbey by the sea, the mudflats
where we go for shellfish, the quick tides

slapping at the rocks. Here, our oxen
hauling at the yoke, here the sheep

that graze around the abbey walls. A hawthorn
bent by wind, a trackway winding inland

to the market town. Whitened grass
the hare ran through, the huge sky

filled with crabshell-coloured clouds.
Look closely and you'll see the monks

– these tiny figures, miniscule as pinpricks
used as the markers on a parchment –

hooded figures scurrying against the wind
or sitting calmly in the chapel's candlelight.

This is what we are, on earth's fresh vellum,
in the place where God inscribes our lives.

But here, in the warm scriptorium,
with my pigments, inkhorns, sharpened quills

and lovely gold leaf, it is I
who fills the fresh-stretched parchment's void

with birds and fish, with trails of flowers and leaves,
and creatures – rabbit, dog or fieldmouse –

hiding among the curlicues of words,
becoming, as I write down and illuminate,

the creator. I look down at the page
and see that it is good.

'Rummers and Ladels'

How close I might have come once, as a child,
to touching, in my granny's sideboard
– place of peppery smells and lining paper,
stoppered bottles of gold and scarlet liquids –
a crystal tumbler from which Sir Walter Scott
sipped whisky. Perhaps I fingered the rim of it,
made the crystal sing. Or perhaps not.
Maybe the glasses that he drank from ended up
in someone else's house, or were long since broken.
Perhaps they were there all along and nobody said
or remembered. I've rooted in my parents' china cabinet
and my father's memory, found nothing.

Only the story, in my grandfather's notebook from the twenties.
His mother tells it him, he gives it a title, writes it in her voice:
I think we should put our Rummers and Ladels
in the Plate Cupboard. You know Sir Walter Scott
probably drank his toddies from one or more of those.

She tells how Sir Walter once stayed for a week
at the home of Provost Marney of Arbroath,
and that the Rummers he drank from were passed down
to the provost's spinster daughters. They gave them to their niece,
a Mrs Mitchell, who'd a brother, *not exactly daft, but just a little queer,*
and bedridden. And on Sunday afternoons, *my father went up*
to give him the news and especially to tell all the jokes he had heard.
So Mrs Mitchell *was very good to us,* and *when she heard*
we had no ladels, she brought us Provost Marney's
together with the crystal glasses from which Sir Walter sipped.

The marks Scott's lips made on the glasses were washed away
two hundred years ago by Provost Marney's servant girl.
But still, if I were to hold one of those rummers, and drink from it
a shot of malt, would some sense of him imbue me?
Illogical as kissing bones of saints, but there's potency
in relics. Even the notebook telling the story has become one:
I turn the soft cream pages with their copperplated ink, fondling
this meagre piece of family history. It's as though we dip our hands
into the huge dark bran tub of the past, grateful for anything we find.

The tumblers are gone, and who knows where.
But I'm listening to my daughter at the age of eight,
reciting to herself the words of Scott:
> The herring loves the merry moonlight
> The mackerel loves the wind
> But the oyster loves the dredging sang
> For they come of gentle kind
and this is in her memory now, together with a tale
as vulnerable as glass that travels through our family like a ballad.

Strawberries
after Edwin Morgan

Were there ever strawberries like the ones
bought on a sunny morning in early June
from a cream-painted greengrocer's shop
in the market square of a Devon town
and eaten that afternoon in a birchwood
with a soft wind shimmering the leaves
and the sunlight making dappled shadows
on the little cousins as they reach into the punnets
for the fruit, so warm and sweet, its ruby juice
already glistening on their fingers and their chins?

Suhayl Saadi

The Saelig Tales

A Novella

Dedicated to Nadia Afza Shirin Hawwa Mirza-Saadi

IVY STRETCHED OVER the walls of the Old Manse, covering the front of the building and most of the sides. Only to the rear was the foliage sparse, revealing patches of dun brick and Tudor oak. The green wooden door that once had been the servants' entrance stood open. Occasionally smells of cooking still would seep from the kitchen window, but now the only scents were those of the red and white roses which grew up the walls of the small garden which abutted upon that part of the house. The foliage was of the old type, with flowers the size of a child's palm. During the day they gave off a barely discernible odour, but towards evening, their scents would swell and flood through overhanging leaves of yew and elder, whose soft rustling fell almost into stillness as the light grew redder and the birdsong epiphanous.

A low iron gate set in the far wall led into the outer garden and orchard, which stretched right down to the slow-flowing Mychelham Water some hundred yards or so due east. On this August evening, smoke rose from the patio at the centre of the garden and coiled around the white canvas parasol under which the Reverend Edward Ingle Synnot was seated, partaking of a supper consisting of succulent green figs from a tree which stood on the other side of the garden wall, hard Danish cheese, freshly-baked bread and a carafe of finest Minho port. Between sips, he leaned back against the hard wicker of his chair and lit up an impressive Cuban cigar. Impressive, that is, if anyone had been watching this septuagenarian vicar, plus-fours-and-all, engaging in the typically bucolic pleasures of his Sunday evening. At that time on the Lord's Sabbath, when prayers had been said, wafers consumed, and robes relinquished with not a small measure of relief, his sole companions tended to be avian or insectiferous.

The vicar switched off a transistor radio to which he had been listening, laid down his cigar and, stretching across the wooden table, picked up a leather-bound book. It felt light in his hands, its faded white leather smooth against his skin. Using the tip of his index finger, he traced out the gold-leaf letters of the title on both jacket and spine and then lifted his right hand and squinted at the finger-tip; using the other fingers of the same hand, with a clumsy elegance he donned a pair of gold-rimmed, half-moon reading spectacles, gazed at the white dust accrued on the whorls of his finger-pad, then sniffed it gently. His nose was long and firm, slightly rounded at its end, like the protuberance of a Henry Moore statue; his lips, once middling full, were pursed through long years of solicitude and intercessionary prayer; his eyes were the colour of well-seasoned oak. He removed a white handkerchief from his trouser pocket and wiped the dust onto the cloth. He undid the clasp, allowed the book to fall open, lifted away the white satin bookmark and began to read. He read inwardly, but if one were to have looked closely enough between, say, the broad leaves of an old yew tree, one might have made out the harmonic movement of his lips and tongue. Perhaps a wandering white dog might have been capable of hearing the melody of his barely conscious vocalisation of the meanings which had been burned into the paper. Whether or not there was such a creature among the apple and pear trees of the orchard remains unknown, but the fact was that Reverend Synnot was no longer alone. Another man was sitting opposite him.

Edward only noticed him when the edge of the cigar-leaf most proximal to his fingers began to singe. As he stubbed out the cigar and glanced beyond the golden upper edge of a new page, his eyes caught the man's face. 'John!' he exclaimed with an easy smile, 'I didn't see you arrive.'

The other swung back on his chair and folded his arms behind his neck.

'Sometimes even the animals don't notice me.'

'Years of hunting for poachers?'

'Aye. And for game.'

'In the old days, parsons used to hunt along with the other men.'

'Before my time, Canon Synnot.'

'Mine too! Come on John, you're as old as I – give or take a year or two. And you know full well that I am not a Canon, I have no cathedral around me, merely a village church.'

'These days the passing of a year assumes an importance, both critical and melancholy…'

'I see you're cheerful as usual. A hard day?'

'You choose to stay in your high steeple-house, protected for all eternity by the body of the Church Invisible.'

'Less choice than calling…'

'Bah! Rain on the window: pitter-patter, pitter-patter.'

John Rotherfield brought his hands down onto the table. They were large hands, calloused, the nails cracked here and there and with dirt ingrained into the knuckles. His hair was full for an old man. It looked as if it had been burned silver by the sun. His eyebrows were bushy and still black. Lines ran in every possible direction around his eyes, mouth and neck. He had come to resemble the crust of a dessicated planet which, aeons past, had been lush and green. Yet his frame was unbent and lithe. His gaze, fixed on a point behind and to the left of the other man's jacket, was so intense that Edward had an almost irresistible urge to turn around. However, he knew that following Rotherfield's deep blue eyes into whatever reveries he held within his head was a dangerous path to take; perhaps he was only looking at the climbing rose that had forced its tangled stem upwards against the crumbling brick ever since the days of Paine and Cobbett.

'You look like you could do with a cigar and a glass of the red!'

And without waiting for a reply, Edward poured him a generous measure of port, filling the glass to the point of overflowing. Without spilling a drop, he placed it before the gamekeeper. For an interval during which it seemed to Edward that he could hear the ticking of the grandmother clock on the wall of his study far within the house, Rotherfield's stare held him, as countless times it had held a pheasant, a deer or a snake. Yet it was he who looked away first. He threw back his head and gulped from the glass, his Adam's apple pulsing up and down the trunk of his throat. Edward noticed that Rotherfield had leaned a small axe and a bag of sticks against the wall and shivered inexplicably.

Rotherfield lit his cigar. When he spoke again, his voice had dropped a quarter-octave.

'What's that you're reading?'

'Oh, a curiosity I picked up at the Sergison Manor sale a few weeks ago.'

Rotherfield reached across and took the book out of his hand.

'*The Architecture of the Blessed*... who is the author?'

'The name has been completely eroded.'

'That's strange, the title's perfectly clear. There's not even an indentation to suggest an author's name was once there. What about inside?'

'Nothing there either,' Edward answered.

Rotherfield began flicking through the yellowed pages.

'Strange...' he said again.

Edward shrugged. 'These old volumes harbour all manner of curiosity. I have one which has been printed in looking-glass type and illustrated in reverse pictures. I have to use a mirror to read it.'

Rotherfield put the book down close to his glass, glanced down at his boots, exhaled slowly and then looked back up. Edward, for reasons he found difficult to identify, felt compelled to speak.

'Do you remember, John, when we were young – before the Great War, before I became a priest – we used to go down to the riverbank and lie in boats and read to one another and sing, you, me and...'

'Of course I remember,' Rotherfield cut in.

'It seems like another life, now. So much has changed.'

'Everything has changed.'

'Everything?'

'All that matters.'

'John, it's time, surely it's time, to... not to forget, we could never do that, but to heal. Or at least to carry on, to realise that God's scheme is unfathomable, that His face is ineffable as even it was to Christ on the Cross in his moment of ultimate despair.'

'Pretty words, Edward. Ragged sermons. Old music.'

It was a conversation which they'd had countless times over the years, and they always reached this same theological dead-end.

In spite of the lack of a breeze, Edward thought he heard the sound of river water rushing over flat stones. He was aware of Rotherfield's eyes on him, that penetrating quality they had, the manner in which they darted away as though suddenly aware of their power. An oppressive sense of animalistic scrutiny made him shift uneasily in his chair. It was as though the presence of this old acquaintance had disturbed the plumb-line of the equilibrium which he had made for himself in the enclosed garden, the equilibrium which, by extension, held together his life within the Church of St Cuthman.

Rotherfield's eyes had not sustained the veined tiredness of old age. Nothing cracked the arc of their perfection. Edward felt the inadequacy, the banality of his own mud-brown irises. Never once in his seventy years had he perceived through those eyes the nature of God. Through all the gallons of blood-coloured wine and high-stacked ricks of bread, through sermons a million words long and christenings sufficient to drown half the host of Hell, cleavings and layings to earth enough to cultivate the seeds of a nation, not once had the Reverend Edward Ingle Synnott felt the living presence of Christ.

'You have sought solace within the pages of your books and the resonance of your stone chancels, while I...' Rotherfield's voice quivered like an arrow-shaft in oak.

'You seek it in the woods, in the bark of dead tree-trunks, in your quarry at the quivering moment of death.'

'How poetic you are. How pathetic.'

'I think you need another drink.'

The woodcutter sighed.

'Perhaps I do.'

The vicar obliged.

Rotherfield nodded.

'Your cigar has gone out.'

Edward picked up the fat Havana, ignited its distal end and puffed away like a jazz cornetist until the smoke rose in perfect circles from the ends of the wrapped leaves. The birds now were of the evening: kestrels, curlews, night herons. Rotherfield breathed in deeply. He felt the garden roses fill his chest; and beyond, the sleeping ivy, the broad, grey beech; and the slowly rising veins of the yew began to course through his body where they met and joined with something that had burned there for years. In the depths of despair, nature had always redeemed him. Perhaps that was why, on the first Sunday of every month, he walked through the forest of Andrieda and crossed the Mychelham Water to take port and cheese and bread with the man with whom, in a manner of speaking, he had shared the same epoch. They would harangue each other and discuss metaphysical matters, or pore over treatises on nature or essays which purported to draw links between the exact geographical locations of various artists' homes and their works. It had become an unofficial fixture in both men's lives, these past ten years or so.

'Read to me, Edward. Read as you used to do, among the hay and upon the green of the river-bank, when we were boys.'

'I haven't done that for years.'

'All the more reason.'

'Time moves on…'

'There are at least three hours of daylight left. Time enough.'

'Well, alright. I'll read as long as I can manage. Sunday services tend to fray the voice.'

'They fray my ears.'

'Thank you, John.'

'I hear the music, through the stone walls of your church. I feel the wind blowing through the organ-pipes.

The vicar did not reply but instead fiddled with his reading glasses, which tended to slip progressively down his nose; because he adjusted them so often, the frame had become bent, so that they tended to sit on the bone at a slightly skewed angle, which made the tops of his ears rather uncomfortable.

Edward flipped through the pages until he found the chapter for which he'd been searching. As though he were about to place the book upon a lectern, he carefully smoothed down the spine, cleared his throat and began to read.

'It says that this section was translated by the author from the original Anglo-Saxon, which means that he or she must have been a seeker-out of obsolete tongues, of languages which are no longer spoken or written, of words which have slipped from thought. It takes a particular kind of person to devote a life to that which is no more. We did a modicum of Anglo-Saxon at Theological College, not enough for me to be able to decipher the original version of this text.'

Edward turned the book around to demonstrate exactly what he meant. Rotherfield leaned across the table and peered closely. He made out a series of oddly-shaped letters, some of which were familiar, others completely alien. It was as though the mundane letters which he used every day had become intoxicated by the passage of time. Some appeared to have been speared through the middle, others resembled thorns, gibbets, musical notes or intertwined fingers. The vicar resumed:

These are the works, in vellum, of Aelfric, Abbott and builder of the Church of Wywurth in the land of South Saxons, who died on the Day of the Feast of St Thomas in 872 Anno Domini. They were discovered sealed in an iron casket held within the walls at the crown-end of a pyramidal-shaped tomb close to the east line of the square chancel in the old churchyard of Oxney, East Sussex. The tomb was of more recent date, and so the assumption must be that the casket had been removed from its original place of secretion, which may have been somewhere beneath the church floor, and moved to the cist of one Sir Cuthman Harris, good Squire of Oxney who was born on the 10th March in the Year of Our Lord 1654 and who departed this world on 15th December in the Year of Our Lord 1729. The reason for its removal and deposition are unknown to the author.

THESE ARE THE words of I, Aelfric, who is the Abbott of Wywurth in the Land of the South Saxons. For some twenty winters, since work on this most holy abode of God hath, with His Grace, been completed, I have been engaged in collecting and committing unto manuscript the songs and customs of this land of mine and of applying to said musics the principles and incantations of Pope Sylvester of Rome who lived among the Saracens in the lands to the south of the Dominion of the Franks and who learned there of many hellish things which yet might lead unto a knowledge of the perfect proportions of Paradise and the various lights with which said garden be illumin'd. Through rain and snow and pestilence and great temptation, have I laboured these twenty years in dark cloisters of the soul, and in my searches, I have travelled across very near the entirety of the Marks of the land of the South Saxons. I have waded through the shadows of wayside Roods, I have inscribed the dances and songs, vigorous and gentle, of the thanes and the ceorls and those, too of their womenfolk; these are folk of mine own stock and yet through this long quest, do I sense a great river flowing between mine own soul and that of the men who live and die around my cell. With crot, horn and monochord, I am as a wave pon the sea. I have grown separate even from the fellow-brothers of mine own abbey. They know little of my work and perhaps tis best that way, since they possess neither the wisdom to comprehend its span, nor the reason to put it to use. If they had their way, they might liken to burn such manuscripts as I create, for such as the Æcer-bót is believed by many in this land of ours to be works of the Devil.

And truth be written, I rest uneasy upon the labours of my stylus, for God knows what twists and coils and devilish airs may be assumed and read into even the most innocent of letters. The Word may have been issued from the moving spirit of Our Lord, yet having descended into this world of men, it is not trammelled with the good as oxen are to plough.

But these nights I must speed my labours, my reed must slip across bull-skin as wax floweth into the flame. A dark wind bloweth from the east, and I know not what our fate will be, a month from now. In this work I am ably abetted by one novice monk, Aetheric, whom very near from the cradle I did school in the arts in which my soul is embroiled through the course of this life. I work with said Aetheric in a space which lieth neath the beams of the tower roof and from this vantageous point can we witness the rise and fall of the sun and the moon and the sway and heave of the tides and rivers of the sky, and also can we spie any intruder, man or woman, thane or ceorl, who might emerge from the depths of the forest. In the past few weeks we have made out, along the far eastern rim, a long line of black and gold. These be the clinker ships of the North-Men with their golden beaks and their massed oars, scything through the white waves along the line of the coast. I have spotted the works of these brutes at close hand, when once I was travelling through the lands of the Jutes of old in search of some ancient manuscripts said to have been quill'd by none other than the Archbishop Elphege of East Kent. From my vantage-point, I watched Norse-Men storm into the town and slaughter all, even unto the whining dogs and gawking hens! They took the Archbishop into the square, where they cast him upright upon whole bone and horns of an ox, and then one of them struck him with an axe-iron on the head, so that with the blow he and the bony frame sank down. Then, him being still alive, they proceeded to slit his back with an axe, twice, and deep, so that he screamed as I have never before heard man or beast scream. Then they turned him over and hacked open his chest, again in form of two straight lines, running in angle parallel. Then they forced apart the rib-sticks of his heart-cage and left him there on the wealden mud of the village square, his heart beating to the white sky, his back broken into wings, to perish in the greatest of agonies. I had heard this devilish practice called by the Dark Strangers themselves, 'The Rite of the Blood Eagle'. After they had completed their terrible deed, the savages did take the body and strip it of skin, laying it thus, raw and open, to the vultures and wolves and mad dogs who do follow the hoofprints of death wherever that great beast doth roam. On their left shoulder they carried an axe and on their right, an iron spear. Each man wore two gold bracelets on either arm and on his head, a gilt helmet. They were bearded and their faces were stamped with expression, most terrible and pagan. I hurried myself away from the awful scene and I did not stop till I reached the wayside cross which sits pon the east bank of the east tributary of the River Mychelham, which divides the lands of the Kentish folk from the marches of the South Saxons. There, as I lay down to rest, I smelled the river most foul and horrid. When I raised my head to look upon the waters, I saw that they did flow red. Yet I had to cross the ford, since if I had remained where I was, the Dark Strangers would surely have found my hiding-place and I would have suffered the selfsame fate of the good Archbishop. I waited a little, in the hope that the waters might clear, but with no sign of this impending, I took up my scapular in my arms and waded through the blood-drenched river. The stench of it caused my head to spin, so that I almost tumbled into the red flood. Yet the current flowed fast and I knew that if once I fell, I would be unable to rise again and would drown in the blood of Mother Church. So I strode on, all the while intoning a bede to Our Lord. At the moment when I felt that I could move no further, at the very middle point of the river, I closed my eyes and implored the skies to come to my aid. For I carried with me manuscripts most precious, which I had obtained that very morning from the most saelig archbishop, and if I drowned, they would be gone forever; the ink of their vellum would run and flow through the rivers of the land and be lost in the southern sea. But already my legs were turning to viscid water and I felt as though I would dissolve into the great river. At that moment, I heard the sound of a woman's voice. It was a song which I had never before heard and the words were in a language which I did not understand, or else which now I have forgotten. On that fateful afternoon in the full-spated river, I found that I understood as though I had long known the words of this song, which, though mournful, was not akin to the funeral dirges of our age, but seemed to issue from a time, long past, or else, yet to come. The fluid of the music rendered unto my sinews the power to continue my journey, and so I was able to cross the river and return by these many leagues, to the abbey. I know not the explanation for this happening, nor yet who the woman was that sang so beautifully to me on that day. Perhaps it was the Holy Spirit. I know not.

Aelfric sat at his desk by the opening between the sloping wooden roof of the church tower and the wall and as he gazed across the village to the rods of farmland which lay outside of ditch, bank and palisade, his eyes came to rest upon the ochre wastes beyond the yew forest. The great Southern Sea was some seven leagues away, yet he could smell its sharp blade. The day was hard and cold and clear and as it turned slowly to night, the freezing air settled in complete stillness over the surface of the forest lake. In the morning he would brush away the thin dust of snow from its surface and see himself as though he were lying on the bed of the lake. The sun had abandoned the eastern sky, yet its beams overflowed from beneath the horizon, turning the columns of smoke which issued from the Moot Hill to bronze. Aelfric imagined the smoke to be earthly angels, sent to protect the abbey from the depradations of the Dark Strangers. The thin trails hung unmoving in the still air, like the sung notes of the dead. As he moved about the belfry, Aelfric felt that he was the only thing on earth whose swing and metal had not been still'd. The smells of the village, smells of poultry and pigs, stale hay and green waste, wafted to the top of the tower, yet like the smoke they thinned as they rose. From where he was, Aelfric could not hear any of the chopping, shouting and grinding that would be going on below; such sounds as had accompanied the building of this humble and yet wondrous church. Aelfric had supervised every aspect of the construction, from foundation ditch to belfry roof. It would have been another man's life's work; under his hand, the church had been completed within a mere twenty years.

The plan for the building had come to him through a dream in the form of musical notches. Upon waking, he had grabbed his quill and rushed to his vellum, but once there, he had been unable to transcribe even one of the sounds he had heard. At first he had despaired, for the music had been beautiful and wondrous, but then he had realised that such celestial notes could never be scratched with the end of a bird feather onto animal skin. For twenty years the song had remained hidden in his head, and yet he had been able, somehow, to reach down as though through a dark firmament and follow that which was held therein and so, winter-upon-summer, his church had been built.

The basic plan was that of a Cross with arms of equal length. The main – north – portal was very plain, with a single rose window above it. The ceiling was vaulted and supported by pillars with ornamental shafts. The building was taller than it was broad and culminated in a large dome resting on spherical triangles. At times, especially when it was empty first thing in the morning and the light angled in appropriate manner, the Abbey of Wywurth seemed more like a cathedral than a humble village church. At the centre of the dome, a great golden sun beamed so brightly down upon apse and nave that the whole building seemed to be illuminated. Painted in faint outline behind the sun was a black, square-shaped rood. Most of the interior was unadorned, save for the east entrance. There, carved into the stone, and protruding from it, was the face of a young woman, complete with hair and neckband. Around the face grew tendrils of reeds and leaves of ivy and the whole was set above the door with the visage inclined slightly downwards so that it seemed as though the woman was gazing at folk as they entered. The bell-tower was reputed to be the highest in the lands of the South Saxons, and though he had not climbed each one and measured the rival steeples, stone-upon-stone, Aelfric believed this to be true.

The church had been built using huge sandstone blocks taken from the ruins of buildings of the Old Romans, blocks so heavy that it had taken eight yoke of oxen just to move them the fifteen leagues. He had no idea where the plan for the Abbey of Wywurth had come from, it was like no house of God he had ever seen or heard of, but it had succeeded, it stood upright, its dome and tower punched into the sky. The perfect music which he had heard in his dream was set now in stone.

Up in the chamber of the bell-tower it was as though he were enclosed in a cell, a monastic cell, yes, but more than that, an enclosed space like that which might exist in a book, or a song, or a tomb. Such a place might exist in the lower reaches of heaven, or the hinterlands of paradise. This land was indeed a holy land.

He sighed and, with a groan, raised his frame from the chair and rubbed his lower back; too many hours of poring over half-decayed manuscripts, styling notes into tablets of wax and finally, once all the calculations had been made and the courses of logic run, drawing reed across vellum beneath a tallow light. For several days he had neglected to shave, or even to follow the Rule of Benedict. As he had done many times over the years, Aelfric asked forgiveness of his Creator for these faults, hoping for some dispensation, given the urgency of his task: to complete the cycle of songs, musics and arithmetical calculations which would yield, if not to him then at least to some future scholar, the ability to dance in seamless, lacertine geometer across this land and thus to scry the future and even the nature of that most elusive of mysteries, death.

Aelfric went over to a low table and poured some wine from an urn into a blue glass, swung back his head and gulped so rapidly that it made him choke and cough. He wiped the back of his hand across his lips and drank some more. These past few days he had existed on wine and stale bread and his legs felt like fish-guts. All his brother monks had fled towards the lands of the West Saxons, which yet held secure, but he and his helper Aetheric had remained here with the intention of hiding the manuscripts and themselves until the North-Men had gone their way. Then they would re-emerge, knowledge and wisdom intact – qualities they would carry on their backs north, south, east and west. They had to stay to complete the work not so much because the Abbey of Wywurth was one of the last places where they might find seclusion and materials with which to continue; more because of the head of Alcuin, which could not be moved from there, e'en until Doomsday.

Aelfric tensed. Footsteps, growing louder. Three knocks, followed by four: it was their code. He went over and turned the iron handle. The door swung open, revealing a breathless Aetheric. The Abbott turned away, folded his hands behind his back.

'Well, didst thou find any meat?' he asked, sternly.

'None, Master Abbott. There is nothing to be found for twenty acres in any direction. I spent the whole day searching.'

'And didst thou return, empty-handed?'

'Aye,' Aetheric nodded. His eyes were bright with the dreams of youth and angels, but he, too, was unshaven and his face had grown long, his eyes red-rimmed with sleepless nights. 'Except for this.'

In the opened palm of his outstretched hand, Aetheric held a sparkling piece of jet, cut in the shape of an eye.

'What is it?' Aelfric asked, taking the stone from him. 'It is smooth and polished like jewellery, yet it is like none which I have seen. Where didst thou find it?'

Aetheric hesitated. 'I was given it.'

'Given it? By whom?'

'By a mendicant with a flowing white beard...' he sighed deeply, 'and eyes the colour of the sea.'

'And where didst thou meet this mendicant?'

'Upon the ruins of Moot Hill.'

'The ruins? But the hoolets do not inhabit the Moot. Who has ruined it? The thane yet guards it with his life.'

Aetheric shook his head. 'No, Father Abbott. The thane has fled and only penniless wanderers now inhabit its hall. They are using the wood of walls and roof for fuel.'

Aelfric walked over to the gap of light. What the novice had said must indeed be true. Smoke, dancing lithe and curvaceous, was rising to such a height over the village as he had never before seen. It must be that, timber by timber, the building itself was being fed to the fire.

The shapes the smoke made against the sky resembled great thorns, or Viking axes, or demons, and the smell it gave out was of sulphur. It was as though Hellfire itself had descended upon Wywurth and upon the world, thought Aelfric, feeling the stone smooth and warm in his hand. He became angry.

'What use is this stone, thou fool? It is a piece of trickery. What didst thou pay for it?'

'One silver pening.'

'Madman!'

'What worth hath money, now? The eye hath special powers. It came from the lands of the Salernii.'

The Abbott's face contorted. 'I tarry all hours poring over these manuscripts, I scry blóts and bedes unknow'd e'en to the most learned amongst us, I neither eat nor drink – save for worm-infested bread and stale Communion Wine (for which I ask God's forgiveness) – and thou, whom I have brought into the light of knowledge these past fifteen winters, thou wandereth among mendicants and render unto them compense for common rocks!'

So saying, he raised his arm and cast the stone to the floor, where it broke into eleven thousand pieces. There was a loud bang and the room filled with smoke so dense it caused their eyes to water. Then, as Aelfric made the sign of the rood across his chest, he thought he heard music. It was of the same rhythm as the music which the thanes played and to which the scops sang in the great Moot Halls across the lands of the Saxons. Yet this leoðsong seemed to issue from the very core of his being. It was soon as though his very bones were singing. Although he could not make out the words, they seemed known to him, as if they had once fallen from the lips of a lover. (Aelfric was surprised that this thought had occurred to him, since, even in dream, he had never possessed a woman.) The song was at once the rise and fall of the tide in spring, the sound of snow falling on a stone tomb, the spinning memory of long galleries and fire-shadows.

And now, at the same instant, Aelfric and his novice discerned the form of a woman dancing in the billowing smoke. A prayer dried on Aelfric's lips as he watched her grow more substantial, until she stood before them, tall and willowy, her black tunic and mantle affixed with a brooch in the shape of a sun, a necklace of jet-stone and silver wire at her throat. Her eyes are river-fish grey, thought Aelfric. Her face, long and unnaturally white, reminded him of his own, reflected in the mirror of the frozen lake. The woman's lips were moving. She started intoning the words of a song:

It was long, long ago –
Yet I recall – when at the forest's edge,
I was hewn down and my stem removed
Resistless were the foes that seized me there,
They fashioned for themselves a spectacle,
Commanded me to bear their criminals.

Aelfric cleared his throat and addressed her. 'From where dost thou hail, and for what purpose?'

She turned towards him and as she did so, her black hair came loose from its clasp and danced across her visage in manner akin to a leafy yew branch caressed by the breeze.

'I am from the river beneath the mountain. I am from the Isle of the Sea-Calf where the fisherman turned the people from the raven to the speaking wood. My name is Aethelflaed. Within me, there rages the passion of eleven thousand virgins.'

Aelfric shot a glance at the novice, who lowered his gaze.

The woman continued, and it was as though she were singing her words.

'Within me, O monk, the heart of Inge-land doth beat strong. I am in the grains of rock, in the silver of springs, in the time between tides, in the moots of the seas where whales and dolphins sing and spinneth tales. I am in shank of bull and breast of cow. I am in the eyes of the lover.'

'Good maiden, dost thou reside also in the ink and gold of my manuscripts?'

'The words which you have scratched across skin and beat into silver and bled into stone, those colours of earth which you have drawn from land and river will be burned and washed away, forever lost to those who come after you.'

Aelfric felt as though his legs were about to give way. He stumbled to his chair, and almost fell into it. The novice went to him.

'Are you alright, Father Abbott?' he said solicitously. 'Thy pale face and silvery hair possesses a gleam more akin to metal than to man.'

'I... I do not know, Aetheric. In the name of God, I do not know.'

'Let me bring thee a drink.' Aetheric lifted a tumbler to his master's lips and the Abbot drank of the Holy Communion wine.

A little recovered, he continued, 'Spirit of the dark stone, for mercy's sake, pray tell us poor mortals what we must do to save the manuscripts, the words and songs of the folk who dwell within this life as from mark to mark. Pray sing to us as thou didst sing to me upon the bloodied ford, that summer's afternoon.'

The maiden smiled and moved toward the two monks. She was taller than the tallest man in the village; she stood over six foot; and she progressed in manner light and subtle, hardly skimming the ground. Her feet were bare. She sat upon the other chair, rested her arms on the table and laid the soft, white skin of her palms upon the coarse vellum of the manuscripts.

'Rest thy fear, good Father Abbott, for this winter's day shalt thou attain the fruit of thy labours. Thou shalt perceive of such that only one mortal man hast seen before thee, and only one other will in days yet to come.'

'Good lady, dost thou mean that I shall seek out and find safe places where this vellum might be secreted?' She motioned across the room, toward the shafts of light which poured in through the wooden frame.

'That, and much more besides.'

'I do not fear death, only the pain of transition. I am old and I have lived here in this abbey for most of my life. I have prayed to my Maker most scrupulously through the Rule of Saint Benedict and if it is time for me to depart, then I am ready.'

'Make not that mistake: I am not sliced from the finger of thy God.'

'Then art thou…?'

'I do not hail from the dark regions, nor from the talon of thy Beast.'

'From whence, then, dost thou arise?'

'Thou shalt gain apprehension of whither I do arise; for now, suffice it to say that I was here before thy God, before thy Devil. I am in the grains of the stone which thy novice didst crack, in the leaves not yet in bud; along the long roots of thine eyes do I sprout, through the blood coils of thy brain do I run. Abbott – I am in thine heart.'

'Lord God, save us!'

'Beyond and beneath salvation and damnation, there am I. Thy manuscripts sing the songs of my soul and of all the souls which dance and sail within mine.'

Aetheric now gulped down some Communion Wine. 'Good lady, forgive me, but when I look upon thee I forget the vows I am to take. I grow dizzy…'

She reached out and took his hand. 'Good novice, I will guide thee on the voyage which thou must undertake.'

'Thy hand is soft, yet cold as ice.'

'The journey is long, and though like Sylvester thou be on't, yet thou wilt not perceive aught of the marks and crosses thereof.'

'I care not. If the journey be into the light, what matter this beat of the sparrow's wing? Death is but a mask on the face of the everlasting.'

'Thy master, Abbott Aelfric, shall be the watcher. His soul has grown greater than most. No hlaford, no guardian of the loaf, can make this journey. No man who liveth in the joys of the mead-hall can venture pon such moots as this voyage will require; only the wraecca will be able to scribe that which he will see. He alone can save thee from the fiery jaws of the terrible green nicor, from the surfeits of this life.'

The Abbott gathered up his writing materials – vellum, reed and pigments – and sat alert at his desk. The light was still strong, yet at its fulcrum was a hint of the darkness which covereth all. He tied the rope tightly around him, so that his clothing seemed more shroud than habit.

The black-haired lady placed her hands upon the shoulders of the novice. Her fingers were long and bony, the nails like icicles on the point of melting. She drew him to the centre of the room. He closed his eyes and began to sway. She threw her head back so that her long mantle of hair swept like the wakes of a thousand long-ships across her tunic. Her mouth opened but at first no sound issued from her throat. Then, as Aelfric watched, the muscles between jaw and collar-bones began to pull and ripple and stretch and her head swung from side to side, as though she were in a trance of prayer. The movements grew until it seemed as though they would rip her skull from her spine. As a trickle of blood began to flow from her neck, she began to sing in a voice high-toned as a lark's, yet strong as a raven's. Aetheric who was now unclothed lay with his spine curved against the pig-iron of the bell, his skin glowing silver like that of the maiden. The notes from which the lines and strokes and dots that wet the vellum had arisen resonated in the Abbott's skull. The white-faced scop began singing in his wanderer's soul.

> *Where is the horse and the rider? Where is the giver of gold?*
> *Where be the seats and the banquet? Where be the hall-joys of old?*
> *Alas for the burnished cup, for the byrnied chief of today!*
> *Alas for the strength of the prince! For the time hath passed away –*
> *Is hid neath the shadow of night, as it never had been at all.*
> *Behind the dear and doughty there standeth now a wall,*
> *A wall that is wondrous high, and with wondrous snake-work wrought.*
> *The strength of the spears hath fordone the earls and hath made them naught,*
> *The weapons greedy of laughter, and she, the mighty Wierd;*
> *And the tempests beat on the rocks, and the storm-wind that maketh afeard –*
> *The terrible storm that fetters the earth, the winter-bale,*
> *When the shadow of night falls wan, and wild is the rush of the hail,*
> *The cruel rush from the north, which maketh men to quail.*
> *Hardship full is the earth, o'erturned when the stark Wierds say:*
> *Here is the passing of riches, here friends are passing away;*
> *And men and kinsfolk pass, and nothing and none may stay;*
> *And all this earth-stead here shall be empty and void one day...*

Her song continued, yet now it was a reflection, a didymus, the form merely of a tale as she swayed back and forth with Aetheric the Novice against the metal arc of the bell and Aelfric the Abbott scribed faster than ever he had scribed, pigments and inks flying from the end of his reed quill. The music which he plyed in the form of words melded with the last rays of light which sleeked into the belfry like the blades of langseaxes.

234

And as he wrote, the land itself rose up, chain upon perch upon rood upon acre, and Aelfric saw far into a realm where energy grows form.

Reverend Synnott laid the book, still open, upon the table. He sighed and sat back in his chair. His face was pale and his eyes flitted like bird seeking perch about the branches of the trees outside the garden.

Rotherfield watched all this. 'How beautiful,' he said, 'and how false.'

'Why false?' the vicar asked, his pallor increasing.

Rotherfield shrugged. 'The seeking after pagan gods or goddesses is as pointless as the quest for the Holy Grail. Myth, constructed out of a longing for meaning and structure, when there is none.'

'Even space possesses inherent structure...'

'Human life, it seems to me, is one great betrayal.'

Edward was silent. He concentrated on the crumbling upper edge of the wall some four feet above Rotherfield's shoulder. The scent of roses was growing stronger, mingled with the inspissated odour of old brick. Soon night would sweep over everything, turn colour to formless black.

'That day, before the war, when we took small boats down to the river, yonder...' Rotherfield jerked his thumb back to indicate the direction of the river which flowed beyond the wood's far edge.

'We rowed boats often.'

'That day was different.' Rotherfield inhaled, looked around him. 'It was a little like today: summer, albeit early afternoon, the sun shining, the heat pouring off the fields, along the branches of the trees, down the shallow banks and into the oxbows of the river.'

'We were very young.'

'Not so young.'

'Strange ideas...'

'We had the idea of rowing for a stretch and then lying down in the bowl of the hull so that, viewed from the bank, it would seem as though the boats were empty, simply flowing with the current.'

'It was silly idea,' Edward said. 'Dangerous, even on a slow-flowing river.'

'The river was low with the dry summer. The reeds had risen almost to the surface, you could see them waft by like the notes of a symphony.'

'You, me, and...'

'Caroline.'

The vicar sighed and thrust his legs out straight, leaned back on his elbows and gazed up at the sky as though he were back fifty years, in the narrow rowing-boat as it bobbed along in the middle of the river. The willows hung heavy over the water. He felt the rough, warm planks of the hull rub against his naked shoulders. Through the soles of his feet, which were planted against the arched walls of the craft, he felt the parting movement of the waters and at the same time, against the curvature of his skull, he felt them come together as though his passage had been merely a solitary bubble moving through their substance.

'I dream of her, often. Even after all these years.' Rotherfield's voice was ragged like the black sky tearing back into stars. 'Her eyes, her hair...'

'Stop.'

'...the smell of her skin amidst the leaves and summer heat. The sound of her voice a particular music.'

'Stop it, John. Stop now.'

'Her soul sings to me across the abyss.'

'I cannot listen to this!'

'Why not? Why should I stop? I will not stop, that you may feel less guilty. So that you, the grand Reverend of the Church of St Cuthman's of Wywurth, vicar of all that he surveys, might continue to enjoy the odd summer's evening with a man whom all these years he has considered a friend?'

'Are we not friends, John?'

'Do not patronise me using my Christian name like that! I am Rotherfield, the local gamekeeper-cum-woodcutter-cum-village-idiot.'

'You were never an idiot.'

'Oh yes, I was. I was the one who followed the clarion call. I was the one who leapt like a fool into the trenches!'

'You haven't brought any of this up for years. Why today?'

'I don't know. That story – it reminds me of something... I could smell the village with its wood fires and its snorting hogs, the stench of its sewage, poxes weeping from the skin, the creeping of the mud dead. I have been there.'

'We all thought you were dead. There was no word for over two years.'

Rotherfield had been captured at Gallipoli and held in a Turkish jail full of Armenians, Greeks and Kurds (then known as Saracens). The absence of any other British prisoners struck had him as strange, and only later did he learn that he had been held apart from his countrymen deliberately. The Turks started moving him further and further east until he ended up in Kars, a God-forsaken huddle of dun-coloured buildings where, for nine months out of twelve, snow and ice ruled.

One day, while he was breaking rocks on a barren, rain-swept hillside, he was approached by a man carrying a long stick He walked with a slight limp and was aged around forty, though it was hard to be sure. Rotherfield had never talked about this before, but now his gaze encompassed the vicar as he described the visitation.

'He wore a short, pointed beard, like a Renaissance aristocrat or stage magician. His eyes were black and almond-shaped, his skin olive. He greeted me by name in English and then he handed me a card. I wiped the sweat and rain from my eyes to read it: THE HOUSE OF DHU'L-KIF, RUM MILET 786 A, FANAR, ISTANBUL.

'Then I realised where I had seen him before – at Gallipoli. He had been on a ridge not fifty yards from me, and he just stood there, outlined against the sky in his Turkish Army battle-cap and greatcoat. It was a miracle he wasn't shot straight off, yet as the sun fell into the sea, releasing its redness over everything, he lit a cigarette and started to smoke in a most leisurely manner. Though my rifle was loaded and ready I did not shoot him, yet I could not tear my eyes away from him. Sunset gave way to intense darkness. There was no moon and I began to shiver with the damp and cold. I assumed that the man had gone back down into his trench, though I couldn't be sure; he had vanished with the light. For all I knew, he might still have been there, staring at me.

'When I returned to the present and looked up, I was shocked to discover that the bearded figure who had handed me his card only moments before had disappeared. The hillside was covered with boulders, rocks and piles of scree and I supposed that it might have been possible for him to hide, but although I scoured it with my eyes hour upon hour, I saw no one emerge on the slope.

'Some weeks later, I was woken in the middle of the night by the sound of clanging. I was so exhausted from stone-breaking that I always slept like the dead. But now consciousness came. There was a party of soldiers at the door. At least, I assumed they were soldiers; they had that bearing and they were holding guns. They were clad from head-to-toe in black. Long, black cloaks and leather boots. They stormed into the hut but despite the noise they made and the light from their torches, not one of my fellow-prisoners stirred. They were still snoring away, some with incongruous smiles on their grizzled faces. The other odd thing was that the soldiers' armaments were at least fifty years out-of-date. Things might have been getting pretty dire for the armies of Europe, but not to the extent of being reduced to the muzzle-loading muskets of the Crimean War. And so these were not regulars of the Turkish Army.

'I was still only half-awake when I felt a hand on my left shoulder and realised they had come for me. I grabbed my greatcoat and stumbled outside. The bitter air smelled of stale lemons and chilled the sweat on my skin. I felt utterly hopeless. I was three thousand miles from home and the woman I loved.

'The shapes of the prison huts loomed like dolmens into the sky. Dawn was a thin line on the rim of the eastern horizon and down in the valley, the minarets of the town caught the first light. The only thing that kept me going as we trudged across the dusty black mountains of eastern Anatolia was the thought that my captors evidently did not intend to kill me quite yet. The men spoke not a word. When I indicated that I needed to urinate, they paused and allowed me to do so, but I was never allowed out of their sight. As the light grew stronger, I tried to make out their faces but somehow my senses could not hold on to any of their features. They seemed like the landscape; rugged, swarthy and endlessly repetitive. All of them wore the same style of moustache. I wondered whether they were deserters, but then how could they have managed to get into the camp, torches and all? It had been strange that no-one had stopped us – unless they had killed the sentries. I had seen no bodies, no blood, no sign whatsoever of a struggle.

'All those months in the prison-camps, breaking stones and eating food that tasted like old leather, had weakened me and I breathed with considerable difficulty in this high terrain. I was certain of one thing. The mysterious figure whom I had seen twice now, was not among this group.

'It was almost noon when at last we stopped and sat among some rocks. The men laughed and talked amongst themselves in a language which I didn't recognise. It was the first time I had heard them speak. They unwrapped some provisions and began to eat and drink with gusto, offering me nothing, although I was slumped on the stony ground, my limbs shaking, salivating uncontrollably.

'After about fifteen minutes, I heard a bugle blast, a sound that brought back terrible memories of the trenches. The bandits – for that was what they must be – leapt to their feet and gathered up their bags, guns and flasks; for the first time, there seemed to be some measure of urgency to their actions. They marched me to the top of a ridge, on the other side of which I expected to see yet another endless plateau. However, it was quite different. A breeze blew into my face, much fresher than any I had experienced since my incarceration. I suppose I was lightheaded with exhaustion and hunger – but I felt as though, if I stayed there for long enough, the skin of my face, and thence the rest of my being, might at last begin to heal. I let my eyelids close and then open again. Before me was a vast body of water, so broad that I could barely make out the far bank. Tiny waves coursed across its surface and with every roll of crest into trough, the colour of the water seemed to change from turquoise to deep blue.

'On the near bank, a small sailing ship was moored. The bugle must have sounded from there. I was taken down to the ship where I was met a man of medium height clad in the same rough, stained clothes and black boots and with an identical regulation moustache as the others. I was certain that in the tiny box cabin, there would be hanging an old wooden musket.

'The vessel had a single, large sail and its prow curved upwards almost in the shape of a scimitar, so that it reminded me of one of those pictures of ancient Greek ships I had seen in picture-books as a child. As the hull coursed through the waves, I let my arm hang over the side and felt the spray leap up onto my fingers. I tasted the water. It was fresh and clean and I scooped some up and drank. I could have drunk the lake. The men were laughing and pointing at me. First the obsolete muskets and now the archaic ship; I felt as though I coursing back in time.

'There were some islets in the lake and we avoided those, but after about an hour of rapid sailing along the keel of the wind, I saw that we were approaching a larger island with a jetty, where we moored. I was soon treading a path that led up a steep hill which turned gradually into a small mountain. The peak was of that grey stone which is the natural bedrock in those parts. Flaky, yet very hard.

'Eventually we came to a ruined church, octagonal in shape. I had spotted similar buildings when I had been brought by horse-drawn truck across the wastes of Erzurum to the prison-camp, but this was by far the largest and most ornate. The stone was decorated with elegant carvings of beasts, both real and mythical, and long, curling fronds of exotic flora. These old churches had been built of white sandstone, quite different from the indigenous slate. We stood before a wooden door, carved across its entire surface with exotica. The ship's captain produced a large, pig-iron key from his greatcoat. At first, the door would not open and four men had to lean their combined weight against its bulk before the hinges began to creak.

'It was cool inside, and musty. A few small animal skeletons littered the stone flags before the altar. The men removed these with incongruous reverence. They indicated that I should sit on the uppermost step and then, without a word, either to me or to one another, they left, closing the heavy door behind them with considerably less difficulty than it had taken them to swing it open. It closed with a finality which made my heart quiver. Their footsteps receded up the mountain path and then there was almost complete silence. Almost, because from outside the church came a choir of birdsong. I had never heard so many different tones.

'I wondered how the dead animals had managed to enter, given that the stained glass of the windows was intact. I wondered whether there might be a cellar, with a drain or suchlike. But if they had managed to get in, how had they been trapped here on the stone flags? I shuddered, drew my arms around myself and pushed the thought from my mind. There, in the strange, eight-sided church, I was completely alone. Apart, that is, from the pictures.

'Behind the altar and that at the opposite end of the nave, the walls were covered with frescos. At first, I thought these were the usual stylised Byzantine images, for the sunlight which penetrated the stained glass illuminated only small sections at any one time. As I gazed more closely, I began to make out other images. The bearded faces of Saints Cyprian and Cornelius and the bleeding, disembodied, yet grimly smiling caput of Cecilia all hung suspended from a great arc which billowed backwards into the stone, an omphalos whose peak was not visible in the fresco. The right eye of Saint Cyprian seemed especially black and hollow and I remembered those old mystery-books where just such a hollow was actually a spy-hole. That made me wish for a torch that I could shine up into the face of the converted magician of Antioch, to prove that the eye had a socket!

'Between the religious icons were mythical beasts and flora similar to those which had been carved into the stone walls of the church. There was something about the lines and curves made by the bodies of these animals which seemed to resonate with the arched brows of the saints and with the whole structure of the building. It was strange that I should have been receptive to such things; after all, I was half-starved and hadn't had much more than a sip of water since I had been frog-marched from the prison-camp, which even though I had been there for so long, now seemed a world away.

'I did not even consider attempting escape; surely if there had been a way out of there, then those poor beasts would have found it. And even supposing I had managed somehow to wriggle out of the church, where would I have gone? The island had seemed utterly deserted, and the vessel that brought me there must have left hours ago. Yet in that ancient space, an immense sense of peace descended upon me. I could feel its weight press down on my shoulders and on the muscles of my scalp, my brow, my eyelids, which seemed, then, to bear the same brushstrokes as those of the saints.

'I awoke with my tongue fixed hard against my palate, my head pounding and one side of my body frozen. In the trenches and in the prison camps, it had never been completely dark. The lamps would shine upwards from the trench-lines, creating the eerie effect of a fire in a burning grave. Which I suppose is exactly what those damned places were. And the camp guards had always kept torches burning around the perimeter, to prevent anyone getting any ideas about slipping out. I had forgotten just how dark it gets in the countryside. I grew up in the heart of the country but only a few months of war made me into a different person; even my memories had changed, some slipping away, while others fashioned themselves into great idols in my consciousness.

'Only a wan light staved off pitch darkness. I could make out the darkened glass of the windows, but could see nothing of the pictures which they bore, nor any details of the wall-frescos. I rose stiffly to my feet. I had no memory of falling asleep. The last thing I could remember was gazing up at Saint Cecilia, right into those doe-brown eyes of hers. There had been something cold and distant about the beatified ones. I had seen so many men perish without meaning in the mud of Flanders, Alsace, Thrace. The old masters knew that we are born into air, we dwell here, perhaps we spawn, then we die. To attribute individuality or significance to this husk of flesh is hubris. They knew romantic love to be little more than a conjoining of lust and the sublimated infantile need to be taken into the warmth of another being. That was all. Their saints were appropriately distant, emotionless; sometimes a half-smile might play about the lips of the female ones, yet when one glanced back at the image, the smile would be gone.

'I needed water. If I didn't get water, I would die. I had one more day, perhaps two, then I would slip by degrees into unconsciousness. I found the font by touch. I turned my wrists with the thumbnails facing forwards along the rim so that I would be able to pull myself back up when I had finished drinking. Closed my eyes. Bent down. Let my head sink into the bowl.

'Dust. I spat. The foul taste of something dead. Feathers, hair. I spat again. The font was empty. Had been, for years. It had become a place where small animals came to die. I felt that I would vomit, but did not even have the strength.

'Now my spirits sank lower than ever and my mind became utterly flat. I cannot say that I was depressed; in those days, no-one used the word. I had become incapable of feeling, or thinking, anything. Inasmuch as being consists of an idea propelled by desire and directed by the will, in that deserted church on an uninhabited island in the vast desolation of eastern Anatolia, the being known as John Rotherfield was an emptied cup.

'I lay on the stone flags and gazed up at the chapel roof. My eyes must have become accustomed to the near-darkness, for now I saw that, like the walls, the arches and beams of the roof had been carved in the shapes of exotic birds and beasts and other semi-mythical beings. The tiredness which for so long had remained incipient became overwhelming. My eyelids slipped shut and I fell into dreams seamed through with some elusive logic.

'I moved through several layers. In the first, the images and feelings were disordered fragments of my journey to this place: the man on the ridge at Gallipolli, my bandit escorts, the grey mountain peaks, the turquoise lake, the dark confines of the prison-camp, the red-and-black hell of the trenches. Images of the trenches had pursued my nights unremittingly for months on end. Now they were muted, as though I had not been personally involved. It was like watching a silent, monochrome newsreel.

'Gradually these visions faded away and in their place, came sensations from home, from this land of ours. Its bubbling streams, long grass burned by the English sun to a ripe gold, the sound of a wooden boat rocking against a decaying wharf. The smell of lichen and moss, the taste of barley in the wind after the scythe-men had swept through the fields, the incomparable bruising of the plough against one's shoulder, the smooth frequency of its transfiguring violation of the soil. The feel of the hot sky on the skin of my back. The smell of sweat. The sound of a jig eddying from across the valley. The groan of a tree as it falls to the ground. Yes, and you, Edward, long before you became a vicar of Christ, your face, that smile of yours, intense, yet shifting. And Caroline, in the days when she was beyond beauty, in a place where love can draw a man into a terror from which he must either escape and never return, or else to which he must succumb wholly, body, mind and soul. The silence which was in her. Her serenity.

'And it was in this almost angelic form that she descended upon me, that day, in that ancient church. From the roof of the place, she descended upon me as a fearsome archangel of light, like Michael of the Sword, or the one who was greater than Michael. All I could hear was the sound of monks chanting in some ancient Germanic tongue.

'When I awoke, it was still night. A moon must have risen, because the whole interior of the church was clearly visible. I was so weak and cold that I could not have moved from where I lay and so I simply gazed up at the scene which unfolded above me. Now, instead of the carvings, there was an enormous map. It was not that the gargoyles and other strange creatures, the fronds, fruits and flowers had vanished; they were there as solidly as before, but the lines and curves, the slopes and dingles formed by their solidity now seemed to lift from the dark surfaces of the wooden beams and to form a hovering structure of its own, separate from the roof. It was an ancient map, drawn in the manner of those times when the un-known stretches were marked with incendiary dragons and horn'd beasts of the sea. And as the giant chart seemed to occupy the entire church, it also came to fill my motionless body. The lines drawn upon the stone by my arms and legs and by the arcs of my skull and ribs and pelvis and the shadowy notion, around these, of my flesh, all of it had become merely a part of the great cartograph which had descended as though from the night sky.

'Through the door of the church flowed the River Rother, its source lost in darkness, while above the altar lay the Hills above Arun Water. The stone convolutions around the chancel rose window now marked the sea-shore of my beloved English Channel. There were no towns on this map, no signs of human activity. I became part of the map of Old Sussex. Saelig Sussex. The Holy Land of the South Saxons. And within the contours of this land, along the banks of its rivers, upon the slopes of its hills, amongst the broken scree of its shore, there lay the patterns of my life, the architec-ture of my being. In the rocks of this unbroken, holy earth, there breathed the music of empty space.

'And then, as I faded once again into a fitful sleep and into the sound of chanting, the map, the roof, became the face of Caroline. She was the reason I had ended up in that place. It was for the love of her I went to war, willing to give up my life because I knew that I would never be able to dwell within the beauty of her being. You, Edward, had poisoned everything that once existed between us.

'Now she came to me, no longer the Caroline of flesh-and-blood, nor yet the Caroline of my dream. I cannot explain this: it was her, and yet it was not her. It might have been the face of any woman, in any time. Can you understand that? It was like one of those faces of the Madonna. They must have belonged to real women, yet they seem so stylised and anonymous.

'Afterwards, when I wondered whether I might have hallucinated the whole episode, it came to me that Caroline's face – the face, Edward, that you and I both knew so well – had become synonymous with... no, had become indistinguishable from the beatified visage of Saint Cecilia of Callistus. This was the presence I felt there, those were the arms which bore me to a side-chapel where I was given small amounts of water and later, bread and cheese.

'When finally I awoke, three days and nights had passed since I had been brought to the church. I was rescued by some Laz fishermen who had spotted a light in the church and decided to investigate. In my very broken Turkish, I learned that when the first two men had pushed open the narthex door, they saw a woman's figure bending over my body. However, as soon as they had moved into the nave, they saw that it had been an illusion created by the position of the altar, combined with the reflection of the moon on the gold of the mosaics.

'I stayed in the Laz village until I grew strong enough to travel. Then, riding on a mule, I trekked across the lower slopes of the Caucasus Mountains until I reached the Aras River. There I was yet again held by a small group of Turkish soldiers, who fancied themselves as border guards. I was eventually rescued by some fleeing White Russians. My Turkish guards thought that they had come to attack the imploding Empire and so they ran away – presumably unaware that Lenin had pulled Russia out of the war. It was chaos. The Russians insisted that I accompany them through the snows and wastes of eastern Anatolia and help with menial tasks. The officers reminded me of ballet-dancers left hopelessly down on their luck, while the men had those rugged, determined faces one saw, much later, on Bolshevik stamps. In their eyes, they held the dusty madness of vast empty spaces. They were not Royalists – only a few months earlier, they had taken part in the February Revolution – but they had been forced out of their army units by the Bolsheviks.'

'I know this story,' Edward said, 'all except for the mysterious bearded man and the church on the island. I can't think why you haven't mentioned them before.'

'I have not yet told you all that I know. It is mine to tell, and I will tell it in my time.'

'Go on then.'

'After six months or so, I crossed the English Channel. The Armistice had been signed some weeks earlier by the same epauletted fools who had started it all in the first place. When I got home, everything had changed.' Rotherfield shot Edward a bitter look.

'She did grieve for you.'

'She married the lawyer, far more suitable than a lowly woodcutter, I'm sure you and her father agreed there!'

'What could she have done? She thought you were dead.'

'And she didn't marry you.'

'She never loved me.'

'But you encouraged her to marry the lawyer.'

'I wanted nothing but her happiness.'

'You wanted to make certain that if I did return, she would be beyond my reach. If you couldn't have her, I wasn't going to have her either. You couldn't bear the thought of her giving her love to anyone else. And perhaps she was afraid of your intensity, your possessiveness. The lawyer was an easy way out, for her and for you.'

'Those were difficult times, John.'

'During those two long years, I constantly asked myself why I had not died like the others. I dreamed of her hair, like wheat, falling around my shoulders. The sapphire of her eyes hunted the sleep from my brain and I would hear her voice in the song-patterns of the rain. I could trace out her features in the sky. Yet she wasted no time. And you encouraged her. You opened the way.'

The breeze got up and flipped over some of the pages of the book.

'You were my only friends. You and she.'

'You wished your friend dead.'

'Never.'

'Look into my eyes and tell me that. Put your hand on your holy book and swear to the god whom you believe died for you, and tell me that. And tell her, too.'

The breeze sifted through more of the pages and Reverend Synnott reached over and picked up the book. Steadying his left hand against the edge of the table, with his right he flicked through chapter after chapter, not really reading any of the words. The movement of the pages seemed to him like the motion of birds' wings.

Without raising his eyes, he spoke nervously.

'I will do no such thing. The very fact that you doubt me... You've never said these things before in all these years. I am not perfect. I never pretended that I was.'

There was a lull, which seemed to both men somehow unnatural, until they realised that the daytime birds had fallen silent and the night birds had not yet arisen. Rotherfield refilled his own glass and swigged down the draught.

To occupy this silence, and because he could think of nothing better to do, Edward began to read again.

The next set of manuscripts were discovered by the author near the base of the pyramidal tomb and had been somewhat damaged by moisture rising from the earth. Moreover, since they were of vellum, they had begun to swell and putrefy, so that as they were removed (with the greatest of care and attention), they resembled nothing more than those ballooning pantaloons known as 'galligaskins' which swath'd the hips of the fashionable around the year 1600. Such observation is notable in this context because the forthcoming section of text, although penned in archaic Black Letter, was created within the desmesne of that era.

Tis pon the first day of May's ship
That lovers fair do dance and drink
Of nectar rose and mandrake form
And with joyfull sadness through mother's belly
The dead raise hands in adze blade:
One sawyer, joined by a second, becometh oratory!

Then in southerly parts by Englande's white shore
A gentle man doth pine by window-frame
For the maiden whose feet doth seam cross stone and sand
And whose smile like lune, half-risen, doth clasp his soul
In bounteous torment.
Yet like the moon, she flieth far beyond his grasp
And ever will remain so, till Day of Doom come to pass.

IN THE LASTE yeare of the reign of Goode Queene Bess, moste deare depart'd from this toil'd earth, didst live in landes to south of Wywurth one Lord Thomas Birkin. Lord Thomas, fair-of-face and scion of baronet, a man pass'd youth yet in action aged not, was not bethroth'd for reason of his master's debts. Lord Thomas dwelt within the pages of his books, the loose scrolls of manuscripts anciente and of planns formulated by the hands of monks long-earth'd. His hair grew wild and he lived on stale ale and currants red and blacke, and stole the occasional hog from the merchant farmer whose lande adjoined that of his lord. Thomas was wont to pass many a night singing, with voice more beauteous than that of the galingale, in the long gallerie of his father's mansion. One such evening, Anne, the daughter of Caburn the Joyner, was passing by.

'What's this I hear?' she said, in voice low and strong. 'A nightjar, or a thorn'd breast? Tis hard to tell, in these days of vers'd love. The young lord must be in love's state most dire, yet his his love hath no object, his adze no timber to carve. What if I, like feather into pillow, mighte slip myself into his inner courte. Then mighte we be recompens'd for the day when the Baronet Birkin did caste from the lande our familie and many another whose forebears' bones have lain within't since ancient times. This loss hath plagued my deare father and made our lives vinegar and pewter. T'would indeed be a revenge grac'd with winter parlour galingale and metheglin!'

Scheming so, did Anne secrete her load of forest gatherings and contrive to porte herself, barefoot, to the lower roof of the Birkin mansion, where she didst proceed to dance in manner moste elegant and when through his fulle glass window, the Lord Birkin did spie her, he did grow transfix'd. With a great sigh did he thrust open the window and resume his song and though Anne did spie her long-haired lord she did assume that pretence of blindness which joyners' daughters porte like woollen biggen and with arm arch'd long akin to yew bow, did she lifte the white cap from her pate and fling it in direction of its moon simulacrum. Her hair was longe and blacke and curious combed and plaited and flowed about her person as the waves of the night sea. Grammar, logic, rhetoric – trivium all – and yet more, arithmetic, geometry, astronomy, music, quadrivium moste fine, all of these did shifte within the breaste of the unshaven Thomas. From that moment on, he resolved to dwelle within the love of this faery, to raise oak pon stone base, to seed garth among rank weed and with everie breath, to turn the great wheele of the post mill in the compass of the stars.

When he ope'd his eyes, the forme moste delirious had vanished and the nighte was blacker than ever. Yet within the longe gallerie of his forefathers, Thomas Birkin was akin to flame or sea-gust. He left his manuscripts as they lay, pon the broad hardbeam, went back to his bed-chamber from whence he gathered up his chattels and made off into the foreste of the May nighte.

But she was gone into air, and gaze as he mighte pon the flat spann of the foreste lake, Thomas could not conjure the face of the one he loved, any more than he might the words of the dead. The whole of the nighte did he sojourn there, yet she did not return and as dawn's mournful light waxed over the lande, the lord's son return'd unto his chamber where he slumber'd, restless and alone.

The next nighte, he did hang pon the likeness of her forme, gazing and singing into ayre's darkness over the empty roof till the moon had set behind the brow of the hill. For hours longe did fine Thomas tarry, sat pon the great chimney stack, yet still no sign of his belov'd; not e'en the faintest breath rippl'd through night's skin. The young lord was newly fayre shav'n and bedeck'd withe pokestick cambric, perfum'd leather cloak and heel'd shoes of the newest kinde, readied for to dance to the rosin'd wheele of the heavens. Just when he felt sleep rush over his mind, there stood his love of one globe turn. The joyner's daughter appeared to him as a bud from the lower garths of paradise.

'Thou art the moste perfecte being,' he said aloud.

'Sir,' she gave reply, 'how canst thou saye such a thing, for I am onlie the joyner's daughter and my mother was the daughter of the miller who dwelleth in the wheeling oak poste-mill. The winds have not filled her sails for many a year and we are off to the filthe and labyrinth of the towne, in quest if not for silver, then at leaste for pewter's bite. You, sir, are a noble lord.'

'I care not, good lady, for the stops and kayles of this world, nor for farthingales and fore-smocks. Verily. I would make common cause with a joyner's daughter or a millers' grand-daughter, if you be she, as I would with mine owne salvation.'

The Maid Anne took Lord Birkin's hand and they did dance for hour-upon-hour as the moon rose and fell and still they danc'd, 'The Lusty Gallante', 'The Pepper's Blacke' and 'The Shakinge of the Sheets' until the verie stars in the firmament didst gather together closer than is naturale in these times and confere as in manner of old. The laste dance they did dance was 'The Vicar of St Fool's'.

The air was warm and hour-by-hour did they dance off their accoutrements until they were bared to the nighte, and still they danced. The maid's hair, which at first trip had been curl'd high and dressed with bejewell'd caul and French hoode, now windblowne and free, wove about her neck and shoulders. And her Lord's long hair mingled in manner moste strange with that of his angel. Any evil thoughte in their beings was drawen out, good and true, by the fire which swept o'er them. And they were like the seeds of the fig-tree spawn'd by Solomon's Brothers. And with the rootes of the figgy green tree, their love grew along paths moste dark and unknow'd e'en to themselves. The wartes of their soules were pierced as though by lances; the boulders of their guts were rolled into sand; the sap colours of their heart, wound longe pon the skins of young bulls, told of plays and tales and poemes of love and death and musick. Then they lay together beneath the heavens and she remember'd her scheme and he, his vellum, but yet they did bring those geometers to minde merely as past course, longe caste asunder from the mainmast of the vessel pon which they did sail. From the Great Hall of the house, did they hear musick of kinde moste exquisite and beauteous, a fantasie issuinge forth from the stringes and tunnels of lute, pandora, cittern, recorder and viol, as composed by those archangels of Orpheus, Byrd, Bull and Gibbons. And as the lovers felt the musick in their bodies, they fancied they could heare, issuinge from far off on the foreste lake, the cry of a white swann. And then the sounde of the instruments faded, for though moste fayre and beauteous, all such are merely tools carv'd pon th'ends of fingers imperfect, while the voice of man or beaste be created in miraculous manner moste true by the breath of Almightie God. And so, as dawn's pale sword emerg'd from the blacke waters of the voide, so did there strike up a swann madrigal such as had ne'er before been heard, and Thomas turn'd towardes his dream of twin nightes and address'd her, thus:

'Mie love, thou art indeede a flow'ring garden, come late to mie life.
So it is I wonder if in truthe, whether this existence
hath reach'd its apogee and my soule returnst unto Paradise bosom.'

And she didst replie:

'My lorde and master, it doth render great joye unto the bosom
of this poor and rankl'd place in which thou hast dwelt
A love moste pure and goode that swanns unblemish'd
Do wake before God's allotted hour and sing His praise
As though t'were our Spem in alium.'

His surprise was yet of no-surprise:

'How com'st thou, a simple tradesman's daughter,
To know of Tallis and musick that twere compos'd some fifty years to thy rear?'

She laughed the laugh of a joyner's scion and to him replied:

'Sir, tis thine owne musick that doste sweet'n my rear
And raise the ayre of our union to madrigal of all nature.'

And Lord Thomas didst engage withe her in this manner:
   'But what evil, my love, can there be in this, thy breast of rime pure
   Caste from Heav'n's frame?'
And she turn'd away her fine-bon'd face as poste-mill spun pon breeze,
   'I cannot saye that which has slow'd in oxbow dregs
   To pile as weed and murd'rous stem
   For the joyner's daughter would ne'er breathe ill pon thy fayre
   countenance
   Any more than she would pon her babe, not yet borne.'
He pulled her forme towardes his lips, but not for kisses sweet.
   'Tis good, thou speaketh in ayre and madrigal, and not in riddle and
   maze moste devilish,
   For tis the wierd of a good man to lose track and rope to Paradise
   When caressed in th'arms of a counterfeit!'
She spake through stale ale breeze, which caused his bodie to shiver and
shudder:
   'I am no simulacrum, mie goode lorde! My love for thee is true!'
   And he in loving embrace did gather her tresses,
   Blacke and twyn'd like bend and flow of stream moste ancient,
   And whisper'd such wordlings in her lug that she didst blush and
   tremble
   Since the memorie of her maidenhood was set in vellum muscle of her
   heart,
   And Goode Anne of the Poste-Mill did lifte herself, more seraphim
   than succubous
   And rais'd her throate, her mane, like laste of Philomele, jug, jug, tereu!
   So that all the byrdes of foreste and lake did awaken and flutter and
   dart, blood-red
   Around the rose-stemmed limbs of the two whose breathe and beat
   like leaf and stem
   Didst arise but from one source, one quill:
   Remember nothing but this: That o'er the tenebrous waves of death's
   longe river
   There are many burninge lamps which light the waye; yet none is
   greater
   Than the lighte of the sky which doth proclaim the olde at an ende
   And the rise of Love's Queendom pon all, stone and glistening lip of
   daye.'
And so singing, they didst love again as the lande didst awaken into breathe

and songe of summer's morn, after which, to scape arch'd houndes and falcones of the hunte so plann'd, she didst hasten away. The next nighte, the third of those related in this passage, the Goode Maid Anne did not come to the Lorde Birkin, though once, as midnight struck iron, he did fancie that he smell'd her skin, like flower'd verse of poesy petal, brush gainst his nare. Nor did she come unto him on the next yet, nor the one after that, and he grew thin and lived once again in his bed-chamber, but now he hadst not e'en his manuscripts from which to drawe succour. As winter fell upon the lande of Sussex, so did the foreste lake by Jacob's Poste freeze o'er and when the bedraggl'd lorde didst venture one morn to walk pon the water of the pond, he sat and brushed away the powder of snow and he remembered the nighte he had danced with the maid moste fayre and he remembered her skin which was softe as the snow pon his and he caste in minde her e'en which were bluer than the face of the winter sky mirror'd in the lake. He broughte to minde the legend of Birkin Hall, which tolde of a skulle most horride that did emerge from the old priesthole on certain nightes, but onlie to those besott'd heavily with the musk of love, those drawn upwards in tall reveries of musick, or else those verie neare to deathe, the three states thus apportion'd being closer to one another than skin be to bone. The skulle was said to be that of some longe-dead priest, or monk, or such-like fiend! Thank God! Master Thomas had never set een pon said white ball caput. He gazed at the heavens and then sighed and his sigh blew yet more snow off the clear ice of the pond. He glanced downe into the darkness of the lake. Rising from the darkness, as on that first nighte of May, he saw her face, whiter than ever before, rising towards his. And beside her face was another, smaller, hairless, and by the cup o' Chanctonbury, the tiny face was that of Thomas Birkin. And verily, his twin love didst make its lips into the shape of a smile, in manner moste akin to that of a lady.

Author's note: Anne the Joyner's Daughter went from that place and sat by the forest lake, gazing into the water as dawn filtered across the sky. Soon after, she found that she was great with child and some months later, she went to live with her grandfather, the miller, and her child was born into this world of betrayals.

Though nightly he waited upon his roof and many times sat by the pond during the years that followed, Lord Thomas Birkin never again saw the joiner's daughter.

In his dotage, when Master Cromwell's Roundheads came to sack what was left of Birkin Mansion, they found him naked and almost blind, lying half-dead by the window of his bed-chamber, clutching a bundle of dirty rags. When their New Model Commander investigated further, he found, wrapped in the bundle of rags, a lock of fine, black hair which was not dirty at all, but gleaming and fresh as the night it had been severed. The old man gazed up at the cuirass'd Roundhead Officer and thought he saw something familiar to his recognition, but though he tried hard, he could not make out the face.

The vicar laid down the book.

'I think it's time we parted for the night.'

Rotherfield shook his head, slowly.

'I want to hear more and besides, I want to pluck and eat a fig or two.'

'The fig-tree is out of season,' Edward said, 'has been, for years.'

But already, Rotherfield had arisen and stepped outside the gate. For a minute or so he remained out of sight behind the high stone wall, searching the wizened branches for fruit.

The Reverend Edward Synnott leaned back against the wicker of his chair and closed his eyes. The port had mulled itself through the fibres and convolutions of his brain so that behind his clasped lids, he felt a sensation like mild giddiness, a subtle shift in space and time which one might feel in the midst of a dream. From somewhere in the forest came the high-pitched warbling of a nightingale. His ears had grown accustomed to the noises of the woods, the steady, pulsatile flow of the river and the soft friction of the leaves, the random interruptions by owls, nightjars and sleek-backed rodents scurrying through the undergrowth. He had sat on this chair each evening and listened for close on fifty years. The sequence of notes varied, subtle differences growing as the night wore on, until it was these unrepeated tones, and his silent anticipation of their arrival, that came to define the entire symphony. And tonight, Edward felt that the substance of his brain had grown to be like that of an animal and that he was receptive to absolutely everything that was occurring, or even which might yet occur, within the body of the forest. Night was his time. The separate tenebrosities held between the pages of the books in his library, each one an individual darkness, or the silent wind within an organ-pipe, or the unseen whorl in the wood of a living tree. They had sung to one another all night, yet somewhere in that warm August blackness Edward had lost the other two, had lost them forever.

And it had been as though he had lost his own soul.

'See – I found some! Three, actually; small, but definitely edible.'

Rotherfield was standing above him, his six-foot frame blanking out the constellations.

The figs were the size of nightingale's heads, and livid green as though the inner substance of the fruit had been sucked through the integument. Without thinking, Edward accepted one. It felt soft and downy in his palm and through the skin it was as if he detected a faint pulse. He dismissed the thought.

'You're sure it's alright to eat?'

Rotherfield made no response.

Edward felt the architecture of the night becoming distinctly oppressive. Quickly, he bit into the fig.

The fruit was gritty between his teeth and tasted slightly pungent, though not unpleasantly so. He chewed slowly.

'You're not hungry?'

Rotherfield shook his head.

'I want to hear the next section. I want to hear the end.'

Edward sighed and a shiver coursed through his body, which reminded him of the pressure of his back against the wood as the boat had moved gently through the black water.

'Look, why don't you read it for yourself? I'll lend it to you,' he said.

'I had my fill in Anatolia.'

'Of figs...?'

'They grew on the hillsides. The White Russian platoon virtually lived on them. That, flat-bread and yoghurt.'

'There are worse things to live on.'

'I followed the man with the face.'

'Man with the face...?'

'I tracked down the address on the card he gave me to a derelict house on a backstreet of Constantinople. The door had not been securely fastened and I broke in without difficulty. It was one of those tall buildings with a central courtyard and barred street-windows. On the top floor I found a pile of ancient manuscripts written in languages I had no hope of comprehending.'

'The tongues of the dead sing on through eternity.'

'Somehow, I knew with certainty that these drawings and texts represented the combined wisdom of Alexandria and Baghdad. The Bibliothèque of Baghdad, with its twelve thousand volumes, much of the learning of the ancient and mediaeval worlds, was flooded by the terrible nicor, the brother of the first and greatest of the Mongol Khans, and a sizeable proportion of the people of that city having sought refuge in the subterranean plexus, suffered the same fate as their books. I could see all this in the old vellum manuscripts, just as I had seen the map of my homeland in the dark roof-beams of that octagonal church on the island. I resolved to remove these manuscripts to a safe place known only to myself. I knew that I had been guided here for a purpose. The last page I looked at bore the semblance of a face which I felt I had known for thousands of years. It was the face of Sinan the Architect, who centuries earlier had built mosques in the shape of poems. Seeing his imprint there, in the filtered half-light which rose from the surface of the Bosphorus waters, I understood that I, too was part of a long poem, of whose verses I would only ever catch faint glimpses.

'The number of manuscripts was so great, I decided to return the next day with cart and horse. Which I did. But I was unable to find the house again. Perhaps it had never existed. I scoured the streets of Constantinople, but found not a trace of those miraculous drawings, musical notations and Dark Letter texts which I had touched with my own hands. I had now lost two loves in my life, and wandered through the city streets of Old Byzantium, half-crazed on aniseed liquor, until I collapsed from total exhaustion. I awoke, days later, in a madrasah, where the students did their best to heal me.

'The day before I was due to leave, they took me into a room without windows, empty except for a life-size brass head. They said it was a replica of the head of Khizr-the-Green, who had only ever appeared in spirit form to poets, saints and prophets. And there, before my eyes, they performed some incantations and they made the head talk. The language was Turkish, so I got a few words. A noun, a verb, a phrase, nothing coherent. Something about a mill shaped like a mosque and a long ship and a lake.'

'How odd.' Edward looked sceptical.

'I know what I experienced. It was something from ancient times. The brass head was hairless. It opened its eyes and parted its brass lips and talked for about twelve hours; it emerged from silence in daylight and when it sank back again into dumb metal it was day once more. This was no dream, nor anything I previously had understood as reality.'

This last was uttered in a whisper and now Rotherfield paused and closed his eyes. Edward could see the globes slip and dance beneath the skin of the lids, so that after a while, each began to resemble a tiny brass head. And then the whole integument seemed to be inordinately stretched across the bone of the woodcutter's skull and his silvery hair was akin to strands growing lank from the scalp of a corpse. Edward shuddered and blinked to dispel the image. When he looked again, Rotherfield was staring at him.

'I live with this knowledge, that once I touched upon the greatest of all treasures, the language which lies beneath all languages, and that its secrets are lost to me. I have cut wood since that day. I have searched for the beauty of line and the music that lies in the creation of silence. I have searched for love through other means. So read on, and since you are in part the cause of all of this, then sing the words which the author of this small tome has penned; whether they be false or true, we will listen.'

The vicar's face grew pale as the falling moon. Automatically, he picked up the book and began to intone the words which his eyes followed, tracing out the architecture of letter, phrase, sentence, as though he were reciting a passage from the Holy Book.

He felt as if he had not space enough in his body to breathe. In the shallow boat, that night beneath the new moon, Edward Synnott held his breath until the moment he knew that he would burst into fragments of himself and scatter across the streams and forests and lakes of old Sussex. And as for the other two, since he could no longer see them, he listened for the sound of their breathing. He became dizzy and fell asleep and when he awoke, his companions had gone. He rode on the current until he spotted an oxbow and steered towards it, using the small tiller at the stern. He was about to leap out of the boat onto the dry bank, when he heard a sound coming from the river. Afterwards he thought it had sounded more like a song but at the time he wasn't certain. He had thrust his body back down into the stinking belly of the boat, the better to listen.

This is the account given by a certain Curate Johnson of the village of Wywurth regarding an incident which was said to have occurred, during the late summer in the Year of Our Lord, 1881. The original manuscript was discovered in an empty bottle of porter found at low tide, lodged in one of the sea-caves, which, once every twelve hours, form the most extrematous parts of this ancient land of Sussex. At first, though no liquid was found in the bottle, the ink seemed to have faded away, so that to the curator of the local history museum the yellowed paper resembled vellum. When placed in complete darkness, however (and this is attested to by the curator, three Parish Councillors and the Grand Master of Wywurth Masonic Lodge), the ink, which later was found to have been drawn somehow from the sap of the fig-tree, gradually became visible once again; and thus was the account deciphered and committed to print by these officials. Oddly, when the scroll was subjected to daylight, or even to artificial light, the writing evanesced again, only to re-appear when placed in the dark room.

'That cannot be,' cut in Rotherfield. 'How could they have read it, if they were in complete darkness?'

The vicar shrugged.

'Perhaps one of them was blind, and could decipher the course of the ink by touch.'

'Hah! Very likely! Typical theological dissimulation.'

'Shall I continue?'

'Yes, yes. Go on.'

The manuscript remained in Wywurth Local Museum until 1940 when, as a matter of security, it was removed to a place unknown. Since the related paperwork was destroyed during the war, the fate of the so-called Saelig Manuscript (sometimes also known as The Daughter of the Wind) is now unknown. There have been reported sightings from as far afield as Azerbaijan, Pantelleria and Odessa, but the author has no means of verifying these alleged sightings. The sections which appear in this book constitute, in part, translated copies from the original manuscript, but since the author was unable to complete this process, he has had to rely on his memory and on accounts related to him by various country folk. Unreliable as they may be, they are reproduced in seamless manner, because the author believes that oral histories hold deeper truths than it has ever been possible to apprehend through the written word.

I, WHO DO go by the name of Henry Francis Johnson, am curate of this ancient parish to the good vicar known around these parts (and no doubt also in the parts hereabouts) as 'the hunting parson', the Reverend Brightling Fulthrope. I am not an educated man, that is, I am not overly-educated like our good Vicar Fulthrope, yet I did attend the Dame School and am school'd by mine own good hand, and I do know of life's viccissitudes to the span of any man in this short sparrow's flutter. Herein does this poor, mortal hand relate a tale of absolute and wondrous verity which did manifest as happenings one summer's night and day, some seven years ago this Lammas.

A sight most common around these parts is that of a tallship wi' top-gallants fluttering along the line of the horizon like the great wings of an albatross. In one day's span, they cross the edge of our world and then vanish as though they had never been. On this Lammas Eve of which I write, the wind had dropped so low that the sea was more akin to lake than ocean. It was as though for the full twenty-four hour, the incoming tide did not turn. The ship sailed in the Devil's direction, from west to east, but barely had it reached one third of the way across this line of coast, when it seemed becalmed and moved no more.

I was busy attending to St Cuthman's. The tower was the oldest part of the building and had carried heavenwards the prayers of thousands of folk, rich, poor, learned and illiterate; it had survived Dissolution and Reformation, Civil War and the shadow of Boney's fleet. But now, without the attention of a master stonemason, there was little doubt that it would not retain its current form beyond the end of this century. The bells, in particular, were in dire need of repair; they had been forged of iron in Saxon times and the metal was very near rusted away, so that the danger (should the ringers be bursting with barrel liquor) of their coming loose and tumbling upon all and sundry was not so very far from truth's oratory.

Though the shadows were growing long over our small parish, the wind still had not got up and the sea remained becalmed. As I walked towards my humble dwelling at the opposite pole of the village from St Cuthman's, I saw that the ship had moved not one half of a degree, compass-wise, along the horizon. However, it seemed larger than before and this seemed strange to me, until I realised that in the absence of a prevailing wind, the incoming tide was drawing the vessel straight towards the shore. Though there was no breeze and the Lammas Eve remained warm, yet as I gazed across the darkening waters, I shivered.

I have never married and next Gooding Day, God-willing, shall I reach my sixtieth year. Unless there be a drowning haar over the coast, from the back window of my house it is possible to make out on the Great Hoe, the Giant Man of the White Way, carved by some pagan ancestor of ours in a time before books, perhaps even before words. To my front is nowt but the sea and the invisible darkness of the French coast. Oftentimes, on Figgy Sunday or All Saints' Eve, have I knelt and prayed out-of-doors, facing southwards, I know not why, and sometimes, though my eyes be closed and my palms clasped in reverence of our Saviour, yet I find that I can see, as through an elder copse, things which in this physical world of ours remain invisible. On one such night, I did see the Bendin-in of the great mackerel nets. Though, in my reverie, Vicar Fulthrope did bless those nets and the fishermen who cast them on the waves, yet the corks which kept the long webs afloat and concertina'd through the water, all of a sudden changed into bones. The mackerel, which danced in the thousand, turned from silver to red and the bread, cheese and beer of celebration lay uneaten on the beach.

The very next day, a great storm did blow up and all but one of the fishing-boats sank, with the loss of twenty men, some of whom had reached to within a few yards of the shoreline. Though God be in everything, yet sometimes, I think that the sea is without God. Please do not suppose that I myself am mired in those peasant fears which, this past fifty year or more, have been banished from the heads at least of those who have letter. Though I be but a lowly official in this very ancient Church, I am yet one for science and the new ways of thinking: I have seen too many of our poorer folk shackled like pack animals to superstitions. I carry no shepherd's crown in my pocket. On no occasion have I so much as drawn breath on these matters in the presence of the Reverend Fulthrope, who is most opposed to such wantonness of the spirit in his parishioners. All is best left to the Almighty, who will see all books balance justly on the Ultimate Day. Nonetheless, as I listened to the water lapping on the stony shore, I fancied that I could make out the creaking of the ship's ropes and timbers and I had the queerest apprehension of some dreadful misadventure hanging like the shadow of the new moon. I drew my cassock around my waist and hurried home and drank a jug of hot, spiced ale, that my sleep pass without fancy.

I was woken from darkness by the sound of banging. I thought one of the shutters had come loose, so in night-dress, and porting pewter-and-candle, I went out to make certain. One shutter had indeed come away from its fastening and I battened it back down. Since the night was warm and windless, it struck me as odd that a shutter should have come loose. My candle fluttered. I held my breath. A pale moth crossed my path. The sea was dark and heaving and there was no moon. I let my breath run out into the darkness. There was a hand on my shoulder. Sharp, cold, bony. I dropped the pewter. The candle rolled along the ground, came to a stop and sputtered, but did not go out. Prayer would not come. I turned around. Stepped back, a cist-length. My eyes had not yet grown accustomed to the pitch black of the night, but I was just able to see the top half of a man's face, disembodied, floating. Then I realised that a black scarf was wound around his mouth and nose. I was able to discern that he was tall, clad all in black and that his limbs hung somewhat loosely about his frame. He was slightly breathless. His hair was bound in a second scarf.

'Curate Johnson, I'm darned sorry to wake ye, sir. I didn't intend to scare ye.'

'You know my name?'

'Never mind about that, sir. Just a-mind what I say. There'll be no harm comin to thy good self nor to any body on this night's world.'

His voice was not familiar to me. I know all the parishioners of Wywurth and most of them in the hamlets round abouts, too and yet, there was something about his form, there, in the summer darkness…

'I knocked on thy door, good curate, but thee must've bin good and truly clasp'd in sleep's swarthy arms, for thou didst not awaken. So I was a'tryin to tap on the glass of yon window.'

'What do you want, man, at this ungodly hour?'

He stepped towards me. I moved back, but halted when I felt against my bare heels the beginnings of the slope which led from my cottage down to the sea's edge. He held up his hand.

'Don't thee fret, now. It's just we want ye to cast open the doors a' the church a' Saint Cuthman's for the night.'

'What do you want with the church? There is no lead on its roof, and precious little gold on the altar. Just a few flowers and some old hymn-books.'

'Never you mind on that. Just bring with ye the keys an come wi me.'

So I went indoors, quickly changed my clothes and drew down the heavy, iron key-ring from its hook above the fireplace.

I had taken care seldom to have been in St Cuthman's alone at night. Mark you, as I said earlier, I'm not a superstitious man, but there are limits and the brain is a funny thing once it gets going. By the Lord, even our own minds are not within our control!

The place smelt as though it had been closed, not for the few hours since I had locked up earlier that evening, but for centuries. I knew the interior of St Cuthman's like my own hand, yet somehow, on this night out-of-joint, everything seemed unfamiliar. I wondered whether I might be dreaming – the ale had been good and strong – but the night air on my face had been too real and the oak doors of the church had been still warm from the sun's touch. And there was something else. At the insistence of my 'guest' we had taken a circuitous route, skirting the field enclosures to the north. On several gateposts were hung linen bags, filled with what looked like large joints of meat and loaves of bread – freshly-baked, I could tell from the odour. My companion had removed these bags and given me some, while he carried others himself, so that by the time we reached the church we both were panting and sweating like dogs.

'I am not a young man,' I said, and sat down in the nearest pew.

How strange the place looked! The altar was half-hidden in shadow, while to north and south the transepts were carved hulking things, more Saxon in style than truly English. There had been an old Saxon church on the site of St Cuthman's, but that had been burned down during the Danish raids many centuries ago and of the original, only the tower and bells remained. No-one ever ventured up the tower after dark; apart from the rational danger of losing one's step and falling, there was a story concerning a haunting by a White Friar who was reputed to appear on particular dates in the old ecclesiastical calendar. Apparently this monk did no-one any harm, but simply wrote all night at high speed using a metal stylus or such-like. In the morning, scrolls of vellum had been found blowing across the floorboards of the belfry of the tower. I have never seen any of these; over the years, successive vicars are said to have burned them in secret. I do not believe in this rubbish, and I repeat it here merely to illustrate the point that, especially for a country person, as my companion most certainly was, to be venturing in the old church at this hour on Lammas Eve meant something very untoward was going on, here, in this village of Wywurth where I was born and where, no doubt, in the balm of the soft, sheltered soil of St Cuthman's churchyard, I shall await the universal Resurrection.

The man had not waited with me but had gone on ahead and disappeared behind the High Altar. Suddenly, there were shadows everywhere and the sound of scraping heels and, aye, in that House of God, there was cursing and taking the Name in vain. What seemed to me like hundreds of men, all garbed-up in double scarfs just as the first, were entering through the old doors and heading for the tower, the entrance to which lay behind the high altar. They carried sacks and barrels, some so bulky they had to be hoisted upon two men's shoulders, and beautiful gilt and silver caskets, the like of which I had only ever seen as a child in picture-books of fairy tales. Some of the boxes they carried had stamped on them words in a foreign-looking language. The parts of their faces that I could see were coarse and some bore terrible scars, as if from cattle-brands, across their foreheads. None acknowledged my presence – for which I was moderately grateful – and though I scrutinized them as much as I dared, I was unable to recognise any as being from hereabouts. The largest of the objects which they brought in was an ancient plough, so heavy it took fully twelve men to hoist it onto the chancel floor.

After what seemed like hours, they had all left, apart from one, the man who had made me come here. He now approached me, limping as though from some old injury.

'Good curate, sir, you are free to go – but mind, now, go only the way by which we did arrive here and at all costs avoid the main street of the village.'

I nodded and rose.

'Tomorrow – today – is Sunday,' I said. 'The bell-ringers will be up early to sound the Sabbath and Vicar Fulthrope always inspects the bells before they are rung.'

The sound of the man's laughter echoed like blasphemy through the dark stone church.

'You needs not worry about that,' he said, and though he still wore his scarf I could tell that beneath it he was grinning from ear-to-ear. 'Just say nothing to man nor beast and no harm'll come to you or to nobody. This church be a horn a'plenty!'

And so saying, he turned away.

'Wait,' I said. 'I will need to lock up. If I leave it like this, the vicar will ask questions.'

'Just go on home, Mister Curate, and remember this night as a dream. Be thankful I didn't send ye up the tower where the White Friar busies himself.'

'I don't believe in the White Friar,' I snorted. 'That's no more than a tale invented by smugglers to keep good folk away on certain nights.'

He came towards me and took hold of my collar with both hands. He was a good six inches taller than I and his breath smelled of red wine and Latakia baccy. His expression had altered. The bonhomie had vanished.

'Now, don't you go blabbin about! Don't you be a damn'd fool!'

He glanced around, as though he was aware of the blasphemy which he had just uttered and which had been absorbed into the sandstone. His next words were just as taut, but spoken in a whisper which was more like a hiss.

'In a bricked-up priest-hole at foot o' the tower, there lieth a skeleton which, come Hallows' Eve, doth talk and sing. No-one goes by the wall there. Tis said by those who sip from Chanctonbury Ring that the cold bones do converse wi' the bees and that the wing'd ones take the form of a naked young woman and dance a hornpipe on a dead elder branch to the music o' an invisible, devilish fiddle! Tis said that the Queen o' the Beggars is married on a black river barge to the King o' the Rooks and that the ghostly choirs o' Didling do sing full-throated at the walls.'

He was working himself up into a frenzy and his body was shaking all over. I noticed that he had cut himself just above the left eye. It was not a deep cut but it had bled and the blood was freshly crusted over.

'Would you let go of my coat, please?'

Slowly, he relaxed his grip. His hands fell to his sides and he slumped like a pig's bladder in that Heaven-and-Hell game where all the village fight over a ball, running and falling and wrestling for miles through the wealden clay. I knew then that he, too, was not a young man and, moreover, that he had led a life of dissolution.

'Tis harder for us land smugglers than for the ones who wade aboard ships. We are more like to be caught. There are precious few watchmen in the sea.'

'Why d'you do it?'

'There's always the possibility that we might strike gold. Besides, everyone needs to eat. E'en a curate!'

'Yes, but we all have God.'

'I never once saw God put bread into a starving bairn's mouth. Never once.'

'There are honest ways of earning a living. Millions do it.'

'Millions are slaves.'

'And you? You are free?'

He sighed, and his scarf blew outward from his face in the shape of a cloud over a hillock.

'Beneath the life which you see, there is another life and beneath that, another, and so on, until, like the great traveller, you ask yourself, what is this life, but the thinnest film on the surface of a lake, blown away as easily as by the flap of a dragonfly's wing?'

He stopped talking and the silence of the ancient church swamped everything; pews, transept, altar, vestry; and its source was the door, hidden in darkness, which led to the tower. I felt the centuries pile with the corpses into the wooden pews, those upturned faces, illumined through the bodies of stained-glass saints. Bearded Saxon kings, transported miraculously to Golgotha hill. Forgotten music lingered in the blown sand images, in the creeping of the tides, in the scratch of stylus on skin.

I whispered, 'Who are you?'

The man receded into the shadows. I wasn't sure whether it was I who had stepped back, or he who had moved closer to the altar. I could no longer make out his face.

'Yesterday, I conversed with the bees and danced with the mackerel Today, I run with the smugglers. Tomorrow, I will fight in an obscure war in some exotic land.'

'Who are you?' I repeated.

He shook his head, and went behind the High Altar.

I should have turned and left that church which once I thought I knew. I ought to have hurried back to my low cottage and closed the door against the darkness and against all of history's knowledge. I could have buried myself in dreams of another life, or of lives untold. I am a humble man, a curate of the church of St Cuthman's in the village of Wywurth in the Pevensey March of the county of Sussex. My entry is of this world and my exit shall be of the like, of that there is no doubt. Yet perhaps in the life of every man, there is a moment when thought and action become one, where matter and spirit are united for a brief shadow's span beneath the arc of a new moon. Before I could stop myself, I was tearing after him along the cold flags, some of which were the roof-stones of the hollow tombs in the undercroft, and up the tower, up the spiral staircase, now crammed almost full with boxes and crates. It took all my strength to clamber up to the top of the tower. I pushed open the door to the belfry and then, barely pausing to catch my breath, I climbed up the ladder to where the old pig-iron bells swing in the wind.

Up here, there was a chilling breeze which tasted of salt. The floorboards were half-rotten, and I steadied myself against the cold metal arc of one of the bells. At first, I could see nothing, but then as my eyes grew accustomed to the dark, I made out his form, standing by the opening which lay between roof and walls. He was facing away from me and was gazing out over the village and beyond, towards the rustling leaves of the forest, and the lake which lay like a dark eye at the centre of the land. The floor was covered in boxes, crates, cases and sacks of all kinds, some of them stamped across with large letters, black and red and quite unintelligible. I wondered how he had managed to get all the way up the tower and across the pile of smuggled goods so quickly and so easily, but then I supposed that he was used to it, hiding, dodging, dancing. He struck a match and lit a long cigar. The white smoke curled upwards and assumed form most lithe and danced at the belfry window, and I felt a great sadness. He did not turn to face me, but I saw that he had removed both scarves. Long, black hair swirled around him, intertwining with the smoke.

'In the depths of winter, when the lake is frozen over, I can see my own face, rising.'

'You are no smuggler.'

'I have been many things, I have travelled far and wide,' he said and his voice was seamed with emotion. 'And yet, always I return to this place of my beginnings where the words are written in blood and feathers.'

'Does the vicar know of this?'

He laughed. 'The vicar will receive a case of good French wine and a box of fat Cuban cigars. There will be no service today, as he will be ill; nothing serious, he will make a rapid recovery.'

'And this has been happening...'

'For years, good curate. It is an arrangement.'

'I had no idea.'

He spun round. 'You are outside of the text, Curate Johnson. You shall die when the time comes and your death shall be an ordinary one.'

I shuddered. He had shifted his position in manner subtle as a conjuror, and now was leaning against the massive iron bulk of the major bell. His form did not wholly obscure the bell, however, so large was the holy monster.

'Not... not tonight?'

He shook his head and I thought I saw the flicker of a smile.

'You will live awhiles yet, I fancy.'

I nodded, more than a little relieved, for that courage which had drawn me up here had quite slipped away.

'Hidden within a tomb is a casket and in the casket is a head.'

'A head?' I repeated.

'Sometimes the head is of brass, sometimes of flesh and bone. When the time is right, it sings of many things; of that which is past and forgotten and of that which is unknown and yet to come.'

As he spoke these words in a low, almost soporific voice, something odd began to occur around the bell.

I rubbed my eyes in an attempt to clear the image. Yet my vision was quite lucid, as was my mind: this was not a dream. I struggled on.

'What have you to do with this... this head.'

He had moved back again to the window.

'I am in the song, nothing more.'

'You are sung into existence?'

'As are we all.'

The surface of the iron was changing, shifting, as though it were a plate of molten metal. And in the grey haze thus evinced, I swear I saw the naked form of a woman, tall, and beauteous to behold. She grew larger, until her face filled the image. Suddenly, talking to this strange man seemed the only way for me to keep a hold on reality. My tongue was stuck to my palate. I forced it to move.

'You said that I was outside.'

'In a manner of speaking, yet we are all caught in the bat-and-trap of stroke and dot.'

'Are you...' my voice trembled as I said this, 'are you the White Friar?'

He laughed. Now that he had on no scarf, I could see that he had an inordinately large skull and that his hair was tousled as though he had lived for years in the wind.

'I am a traveller: one moment smuggler, the next, merchant or lover or dancing spirit. Why not a monk of the Most Saelig Order of Saint Benedict?'

The woman had become smaller again and now, facing her, was the figure of a man, also naked. They were swaying together, or dancing, I could not decide which.

'Is something distracting you from our conversation, good curate?'

'I don't know,' I began, and then an impotent anger welled up inside my chest. 'I think that you are mad; either that, or a prankster.'

He shrugged. 'Perhaps I am both. Do you see the casket at your feet?'

I looked down and sure enough, there at my feet was a silver casket which I hadn't noticed before. He handed me a key.

'Open it!' he commanded.

I glanced quickly towards the bell, but the image had faded and the surface had returned to hard, cold metal.

I followed his instructions.

Beneath a velvet flap was a roll of something that looked like an old piece of wood. Carefully, I drew it out. It was a scroll of some sort, tied with a ribbon in like manner to a deed or other such legal document.

'What is it?' I asked.

He said nothing. I could barely make out his eyes. I undid the scroll.

The sheaves fell from my hands and scattered on the floor. There must have been enough to fill a book. I scrambled around, trying to collect them up as they blew across the belfry. He laughed again.

'These, dear curate, these pieces of skin after which on hands and knees you scramble, are the last remaining works of Master Aelfric, great architect of Wywurth, he who sang churches in the shape of love.'

I was breathing so heavily as I gathered up the sheaves, that I had no idea what he was saying.

'Do you understand?'

'I... I'm sorry. I'm not a young man. Coming up here... all this.'

He rushed forwards again and though this time he did not grab my collar, his face was so close to mine that I could almost feel the stubble on his jowl.

'Stretch yourself. For once in your miserable life, leap off the belfry and fly!'

I stepped back, alarmed. I tried to steady my voice.

'Why have you come here, this night?'

'Why have you?'

'I was dragged out of bed!'

'Like stone was I dragged from vellum, through love, death, music.'

'There is no music here.'

'Listen...'

He brought his arm around in the shape of an arc, as though in that one sweep, he were gathering all of the country; the moot lands of thane and ceorl, the swans' roads, the bone-houses, the spheres of spinning poste-mills, the trace of a dancer's steps on stone, the dark hiding-places of priest and smuggler, the flow of generations across land and water into the forgetfulness of the House of Life that is the final honouring of the dead. And in that arc, as though from a great distance I found that I could hear the trip and stamp fantasie of naked soles upon the bare stone flags of the long gallery, the ash and lime songs of scops and the scratch and tear of skin against pig-iron bell ringing dully on winter's morn of the Dark Strangers, and I was cleaving rock on a hillside in a strange and distant land and the guns of hell were screaming all around me. And a voice boomed in my ears and shook the bones of my skull till I feared it surely would split apart.

'And then turn to the east and bow humbly nine times, and say then these words: 'Eastwards I stand, for favours I pray.' Then turn three times with the course of the sun, then stretch yourself along the ground and say a dark bede.'

And in the midst of all of this, I did fall into a swoon and when I awoke the man was gone and I was lying, half-frozen, on the belfry floor. My mouth was filled with the pungency of ripened corn, and the cool breeze carried with it the taste of stale pig-fat, mixed with salt blown off the tops of new-risen waves. My thumb and the first two fingers of my right hand were covered in dried black ink of type most pungent and the small joints ached as though I had been writing all night. I massaged my fingers back to life, blowing onto them in a vain attempt to warm the flesh. As I prepared to make my exit from the tower, I walked past the bell. It was then I noticed that inscribed upon its dark, iron surface, was the image of two elongated, figures. I moved closer and brushed away an accumulation of dust and dirt which had accrued in the lines and hollows. As curate, I had ascended the tower of St Cuthman in times numbering the hundreds, but never before had I set eyes upon any such image. Yet this imprint seemed to have been burned into the substance of the bell for many long centuries, so pronounced was it, and yet so faded. The style belonged to the period of Good King Alfred, when those of our ancestors yet to have ben brought into the ways of Our Lord are said to have carved the ungodly horses, men and demons up on the white hills of the South Downs. On the bell were etched a man and a woman, their forms set in relation to each other in such a way as to connote that they were dancing. The face of the woman I recognised from the night before, though still I did not know who she was; however, as I ran my index finger along the lines, it seemed as though I had known the man's visage for longer than I had known my own.

I hastened down the steps of the tower and quickly locked the church and made my way back home, carefully avoiding the village. That Sabbath day, no bells were heard in Wywurth and no service was held. When next I ventured into St Cuthman's, it was as though nothing had happened. One evening, a few days later, I found a large cask of red wine and a box of cigars at my doorstep.

The first of the night birds began to sound out. The vicar put down the book. The two men looked at each other. There were no words between them. Both were back fifty years, floating on the face of the river which flowed over stone and reed. A silly summer's day in deepest Sussex. The Pevensey March.

At first, the three of them sang as one, Edward's voice being almost a Russian bass, while John's was towards the baritone and Caroline's a mid-alto. Though none were trained singers, they were all young and filled with health and happiness and their lungs pushed the air through their throats so that to each one of them the noise of the river was almost drowned out and all they could hear was their song.

As I walk'd out_one day, one day, I met an a-ged man by_ the way;

His head was bald, his beard was grey_His cloth-ing made of the
cold earthen clay, His cloth-ing made of the cold earth-en clay.

I said: Old man_what man are you? What country do you be-long
un-to? My name is Death; hast though heard of me_All kings and
prin-ces bow down un-to me, And you, fair maid, must come a-long
with me.

I'll give you gold,_I'll give you pearl, I'll give you cost-ly rich robes
to wear, If you will spare me a_ lit-tle while, And give me time my
life to a-mend, And give me time my life_to a-mend.

I'll have no gold, I'll have no pearl, I want no cost-ly rich robes to
wear. I can-not spare you a_lit-tle while,_Nor give you time_ your
life to a-mend, Nor give you time your life to a-mend.

In six months' time this fair maid died. Let this be put on my tomb-
stone, she cried: Here lies a poor,_dis–tress-ed maid;_Just in her
bloom she was snath-ed a-way, Her cloth-ing made of the cold
earth-en clay.

And so the boats sailed on through the forest, along that stretch of
river where the current slackens as the land beyond its banks broadens out
and grows flatter. The trees – yew, elder, willow, oak – were in full, dark
leaf and the branches overhung the oxbows which had been formed many
thousands of years earlier when the great glaciers far leagues to the north
had melted and the river been created, much as in the tale of Noah. And
the land and the waters, both, had moved again and had changed since
Saxon times and by the long reign of Queen Victoria, the sea, once some
seven leagues distant, had swept up to the very foot of the hill on which St
Cuthman's Church had been built.

The boats began slowly to drift apart.

Edward ended his song with great gusto (it is possible to sing thus
about death only when one is in the first flush of life) and then stared up at
the sun through the leaves. The creaking sounds of the boat's hull filled his
ears, and he fell asleep. He dreamed of a great tower, around which were
being played games of Nine Men's Morris and Bat-and-Trap. He dreamed
of Gooding women, their breath turned to smoke in the frozen air, carrying meat-and-raisin pies and sugar-loaves shaped like conical tombs to

one another's houses through the snow on the Day of the Feast of Saint Thomas Didymus; of Wealden houses where, at dead of night, lovers crept downstairs and through the servants' gate and ran towards the owl eyes of the dark woods; of the bottomless lake where the ghost of the green nicor screams in coiled poisoned agony; of eleven thousand virgins chanting and skipping to draw the seeds up through the corpse'd earth; of shoals of gleaming, silver mackerel caught in the long, corked nets of fishermen in boats bedecked with ribbons and flowers; of magical Yule babies roasting in elder log fires; of shepherd's crowns, grinning on the mantelpiece; of a naked man climbing up a cliff-face to collect honey out of a cranny; of the horns of spiced ale blown over swarms of bees as they hived on living branches; of ancient, wrinkled demons who danced around the Ring of Chanctonbury and who offered ten-foot long suet puddings and fire wine to the eleven thousand virgins...

When he awoke, his boat was stationary. He levered himself up and peered over the edge. The other boats were nowhere to be seen.

Panic rose like a spring flood into his throat.

They must have gone on without him.

Edward had ended up at the end of a stagnant oxbow. Gnats and drag-onflies danced courtship rituals across the transparent skin of the grey water. Deep down, near the shifting layers of river-mud, the water had remained unchanged, unmoving, for centuries. The prow of his boat was wedged in the mud of a bank, too steep to climb. It would take all his effort to push the boat back into the water and row all the way back to the river proper. But he was unable to make out the main body of the river. He had heard that Mychelham Water had never fully been cartographed. Even the horn-rimmed men from the Ordnance Survey, with their dividers and compasses and stiffened suits had had difficulty; the mud was so shifting, the land around it so oily and fickle.

As he tried to trace the chain of events, the whole day reduced to a blur.

They had gone off together, the three of them, in their rickety rowing-boats. At some point along the river, he had fallen asleep. He tried to catch his dreams, but they were elusive as river reeds. What if the others had drowned? He shuddered. But the river was slow-moving and both Caroline and John were excellent swimmers. The three of them had often leapt into the forest lake and for a delicious, skin moment, had died in its dark, freezing waters. But rivers were different; like snakes, they changed form constantly while yet remaining the same, they sought out points of weakness, then wound their reeds around ankles and necks. Edward felt so drained, he wondered if he had the strength to row the boat homewards. Then he had the vision of a dream, which seemed real: John and Caroline, naked and joined on the felled trunk of an ancient yew. What once had been the upper end, the growing end, of a tree was now submerged beneath the waters of the Mychelham, while the thousand year-old trunk reared into the sun-scaped air, malevolent, green shoots sprouting from its centre. And as their bodies shifted, one upon the other, their skins rubbed into the bark and merged with the skins of other, earlier lovers. Each whorl of wood bore the rune-marks of such conjunctions, all the way back to when the abbott had leaned against its trunk and dreamed of three long-boats dancing in the spume of the river-mouth and of a Roman fig-tree sagging with fruit. The faces of all the lovers, past and future, were turned as one toward the slowly-flowing water and their breath was the air which danced across its surface and formed bubbles that pulled carp and trout and roach up from their dark holes and into the sunlight. Then the vision evanesced and Edward was left, cold and sweating and alone in the bottom of a rotting boat. He felt a fist of rage in his belly. Possessed by his own dark spirit, he leaned over the rim of the boat and spat into the river and watched the spittle swirl and merge with the cold water. He picked up the oars and began to row, not knowing whether he was going up or down stream, towards home or away from it. He needed to immerse his body in an act of total physicality. He did not notice the pair of rowing-boats, half-sunk like crocodiles in swamp, nor the massive tree-trunk toppled into the river, nor the shape, like an archetypal majuscule, of two lovers pressed upon its surface, nor the runes which their corpses carved into the wood.

It was at the moment when he knew his body could row no more that Edward found the river again. He let the oars fall into their metal sockets, slumped back and watched the wispy clouds sail through the blue. Gradually, the pain in his chest subsided. And it was then that he had heard the song.

The vicar shifted in his seat. His body felt as though it was turning slowly to wood. Rotherfield spoke first.

'You saw us that day, you saw us and you told.'

'I saw nothing. Yes, it's true. I did love her. Even though I always knew that she would never want me, that I would never dance in the notes of her song.'

'So, was it repentance, or revenge?'

Edward shrugged. 'The worst betrayals, the ones for which we suffer all our lives, are those of which we are least aware. Ultimately, we betray only ourselves.'

'I went to war, became no more than a worm in the swarming mud. I volunteered for death. That's why I stood up and watched the man in the greatcoat. Even now, I don't know whether he really existed.'

'That's not what you said. You didn't mention standing up yourself. And you said that, later, he handed you his card. What about the prison-camp, the ruined church, Saint Cecilia? The brass head, the wooden house in Constantinople? The chants, the manuscripts? Caroline.'

Rotherfield pointedly ignored him. 'I thought, if he's able to stand erect, then so shall I. And on the prison hill, when I turned the card over, it was blank.'

'We heard you were dead.'

'I was never more than a ripple on the surface of time. I was already as nothing.'

'Not to Caroline.'

'Life goes on: she married the law-giver.'

'And plays the church organ.'

'Yes, I've heard her play.'

'She plays with such sadness. Her fingers dance runes along the wood, the bone.'

'She no longer sings?'

'Never.' Edward took a deep breath. 'John, we are different people now, different than we were then.'

Rotherfield shook his head. 'I think not. We dance the same dances and sing the same words, over and over again.'

'There was something wrong with each section of this book,' Edward cut in. 'Were I to submit the text to an Anglo-Saxon scholar, a Tudor specialist and an expert in early nineteenth century south coast smuggling, I'm certain they would expose it as a fake – and, I might add, written by a man who lived a fake life.' He paused, then raised himself up and half-arched the upper part of his body over the edge of the table. 'You wrote this, didn't you? You are its author.'

A crescent moon had just emerged from behind the clouds. Rotherfield gazed up at it. 'My body was never found.'

'Caroline received a box of Latakia cigarettes and a musical score for church organ. A score which she has never played. Cigarettes she has never smoked.' The vicar picked up the book and brandished it at the woodcutter. 'And decades later, from the sale of Birkin Mansion, the last inheritance of Caroline's long-dead father, the last remaining stone in the doorway of the old Saxon earls of the South, there came this book. She couldn't bring herself to destroy it. Perhaps she had hoped that some stranger would buy it and take it far away.'

'I think it's time I left. Dawn will be upon us soon.' Rotherfield rose. 'But before I go, I want to ask you one question.'

The vicar's face sagged, as though all of his years had descended upon him at once. He remained silent.

'Did you really see us?'

Edward shook his head. 'I heard your song, smelled your love on the river-wind. And in the dark reeds of the oxbow, I foresaw your death.'

Rotherfield nodded. 'Then you, too are in the text. In the last chapter. Read it, when I am gone. Then give it to Caroline. Ask her to play the score 'The Palace is Beautiful'. It is a perfect unity of the mundane, the human, the instrumental. No living soul has heard it for three thousand years.' And gathering up his axe, he limped away. And as Rotherfield passed through the outer gardens and orchards and approached Mychelham Water, his form took on the aspect of a shadow, a moving pyramid that merged with the uncertain light and became imperceptible.

In the distance, smoke from fires lit by drovers rose into the opalescent dawn. There was a hint of charcoal in the fresh morning air.

Edward bent and lifted the small pile of logs, walked stiffly into the house and locked the door behind him. Going straight to his study, he placed the wood in the grate, took a taper from the mantelpiece and lit it with his cigar-butt.

When the hearth-stone was burning to the touch, he grasped the book and flung into the rear of the fire.

Note: 'The Dream of the Rood' (anon), p. 231, is translated from the Old English by L. Iddings; 'The Wanderer' (anon), p. 234, is E. Hickey's translation. Both appear in *Translations from Old English Poetry*, Ginn and Company, Boston, 1902. 'Death and the Lady', p. 268, is from Cecil Sharp's *English Folk Songs*.

Acknowledgements: Thanks to Stuart Airlie, Emily Anson Blake, Caedmon, The Reverend Francis Calthrop, St Christine of the Auld Kirk, Cynewulf, Peter Daltrey, John Dee, Rosemary Eadie, Grey St Lorraine of Mirin, Amjad Ayub Mirza, St Mochaoi of Dumfries, Jennie Renton, Mulla Sadra, Lousine Zakarian.

Nuala Ramage

Mummy

I give you a kiss
that makes you alive
with oozing pure water
that keeps you alive
with black satin sashes
that shine like a piece
of gold in a mirror
in night or light
oh please don't
die I will give you a
chocolate that's sweet
as a bead of me

Ray Catoot

Ray Catoot came walkin by.

    He fell on the floor.

        Aye a said.

            A didny help im.

        Why? yi say *Why?*

        He took awa ma life.

        How? yi say *How?*

            I'll tell yi how.

                He stole my wife and child.

                    A dinny like Ray Catoot at all.

That is how ma sad tale ends

        on a steep steep hill

        on a cold cold road.

            A've told you a story to do wi pain.

Paul Ballingall is a self-taught artist fae the Kingdom of Fife who has worked in various media. He has created a large body of work in the form of linocuts and sometimes uses these images as the basis of large paintings. He can be contacted at Out of the Blue (Studio 12), 36 Dalmeny Street, Edinburgh. www.outoftheblue.org.uk.

Stefan Blöndal, the Danish artist, who provides our 'Snow Queen' cover image, has participated in numerous international exhibitions and has received many awards for his highly imaginative, often surreal work.

Kathryn Berthelsen was born in 1979 and holds an MSc in Creative Writing from University of Edinburgh. Her poems have appeared in the *Herald* and the *Eildon Tree*. In 2005 she was a prizewinner in the Grierson Verse Competition. Poems included in *Textualities~Magic Afoot* are part of a longer sequence, *Restoration: Thirty Poems for Rosslyn Chapel*. She currently lives in Houston, Texas.

Michael Brown is a Professor of Communications at Mount Ida College, Massachusetts. His poetry collections include *Falling Wallendas, The Man Who Makes Amusement Rides* and *Susquehanna*. With Valerie Lawson, he co-hosts the Boston Poetry Slam at the Cantab Lounge in Cambridge, Mass.

Gordon Bruce plays in the Royal Scottish National Orchestra. Also a magician, he has an avid interest in the history of conjuring and allied arts. As curator of the Scottish Magic Archive, he welcomes any information regarding performers and performances in Scotland and may be contacted at the Scottish Magic Archive, 32 Cathkin Road Glasgow G42 9UH (visits to the archive are by appointment only).

Elizabeth Burns has published two collections of poetry and her work has appeared in many anthologies, most recently the Scottish Poetry Library's *Handsel: Poems for Births and Baby Namings* and Canongate's *Modern Scottish Women Poets*.

David Campbell has published three books for children, two CDs, poems and various magazines and is now working on a book of early Celtic tales. His early schooling in the rich culture of the north-east has nurtured his work as teacher, radio producer and internationally known storyteller.

Gerry Cambridge is a writer, musician and photographer. Founder-editor of the *Dark Horse* literary magazine. His books of poetry and poetry projects are numerous, the most recent being *The Dynamite Project*, a 270-line poem based on Alfred Nobel and his explosives factory at Ardeer near Stevenston, Ayrshire.

Tess Darwin's main interest is reconnecting people with the natural world. She is the author of *The Scots Herbal* (Mercat, 1996), on the folklore and uses of wild plants in Scotland. She lives in Fife and works in environmental education.

Regi Claire was born and brought up in Switzerland. Her collection of stories, *Inside~Outside*, was shortlisted for the Saltire First Book Award, and her first novel, *The Beauty Room*, was longlisted for the Allen Lane/MIND Book of the Year Award. She has just completed a new novel, *Women Without Men*, and is currently writing a collection of stories, *Fighting It*.

Anita Govan is a performance poet whose first collection, *Jane*, appeared in 2005.

Major themes in her work include love and loss, motherhood, war and her personal struggle with dyslexia. She is strongly involved in mounting poetry slams, events and workshops and has performed internationally.

Robert Alan Jamieson is a poet and novelist who writes in both Shetlandic and English. The poems appearing in *Textualities* are from a sequence *Ansin t' Sjaetlin: Responses to the Language Question*. He tutors creative writing at the University of Edinburgh.

Lawrence Krauser is a novelist and playwright living and working in New York. He is currently directing and writing the music for a film version of his play *Horrible Child*, which was first produced by Printer's Devil Theatre in 1998. A film of his first novel, *Lemon*, is also being planned.

Valerie Lawson has been published in numerous journals, anthologies and websites. *Ribbon Anvil* was a finalist for Best Poetry Publication at the Cambridge Poetry Awards and she has won several other literary awards. She was a participant in Optimal Avenues multimedia cultural exchange between Massachussetts and Ireland, celebrating the United Nations mandate for a culture of peace.

Tom Leonard was born in Glasgow in 1944. His two collections *Intimate Voices* and *access to the silence* are published by Etruscan Books, Devon. He teaches Creative Writing at Glasgow University. Website: http://www.tomleonard.co.uk

Harriet Lyall has recently completed a series of essays exploring new angles on literary classics. 'Literally Fabulous: Andersen for Adults' was first delivered as a talk at the Danish Cultural Institute as part of the programme marking the bicentenary of the author's birth.

Janis Mackay, a journalist in the distant past, trained as a voice coach and storyteller. Writing being her first love, she recently graduated from the University of Sussex with an MA in Creative Writing and Personal Development.

Susie Maguire's short stories are published in two collections, *Furthermore* and *The Short Hello*. She is also deviser and editor of *Little Black Dress*, an anthology of short stories by women on the theme of the ubiquitous and iconic frock.

Brian Moffatt is an archeo-ethno-pharmocologist and director of investigations at the Soutra Project on the site of a medieval hospital in the Scottish Borders. Discoveries there about mediaeval medical treatments and herbal remedies are published in a series of SHARP reports.

Mark Oxbrow is an authority on Arthurian and grail legends, Freemasonry and the history and lore of Rosslyn Chapel. He is the author of *Halloween* (a history), and contributed to the screen documentary *Cracking the Da Vinci Code*. A Fellow of the Royal Society of Antiquaries of Scotland, he has lectured widely.

Nuala Ramage is eight years old and is a pupil at Springfield Primary School, Linlithgow. She has written a 3000-word story, *The Beginning of the End*, about a forgetful girl called Jade. She wrote her poem 'Ray Catoot' on 25 January 2004, because her brother had to to write a Burns Day poem and she decided to write one too.

Julia Rampen is a poet, musician and artist. A student at James Gillespies' High School in Edinburgh, she was chosen as one of Foyle's Young Poets of the Year in 2005 and in 2006 was a runner up in the Tower Poetry Competition.

Shampa Ray was born in India and lives in Edinburgh. Her poetry has been published in a number of magazines and anthologies. She finds constant inspiration in the natural world and her Buddhist practice – living in the present moment – is a current theme.

Bob Read died on 20 November 2005. His fellow magician Todd Carr wrote of him: 'Bob was a superb performer, a master of misdirection, an achingly funny humorist, a great writer, and the world's top authority on the history of the Cups and Balls as depicted in prints and artworks.'

Dilys Rose, novelist, short story writer and poet, has won several prestigious literary awards. Her publications include *Our Lady of the Pickpockets, Red Tides, Pest Maiden, War Dolls, Selected Stories* and *Lord of Illusions*. She teaches Creative Writing at the University of Edinburgh.

Suhayl Saadi is a novelist and dramatist based in Glasgow. His hallucinatory realist novel *Psychoraag* (2004) won a PEN Oakland Josephine Miles Literary Award, was shortlisted for the James Tait Black Memorial Prize and the Patras Bokhari Prize and was nominated for the Impac Prize. His short story collection, *The Burning Mirror* (2001) was shortlisted for the Saltire First Book Prize (2001).

Gwen Suominen is a visual artist and potter based in Edinburgh. The sea and the sky are strong themes in her work. 'You think it's crazy here, wait till you get out there' is her first published poem.

Claire Thomson is UCL Mellon Research Fellow at University College London, researching narratives of European national identities in the visual arts and literary genres. She holds a PhD in Danish literature from the University of Edinburgh and is editor of *Northern Constellations: New Readings in Nordic Cinema* (Norvik Press, 2006).

Ruth Thomas's forthcoming novel, *Things to Make and Mend*, will be published in 2007 by Faber. She is the author of two short story collections, *The Dance Settee* and *Sea Monster Tattoo*.

Zsuzsanna Varga's main research interests are Victorian studies and studies into travel writing and the travels of the text. In 2005–06, she worked for the Britain in Print Project at Edinburgh University and the Mitchell Library. She is equally proud of having co-edited *Cencrastus* and the Bibliography of Scottish Literature in Translation.

Arthur Watson – Gordon Bruce and Bob Read have said it all.

Ariadne Xenou is a photographic artist. Born in Athens, she is now based in Scotland. She enjoys using alternative photographic processes such as gum dichromate and salt prints and has recently started experimenting in animating her images. Email liubova@btinternet.com.

Tim West was born in Kent but doesn't remember it. He grew up in the North East of Scotland and remembers it all too well. 'William's New Friend' is his first story in print. He's pleased to get it there.